MODERN

ALGEBRA *with*

TRIGONOMETRY

A series of undergraduate mathematics texts under the editorship of
CARL B. ALLENDOERFER

MODERN
ALGEBRA *with*
TRIGONOMETRY

JOHN T. MOORE
The University of Florida

The Macmillan Company, New York
Collier-Macmillan Limited, London

PREFACE

The purpose of this text is to provide an adequate foundation for an intensive study of analytic geometry and calculus. It can be used also as the basis of a terminal course for students who are not planning to pursue any further study of mathematics. At most schools the material in the book can be covered completely in one semester, trimester, or quarter, with naturally a more leisurely pace in the case of a school on the semester system.

The underlying philosophy of the text is to give a careful and logical foundation for any topic discussed, if this seems feasible, but not to disdain the use of intuition for the sake of clarification. It is the firm opinion of the author that, while the material of the book could be framed in a strait-jacket of formal logic, the result would be to reduce it to an extremely dull and insipid study of "dry bones." This is not to discount the value of logic in mathematics, for all mathematics is based on it, and mathematical propositions must depend ultimately on it. However, at an elementary level, it seems healthier to demand something less than complete rigor (if complete rigor is even possible!) and to let the student gradually acquire a respect and an appreciation of the need for higher levels of rigor as he proceeds with his mathematical education.

The two principal ingredients of the text are the system of real numbers and the notion of a "set," both of which are left largely at an intuitive level, although some formal discussion of real numbers is included in Chapter 1. The idea of a function is a unifying concept, which ties together—by means of sets—the elementary polynomial, exponential, logarithmic, and circular functions. While complex numbers are introduced in Chapter 8 and used further in Chapter 9, they are not emphasized to the same extent as real numbers, and the chapter on analytic trigonometry appropriately precedes this introduction. In view of the difficulty with which it is usually grasped by the neophyte mathematics student, the subject of mathematical induction has been delayed until Chapter 10, in preference to inserting it in its "logical" place in Chapter 1. I justify this placement in my belief that the student may be in a better position to grasp the significance of this important principle at the end of the course than he would be if it were introduced earlier. The material on trigonometry is concentrated largely in Chapter 6 and Chapter 7, the earlier chapter being essentially a survey of "angle" trigonometry. There is a tendency in some quarters to reverse the order followed here and to introduce analytic trigonometry first with a subsequent discussion of "angle" trigonometry as a special case. However, most students at the course level of this book have already had some basic trigonometry at an early stage of their education, and I have found that it is quite bewildering to such students if their instructor ignores this and presents what seem to be artificial definitions of familiar concepts. I believe it to be much better to face up to this situation and to review and further substantiate what has gone before, and *then* to *build* on this to obtain the more abstract notions of analytic trigonometry.

In general, the subject matter of the book is much the same as any other book on algebra and trigonometry. However, an attempt has been made to introduce modern concepts, methods, and notations whenever this appears feasible. Moreover, it is my fond hope that, while there may be some omissions, there are no ideas in this book which the student will have to "unlearn" at a later time. In connection with omissions, it may be well to point out that the text contains no discussion whatever of probability and statistics. It has been my experience throughout my teaching career that these topics—although appearing in many books on algebra and trigonometry—are regularly omitted in courses similar to the one we have in mind. This is not because they are unimportant, but, rather, because they are usually covered separately in other more specialized courses.

There are several special features of the text proper. In Chapter 3, there is a discussion of inequalities which is somewhat more extensive than usual, including a brief introduction to the modern subject of linear programming. The matrix solution of systems of linear equations, as given in Chapter 2, is more detailed than in most books of a similar nature, while Appendix B contains, in addition, a discussion of methods of matrix inversion with applications to linear systems. A study of the algebra of functions is given in Chapter 4, including a general discussion of inverse functions. The student is then ready to appreciate the fact that logarithmic functions are inverse to exponential functions, and inverse circular functions are inverses of circular functions with somewhat restricted domains. In most textbooks at this level inverse functions are introduced merely to enable one to obtain definitions of these inverse circular functions.

Answers have been given at the end of the book to most odd-numbered problems, while answers to even-numbered problems are available to instructors in a separate booklet upon request to the publisher. All numerical answers and brief pertinent facts for requested proofs are included in one or the other of these two locations, as are a great many graphical answers. While not all answers of the latter kind have been made available, they have been included whenever graphs have been considered to be of particular importance.

A review of high-school algebra is given in Appendix A for the benefit of those students whose backgrounds in elementary algebra are deficient. Since it is assumed that this section will be used by students, generally without the aid of an instructor, *all* answers to the problems in this section have been given in the answer section of the book.

There are a number of personal acknowledgments that I would like to make. Mr. William S. Cannon, of the Department of Mathematics, Presbyterian College, Clinton, S.C., made a careful reading of the entire manuscript under somewhat adverse circumstances. He was also of great assistance in the preparation of answers to the problems in the text and was ably assisted in some of this work by Mr. Paul Campbell of the same department. In addition, the following students at the University of Florida were most helpful in preparing answers: Don Cook, Charles Daniher, Travis Gordon, George Mendonsa, Pedro Sanchez, Anthony C. Shershin, and Betsey and Carl Whitman. To all of these people I express my sincere apprecation for their time and effort. I am also deeply indebted to my colleague Dr. W. P. Morse, of the University of Florida, for a final reading of the text, with many useful last-minute suggestions for improvement. Dr. C. B. Allendoerfer, the editor of this series of texts, was very kind in giving me his impressions of an earlier version of the manuscript, along with several worthwhile comments at later stages of its development. Finally, to the staff of The Macmillan Company, and, in particular, to the mathematics editor, Mr. A. H. McLeod, I would like to express my thanks for patience, perseverance, and extremely pleasant cooperation.

JOHN T. MOORE

Gainesville, Florida

TABLE OF CONTENTS

CHAPTER 1

Our Number Systems

1.1 Introduction

The number systems of arithmetic and algebra are, for the most part familiar from the early grades of elementary school. In this environment, the student has learned that the main use of the natural, or "counting," numbers 1, 2, 3, . . . is to measure the size of a collection of objects. Two collections, or "sets," of objects are said to be *cardinally equivalent,* or to *have the same number of elements*, if it is possible to pair them off so that every element of each set is paired with an element of the other set, and no element of either set is used twice. A pairing of this kind is said to establish a *one-to-one correspondence* between the elements of the two sets. This notion is actually more primitive than counting, for, if such a one-to-one correspondence is possible, the two sets have the *same number* of elements—and we are able to make this assertion without any attempt at counting to find out what this number is. For example, if an instructor tells his class to be seated and observes afterwards that there are no empty chairs and no student is standing, he knows immediately that the number of chairs in the room is the same as the number of students. Expressed otherwise, he makes the observation that the set of chairs and the set of students are cardinally equivalent. If the instructor wishes to know how many students there are in the room, he "counts" them, which means that he sets up a one-to-one correspondence between the set of students and a certain set of natural numbers. If the natural numbers used in this correspondence are 1, 2, 3, . . . , k, we know there are k students in the room, or the *cardinal number* of the set of students is k. Any set whose cardinal number is one of the natural numbers is said to be *finite*. A nonempty set (i.e., one which is not void of elements) which is not finite is *infinite*, and an infinite set which is cardinally equivalent to the set of *all* natural numbers is *denumerable*. Probably the simplest example

1

of a denumerable set (distinct from the set of all natural numbers) is the set of all even natural numbers, because it is possible to establish the correspondence $2n \leftrightarrow n$ between the even numbers and all natural numbers, and it is immediately apparent that this correspondence is one-to-one.

The natural numbers (which we shall usually designate by N) are quite adequate for the job of *counting* any *finite* set, but how are they adapted for other kinds of measurements? It is a trite remark that "two and two make four," but is it true?! If you take two steps from where you are and follow this with two more steps, are you necessarily four steps from your original position? The answer, of course, is NO (if you have distance in mind), for this distance may be much less than four steps. It is four *only if* the four steps were taken in the *same direction*. This intuitive notion of direction leads us now to our next type of number, the *integer*. The *integers* are the numbers designated $\ldots -3, -2, -1, 0, 1, 2, 3, \ldots$, where we notice the presence of "negative" numbers and zero, along with the "positive" or natural numbers. With the use of the integers, we are able to attach a *sign* to a number ($+$ or $-$) and so make measurements in each of two directions—one called "positive" and the other "negative." Unless it is needed for emphasis, however, the sign $+$ is usually omitted from the positive integers, so that, for example, we usually write 3 instead of $+3$.

With nothing but integers available for our use, however, it is well known that measurements often fail to come out "even." If we measure the length of a table, this length may be close to four feet but not four feet exactly. Hence, it is necessary to introduce "fractions," or "rational numbers," to make such a measurement more precise. The rational numbers are numbers expressed in the form of a ratio $m/n, n \neq 0$, where m and n are integers. Just as the positive integers are not to be distinguished in any practical way from the natural numbers, so the rational numbers of the form $m/1$ may be identified with the integers m. (There are logical distinctions between the identified sets of numbers, but we shall not discuss them here.)

With the advent of rational numbers, all measurements of any practical importance can be made, but our number system is still deficient. It was known to the early Greeks that the measure of length of the hypotenuse of a triangle with unit sides is not a rational number. The argument can be made by the method of *reductio ad absurdum*. Let us assume that x in Figure 1 is the rational number m/n (see page 3). Then, by the Pythagorean theorem, $x^2 = m^2/n^2 = 1^2 + 1^2 = 2$, and so $m^2 = 2n^2$. The square of any integer involves any of its prime factors an even number of times. Hence, the left member of this equation involves the factor 2 an even number of times or not at all, while the right member definitely involves 2 an odd number of times. Since this is absurd, our assumption that $x = m/n$ is untenable. If we wish to make measurements of length of line segments such as the above hypotenuse, it is then necessary

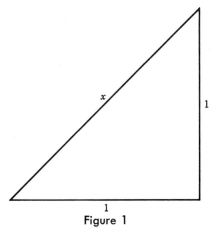

Figure 1

to introduce nonrational, or *irrational*, numbers. In the case of the hypotenuse of Figure 1, the irrational number needed is designated $\sqrt{2}$. It is true, of course, that this measurement of length can be made to any desired degree of accuracy with a rational number, which is to say that we can approximate $\sqrt{2}$ as closely as desired by a rational number. All irreducible "radicals" such as $\sqrt{2}$, $\sqrt[3]{5}$, $\sqrt[7]{12}$ (to be discussed later in more detail) are irrational numbers, as are also such well-known numbers as π (the ratio of the circumference to the diameter of a circle), and e (the base for natural logarithms, to be discussed later). We are then implying that none of these numbers can be expressed as a quotient of two integers.

It can be shown by division that a rational number can be expressed as an infinite decimal with a repeating sequence of digits. (In the case of a decimal which "terminates," the repeating sequence of digits consists entirely of zeros.) Conversely, it is not difficult to show that any such "repeating decimal" can be expressed as a rational number in the form of a quotient of integers. This leads us to a very simple definition of a real number: *A real number is an infinite decimal.* If the number has a repeating sequence of digits, it is rational; if otherwise, it is irrational; but together the rational and irrational numbers comprise the *set of real numbers.* While the rational numbers can be shown to comprise a denumerable set, the irrationals do not and in this sense are more "numerous" than the rationals. The set of real numbers, which we shall designate by R, will supply most of the numerical ingredients of this text. A further extension of this set to include the complex numbers will be made in a later chapter.

PROBLEMS

1. List the numbers that are natural numbers, integers, rational numbers, and irrational numbers in each of the following collections: (a) 2, $-\frac{1}{2}$, $\sqrt{3}$, $\frac{1}{5}$,

$0.272727 \cdots$; (b) $-\sqrt{2}/2$, $\frac{1}{2}$, $\sqrt[3]{5}$, $1.571571571 \cdots$, -6, 0; (c) $2/\sqrt{5}$, -2, $\sqrt[7]{2}$, 3, $\frac{5}{6}$, $\sqrt{2}/\sqrt{2}$.

2. Use an argument similar to that used in the text for $\sqrt{2}$ to show that the diagonal of a cube of unit side cannot be measured by a rational number. Then deduce that $\sqrt{3}$ is irrational.

3. Show by actual division that the following rational numbers can be expressed as repeating decimals: (a) $\frac{11}{13}$; (b) $\frac{27}{37}$.

4. Use a one-to-one correspondence to show that there are just as many natural numbers which terminate in the digit 3 as there are natural numbers which terminate in the digit 7.

5. What would be the simplest way—without counting—to determine whether there are the same number of ladies as gentlemen at a dance party?

6. Explain what is meant by the statement that π is not a rational number. Is it true that $\pi = \frac{22}{7}$?

7. Explain how you could tell—without counting—whether there are the same number of oranges as there are grapefruit in a certain basket of fruit.

8. Consider the fact that there is only a finite number of reduced fractions m/n, with m and n positive integers, such that $m + n = k$, for any fixed integer k. Now let k vary and prove that the positive rational numbers form a denumerable set.

9. Is there any difference between 2 and II? Between 4 and IV? Explain.

10. From your past experience, identify one operation which can always be performed within the set of all: (a) integers, but not always within the set N; (b) nonzero rational numbers, but not always within the set of all integers; (c) real numbers R, but not always within the set of all rational numbers.

1.2 The Real Numbers as an Additive System

Many aspects of real numbers are so familiar to us that it is rather difficult to examine them objectively. However, if we are to get a proper understanding of these numbers, we must make a careful analysis of even the "obvious" properties which we have always accepted without much question. *In this chapter and in the sequel, unless otherwise specified, it will be assumed that letters designate real numbers, which are arbitrary except as indicated.*

An algebraic "system" differs from a mere set of numbers, in that a certain structure has been assigned to the set. By this we mean that some "relations" and "operations" have been defined in the set. The operations of addition and multiplication are without a doubt familiar to the student, and, while there is probably some misunderstanding about what a "relation" actually *is*, the student will have had some practical experience with some of the common relations. In a very intuitive sense we say that a "relation" $\Re$ has been defined in a set of numbers if it is possible to decide whether $a \Re b$ is true or false for any numbers a and b of the set. The relation of *equality* $(=)$ probably is the most common of the relations, and if we make a critical analysis, we see that the statement $a = b$ means that a and b are merely *different names or representations of the same number.* For example, $2 + 5 = 4 + 3$ is valid because both members of this equality represent the *same* number 7. The relation of equality obeys three important laws:

E_1:	$a = a$	(reflexive law);
E_2:	If $a = b$, then $b = a$	(symmetric law);
E_3:	If $a = b$ and $b = c$, then $a = c$	(transitive law).

Any relation—such as equality—which satisfies three such laws is known as an *equivalence* relation. An example of a relation which is *not* of this kind is the "order" relation $<$ (to be discussed in §1.5). For it is apparent that $a \not< a$; and if $a < b$, it follows that $b \not< a$, in contradiction to E_1 and E_2. (A line drawn through the symbol for a relation, such as $\not<$, indicates a denial of the relation.) The effect of an equivalence relation in a collection of elements is to separate the collection into smaller classes of "equal" elements with no element common to two classes. We shall not prove this assertion, however.

In practice we very seldom need refer to E_1, but while E_2 and E_3 are used a great deal, it is convenient to replace them by equivalent but more useful formulations. We shall refer to these newer rules as E_2^* and E_3^*.

E_2^*: The two members of any equality may be interchanged.

E_3^*: If $a_1 = a_2 = \cdots = a_n$ is a finite "chain" of equalities, it follows that $a_1 = a_n$. This rule is just an extension of Euclid's familiar axiom that "things which are equal to the same thing are equal to each other."

EXAMPLE 1.   If we know that $3 = a$, for some real number a, an application of E_2 or E_2^* will allow us to write $a = 3$.

EXAMPLE 2.   If we know that $a = b$, $c = b$, and $c = 5$, we can use E_2^* to write $a = b = c = 5$. An application of E_3^* will then show us that $a = 5$.

In our system of real numbers, we have two primary operations known as "addition" and "multiplication" and indicated, respectively, by $+$ and $\cdot$. The $\cdot$ for multiplication, however, is frequently replaced by the mere juxtaposition of the elements multiplied, provided there is no confusion with the decimal point of our real numbers. The laws of addition may be listed as follows.

A_1: The "sum" $a + b$ is a uniquely determined real number. Since $a + b$ is real, as well as a and b, we say that the system of real numbers is *closed* under addition.

A$_2$: The *associative* law of addition, or $(a + b) + c = a + (b + c)$.

A$_3$: There exists a real number 0, known as the *additive identity*, with the property that $a + 0 = 0 + a = a$.

A$_4$: There is associated with each real number a a real number $-a$, known as the *additive inverse* of a, such that $a + (-a) = (-a) + a = 0$.

A$_5$: The *commutative* law of addition, or $a + b = b + a$.

The properties A$_1$, A$_2$, A$_3$, A$_4$ characterize an algebraic system known as a *group*, while A$_5$ makes the group *commutative*, or *abelian*. Hence, the five laws of addition assert that the real numbers comprise an *abelian group under addition*, or an *additive abelian group*.

There is usually associated with any operation another operation which in some sense is "inverse" to the original. If the basic operation is addition, the inverse operation is *subtraction*. Let us suppose that three numbers a, b, c are so related that $a = b + c$. If we now add $-b$ to both members of this equality, being mindful of the commutative and associative laws, we obtain:

$$a + (-b) = -b + (b + c) = (-b + b) + c = 0 + c = c.$$

It is customary to replace $a + (-b)$ by $a - b$ and to say that we have obtained $c (= a - b)$ by *subtracting* b from a. That is, *by definition of subtraction*, the result of subtracting a number is the same as adding its additive inverse. This "rule of subtraction" is usually memorized in elementary arithmetic.

The intuitive effect of an inverse operation, in general, is to undo the results of the basic operation. In the case of subtraction, this means that the subtraction of a number b from some given number annuls the effect of the prior addition of b. This is true because, by definition of subtraction, $(a + b) - b = (a + b) + (-b) = a + [b + (-b)] = a + 0 = a$. Similarly, the addition of b annuls the effect of a prior subtraction of b, so that each operation is the inverse of the other.

While there is probably no great confusion about the matter, it may be well to point out that we are aware of a double usage of the signs $+$ and $-$. They have been used to designate both the sign of a number and an operation. In the case of the $+$ sign, since it is rarely attached to a number, it is usually a symbol of operation, and in the exceptional cases its usage should be clear from the context. As for the $-$ sign, since we have defined $a - b$ to be the same as $a + (-b)$, it really makes no difference whether the $-$ sign is to be associated with b or to be regarded as the symbol for subtraction. Hence, the apparent ambiguity is of no great consequence, even though the sign of a number and the symbol of an operation are entirely different logical notions.

EXAMPLE. Prove that $a + (b + c) = (b + a) + c$, indicating the justification for each step.

SOLUTION

$$a + (b + c) = (a + b) + c, \qquad \text{[A}_2\text{]}$$

$$(a + b) + c = (b + a) + c. \qquad \text{[A}_5\text{]}$$

Hence,

$$a + (b + c) = (b + a) + c. \qquad \text{[E}_3^*\text{]}$$

PROBLEMS

In problems 1 through 5, use the given additive properties of the real numbers to establish the equalities, including the proper justification for each step.

1. $a + (b - a) = b$.
2. $a + (-b) + b + (-a) = 0$.
3. $(a + 1) + (1 + b) = a + b + 2$.
4. $(a + b) + (c + d) = (d + a) + (c + b)$.
5. $(b + a + 1) + [(-a) + (-b) + 2] = 3$.
6. Use an example to show that subtraction is not an associative operation.
7. We have shown above that subtraction is an operation which annuls addition. Use a similar argument to show that addition likewise annuls subtraction.
8. Use the geometric notion of similarity ($\sim$) to show that similarity is an equivalence relation in any set of plane triangles.
9. Show that "is divisible by" is not an equivalence relation in the set of integers.
10. Decide which of the following number systems are closed under the operation of addition: (a) all odd integers; (b) all even integers; (c) all prime integers; (d) all integers divisible by 3; (e) all irrational numbers.
11. Designate which of the above properties are used in order to make the assertion that $- (\alpha + 0 + \beta) + (\beta + \alpha) = 0$.
12. If $a + t = a$, prove that $t = 0$, thereby establishing the uniqueness of the additive identity 0.
13. If we replace c by a in E$_3$, it would appear (!) that E$_2$ and E$_3$ together imply E$_1$. Is this true?
14. If we define an equality relation ($=$) so that $a = b$ provided a and b are both even or both odd, is this type of equality an equivalence relation in the set of integers? How many distinct (i.e., "unequal") integers would there be with this definition of equality?

1.3   The Real Number System as a Field

In the set of real numbers, we also define the operation of multiplication, and the familiar multiplicative properties are quite similar to those for addition. We use the juxtaposition of symbols as an indication of multiplication, and the following list of properties parallel those which we listed in §1.2 for addition.

M_1: The "product" ab is a uniquely determined real number, so that the system R is closed under multiplication.

M_2: The *associative* law of multiplication, or $a(bc) = (ab)c$.

M_3: There exists a real number 1, known as the *multiplicative identity*, with the property that $a(1) = (1)a = a$.

M_4: There is associated with each nonzero real number a a real number a^{-1}, known as the *multiplicative inverse* of a, such that $aa^{-1} = a^{-1}a = 1$.

M_5: The *commutative* law of multiplication, or $ab = ba$.

In view of the remark following the parallel listing of the additive properties of R, it should be evident that the nonzero real numbers form a commutative, or abelian, group under multiplication. We may also say that the nonzero elements of R make up a multiplicative abelian group. The operation symbols for the additive and multiplicative groups of R are different, and the additive and multiplicative identities and inverses are quite different numbers. However, the basic listings of the rules are the same for the additive and multiplicative systems.

The two characteristic properties of real numbers which connect the operations of addition and multiplication are called the *distributive* laws (left and right). We designate these by D.

D: $a(b + c) = ab + ac$,
$(a + b)c = ac + bc$.

Actually, it is possible to prove either of these distributive laws from the other, but we shall find it convenient to use D to refer to either or both of them.

A set of elements, with an equivalence relation (such as equality) and two operations (such as addition and multiplication) which satisfy the requirements $A_1, A_2, A_3, A_4, A_5, M_1, M_2, M_3, M_4, M_5,$ D, comprises an algebraic system known as a *field*. It is then a consequence of our definition that the system of real numbers constitutes a field.

There is one final "rule of substitution" which is useful in many algebraic manipulations and which should be mentioned. We use S to designate this rule.

S: In any algebraic expression, it is permissible to replace any element by an equal element, without affecting the value of the expression.

Basically, this means that if $a = a'$ and $b = b'$, then (1) $a + b = a' + b'$

and (2) $ab = a'b'$. Hence, sums and products of equal quantities are themselves equal. It then follows that any sum or product is independent of "equal" representations of the numbers which appear in its formation, and we sometimes express this by saying that the operations of addition and multiplication are *well defined* in *R*.

Just as subtraction is inverse to addition, so is *division* the inverse operation to multiplication. The division or quotient of a by b, designated a/b, is *defined* to be the product ab^{-1}, if $b \neq 0$. If $b = 0$, $a/0$ is without meaning, which is to say that **division by 0 is undefined.** The identification of a/b with ab^{-1}, in the multiplicative system, may be seen to parallel the identification of $a - b$ with $a + (-b)$ in the additive system.

EXAMPLE 1.   If $\alpha = a$ and $\beta = b$, the substitution principle S allows us to state that $(2\alpha + 3\beta)(\alpha - \beta) = (2a + 3b)(a - b)$.

EXAMPLE 2.   Prove that $(a + b)(c + d) = (ac + bc) + (ad + bd)$, including the justification of each step in the proof.

SOLUTION

$$(a + b)(c + d) = a(c + d) + b(c + d) \qquad\qquad\qquad [\text{D}]$$
$$= (ac + ad) + (bc + bd) \qquad\qquad\qquad [\text{D}]$$
$$= ac + [ad + (bc + bd)] \qquad\qquad\qquad [\text{A}_2]$$
$$= ac + [(bc + bd) + ad] \qquad\qquad\qquad [\text{A}_5]$$
$$= [ac + (bc + bd)] + ad \qquad\qquad\qquad [\text{A}_2]$$
$$= [(ac + bc) + bd] + ad \qquad\qquad\qquad [\text{A}_2]$$
$$= (ac + bc) + (bd + ad) \qquad\qquad\qquad [\text{A}_2]$$
$$= (ac + bc) + (ad + bd). \qquad\qquad\qquad [\text{A}_5]$$

Hence,
$$(a + b)(c + d) = (ac + bc) + (ad + bd). \qquad\qquad\qquad [\text{E}_3^*]$$

EXAMPLE 3.   Prove that $ab + (a + b)c = (a + c)b + ac$, including the justification of each step in the proof.

SOLUTION

$$ab + (a + b)c = ab + (ac + bc) \qquad\qquad\qquad [\text{D}]$$
$$= ab + (bc + ac) \qquad\qquad\qquad [\text{A}_5]$$
$$= ab + (cb + ac) \qquad\qquad\qquad [\text{M}_5]$$

$$= (ab + cb) + ac \qquad [A_2]$$

$$= (a + c)b + ac. \qquad [D]$$

Hence,

$$ab + (a + b)c = (a + c)b + ac. \qquad [E_3^*]$$

PROBLEMS

In Problems 1 through 5, use the given properties of real numbers to establish the equalities, including the proper justification at each step.

1. $(a + b)c + ab = b(c + a) + ac.$
2. $(a + 1)(b + 2) = ab + (b + 2a + 2).$
3. $b(a + 1) + [(-b) + a] = a(b + 1).$
4. $(a + b + c)d = d(a + b) + cd.$
5. $(ab)(cd) = (cb)(ad).$
6. The system of integers, with the equality relation and the usual operations of addition and multiplication, fails to be a field because it lacks one property. Which property is lacking?
7. Decide which of the algebraic systems of Problem 10 of §1.2 are closed under ordinary multiplication.
8. If $a = 2$ and $b = 5$, use the substitution principle S to simplify $3(a + 2b) + 4ab.$
9. Use an example to show that the operation of division is neither commutative nor associative in R.
10. Show that division is the inverse of multiplication in the sense that dividing and multiplying by the same nonzero number are processes which annul each other.
11. If $b \neq 0$, show that $ab = b$ implies that $a = 1$, thereby proving the uniqueness of the multiplicative identity.
12. Examine the system of all proper fractions with the usual operations of addition and multiplication, and decide which of the 11 additive and multiplicative properties of real numbers listed in this and the preceding sections remain valid.

1.4 Important Properties of Real Numbers

In the two preceding sections we have given a brief description of the basic axioms at the foundation of our system of real numbers. It is the purpose of this section to show how these axioms can be used to derive other familiar properties of real numbers. It may be well to point out that these properties are probably as well known as the axioms, and it is our intention to show *why* they are consequences of the axioms rather than to derive any intrinsically new properties. We ask the student to keep this purpose in mind, as we derive the results of this section, for without this understanding the study in this section will appear quite pointless.

THEOREM 1.41. (Additive cancellation law). If $a + b = a + c$, then $b = c$.

PROOF

$$a + b = a + c, \qquad \text{[Given]}$$

$$-a + (a + b) = -a + (a + c), \qquad \text{[S]}$$

$$(-a + a) + b = (-a + a) + c, \qquad \text{[A}_2\text{]}$$

$$0 + b = 0 + c, \qquad \text{[A}_4\text{]}$$

$$b = c. \qquad \text{[A}_3\text{]}$$

THEOREM 1.42. The number 0 is the only real number such that

$$a + 0 = a.$$

PROOF. Suppose t is a real number such that $a + t = a$. Then,

$$a + t = a + 0. \qquad \text{[S]}$$

Hence,

$$t = 0. \qquad \text{[Theorem 1.41]}$$

THEOREM 1.43. The number $-a$ is the only real number such that

$$a + (-a) = 0.$$

PROOF. Suppose $a + x = 0$, for some real number x. Then,

$$a + x = a + (-a). \qquad \text{[E}_3^*\text{]}$$

Hence,

$$x = -a. \qquad \text{[Theorem 1.41]}$$

THEOREM 1.44. The number 1 is the only real number such that

$$a(1) = a, \qquad a \neq 0.$$

PROOF. Suppose $ax = a(1)$, for some real number x. Then,

$$a^{-1}(ax) = a^{-1}[a(1)], \qquad \text{[S]}$$

$$(a^{-1}a)x = (a^{-1}a)1, \qquad \text{[M}_2\text{]}$$

$$(1)x = (1)1, \qquad \text{[M}_4\text{]}$$

$$x = 1. \qquad \text{[M}_3\text{]}$$

THEOREM 1.45.   The real number a^{-1} is the only real number such that

$$aa^{-1} = 1, \qquad a \neq 0.$$

PROOF.   Suppose $ax = 1$, for some real number x. Then,

$$a^{-1}(ax) = a^{-1}(1), \qquad\qquad\qquad \text{[S]}$$

$$(a^{-1}a)x = a^{-1}, \qquad\qquad\qquad \text{[M}_2\text{, M}_3\text{]}$$

$$(1)x = a^{-1}, \qquad\qquad\qquad \text{[M}_4\text{]}$$

$$x = a^{-1}. \qquad\qquad\qquad \text{[M}_3\text{]}$$

THEOREM 1.46. $a0 = 0$.

PROOF

$$aa + a0 = a(a + 0) \qquad\qquad\qquad \text{[D]}$$

$$= aa. \qquad\qquad\qquad \text{[A}_3\text{]}$$

Hence,

$$a0 = 0. \qquad\qquad\qquad \text{[Theorem 1.41]}$$

THEOREM 1.47. $a(-b) = (-a)b = -ab$.

PROOF

$$ab + a(-b) = a[b + (-b)] \qquad\qquad\qquad \text{[D]}$$

$$= a0 \qquad\qquad\qquad \text{[A}_4\text{]}$$

$$= 0. \qquad\qquad\qquad \text{[Theorem 1.46]}$$

Hence,

$$a(-b) = -ab. \qquad\qquad\qquad \text{[A}_4\text{, Theorem 1.43]}$$

The proof that $(-a)b = -ab$ is similar.

THEOREM 1.48. $-(-a) = a; (a^{-1})^{-1} = a,$ if $a \neq 0$.

PROOF.   Since $-a + a = 0$, an application of Theorem 1.43 shows that $a = -(-a)$. A similar application of Theorem 1.45 to $a^{-1}a = 1$ shows that $a = (a^{-1})^{-1}$.

THEOREM 1.49. $(-a)(-b) = ab$.

PROOF

$$-ab + (-a)(-b) = (-a)b + (-a)(-b) \text{ [Theorem 1.47]}$$

$$= -a[b + (-b)] \qquad \text{[D]}$$

$$= (-a)0 \qquad \text{[A}_4\text{]}$$

$$= 0. \qquad \text{[Theorem 1.46]}$$

Hence,

$$(-a)(-b) = -(-ab) = ab. \qquad \text{[Theorem 1.48]}$$

THEOREM 1.410.   If $ab = 0$, then either $a = 0$, $b = 0$, or $a = b = 0$.

PROOF.   If $a = 0$, or $a = b = 0$, there is nothing to prove, so let us assume that $a \neq 0$. Then,

$$a^{-1}(ab) = a^{-1}(0), \qquad \text{[S, M}_4\text{]}$$

$$(a^{-1}a)b = 0, \qquad \text{[Theorem 1.46, M}_2\text{]}$$

$$(1)b = 0, \qquad \text{[M}_4\text{]}$$

$$b = 0. \qquad \text{[M}_3\text{]}$$

It is Theorem 1.410 that is so invaluable in the solution of equations. For example, if x is a real number such that $(x - 2)(x + 3) = 0$, it is a consequence of this theorem that either $x - 2 = 0$ or $x + 3 = 0$. This would then lead to the solutions of the equation as 2 or -3.

PROBLEMS

1. Use a proof similar to that of Theorem 1.47 to show that $(-a)b = -ab$.

2. Prove that $(-1)a = -a$.

3. Prove that $-(a + b) = (-a) + (-b)$.

4. Use a proof similar to that of Theorem 1.41 to show that if $ab = ac$, $a \neq 0$, then $b = c$. (This is the cancellation law of multiplication.)

5. If $a = b$, why can we conclude that $-a = -b$?

6. Prove that $(a + b)(a - b) = a^2 - b^2$, including all steps in the proof with their references.

7. If x is a real number such that $(x + 1)(x - 2)(x - 1) = 0$, why can we conclude that either $x = -1$, $x = 2$, or $x = 1$?

8. Give the steps of the argument, implied in the proof of Theorem 1.48, that $(a^{-1})^{-1} = a$, for $a \neq 0$.

9. Prove that the right distributive law $[(a + b)c = ac + bc]$ implies the left distributive law $[a(b + c) = ab + ac]$.

10. Give reasons why $a/b = 1$ requires that $a = b$.

11. Explain why $(a + b)/c = a/c + b/c$, $c \neq 0$.

12. Explain why $-(a/b) = (-a)/b = a/(-b)$.

13. Give the basis for the cancellation process: $a(b/a) = b$, $a \neq 0$.

1.5   Order Properties of Real Numbers

The properties of the real numbers, as we have discussed them so far, have not involved any reference to the important "less than" relation ($<$). However, it is a well-known fact that this "order" relation is defined in R so that, for any two distinct real numbers a and b, it is true that either $a < b$ or $b < a$. The symbolism $b > a$ means the same as $a < b$, while $a \leq b$ and $b \geq a$ allow for the possibility that $a = b$. A number x such that $x > 0$ is said to be *positive*, while x is *negative* if $x < 0$. Every nonzero real number is either positive or negative, and the relation $a < b$ may be considered equivalent to the assertion that $b = a + h$ for some real number $h > 0$. For example, since $1 = 0 + 1$, it follows that $1 > 0$; and a similar remark shows that $-1 < 0$. It thus appears that the notions of "positive" and "negative," which we have used earlier in an intuitive fashion, are intimately connected with the order relation "less than."

In the geometric representation of the real numbers, we associate each real number with a fixed point on a straight line of infinite extent—known as the "real line." The point associated with the number a is located to the left of the point associated with b provided $a < b$. In this way all positive numbers are located to the right of 0 (the *origin* of the number scale), while all negative numbers are located to the left of 0. It is the *fundamental postulate of analytic geometry* that there is a one-to-one correspondence between the real numbers and the points of the real line. In fact, this correspondence is so closely ingrained in our thinking that we often appear to identify the points with the numbers and speak, for example, of "point 2" on the real line. In Figure 2 we have portrayed this geometric representation of R. We sometimes refer to this representation as an "algebraic scale."

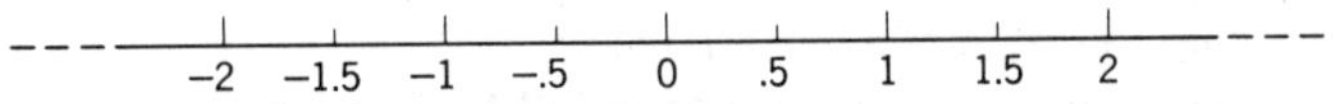

Figure 2

We now list the basic properties possessed by the "less than" relation, and we shall accept them without proof.

     O_1:   Exactly one of the following holds: $a < b$, $a > b$, $a = b$. This is known as the law of *Trichotomy*.

     O_2:   If $a < b$ and $b < c$, then $a < c$.

     O_3:   If $a < b$, then $a + c < b + c$.

     O_4:   If $a < b$ and $c > 0$, then $ac < bc$.

A field, in which is defined an order relation $<$ possessing the above properties, is said to be an *ordered* field.

The system of real numbers is then an ordered field.

The many other familiar properties of the "less than" relation can be derived from the four basic ones above. We illustrate this dependence with two examples.

EXAMPLE 1.   If $a < 0$ and $b < 0$, then $ab > 0$.

PROOF

$$a + (-a) < 0 + (-a), \qquad\qquad [O_3]$$

$$b + (-b) < 0 + (-b). \qquad\qquad [O_3]$$

Hence,

$$0 < -a, \text{ and } 0 < -b \text{ or, equivalently, } -b > 0. \qquad [A_4]$$

Then,

$$0 = 0(-b) < (-a)(-b), \text{ and so } (-a)(-b) > 0. \qquad [O_4]$$

EXAMPLE 2.   If $a < b$ and $c < 0$, then $ac > bc$.

PROOF

$$a + (-a) < b + (-a), \qquad\qquad [O_3]$$

$$0 < b - a, \qquad\qquad [A_4]$$

$$c(b - a) < 0(b - a), \qquad\qquad [O_4]$$

$$cb - ca < 0, \qquad\qquad [D]$$

$$cb - ca + ca < 0 + ca, \qquad\qquad [O_3]$$

$$cb < ca, \qquad\qquad [A_3, A_4]$$

$$ac > bc. \qquad\qquad [M_5]$$

Other familiar properties of the real numbers are included in the problems following this section.

The important notion of "absolute," or "numerical," value of a real number is closely associated with order. Intuitively, we often think of this absolute value of a number as its magnitude, without any regard to its sign. [In this connection, it must be noted that a number $-a$ is not necessarily negative. It may be, for example, that $a = -2$, so that $-a = -(-2) = 2$.] However, the following definition is more satisfactory.

Definition.   The *absolute*, or *numerical*, *value* of a real number a is the nonnegative number, designated $|a|$, defined so that

$$|a| = a, \quad \text{if } a \geq 0$$
$$ = -a, \quad \text{if } a < 0.$$

For example, $|-3| = 3$, and $|5| = 5$. Furthermore, $\sqrt{x^2} = |x|$, for any real x.

One of the most important consequences of the definition of absolute value is the theorem given below. Other useful results will be found in the problems of this section.

THEOREM 1.51. $-|a| \leq a \leq |a|$.

PROOF.   If $a \geq 0$, $a = |a|$ by definition; if $a < 0$, $0 < -a$ and $|a| = -a$, so that $a < |a|$. Hence, for any real a, $a \leq |a|$. A similar argument shows that $-|a| \leq a$, and so $-|a| \leq a \leq |a|$.

PROBLEMS

NOTE: The solutions of some problems may depend on earlier problems of this set.

1. If $a < b$ and $c < d$, prove that $a + c < b + d$.
2. If $a < b$, prove that $b - a$ is positive.
3. If $a < 0$, prove that $-a > 0$.
4. If $a > 0$ and $b > 0$, prove that $a + b > 0$.
5. If $a < b$, prove that $-a > -b$.
6. If $a > 0$ and $b > 0$, prove that $ab > 0$.
7. If $a \neq 0$, prove that $a^2 > 0$.
8. Prove that $1/a > 0$ if and only if $a > 0$.
9. If $a > b$ and $ab > 0$, prove that $1/a < 1/b$.
10. If $a > 0$, show that $a + 1/a \geq 2$.
11. Prove that $a^2 + b^2 \geq 2ab$.
12. Use the result in Problem 11 to prove that $a^2 + b^2 + c^2 \geq ab + ac + bc$.
13. Determine $|x|$ if $x =$ (a) -2; (b) 3; (c) -4; (d) 0; (e) $-\sqrt{2}$.
14. Express the inequality of Theorem 1.51 if $a = -6$.
15. Prove that $|ab| = |a| \cdot |b|$.
16. Prove that $|a/b| = |a|/|b|$, $b \neq 0$.
17. Determine x if $x = |\frac{1}{3} - \frac{3}{4}|$.
18. Determine x if $x = |\frac{1}{2} - \frac{2}{3}|$.
19. Prove that $-m \leq x \leq m$ implies that $|x| \leq m$, if $m \geq 0$.
20. Use the result in Problem 19 to prove that $|a + b| \leq |a| + |b|$. [Hint: Apply the result in Theorem 1.51 to both a and b.]

1.6   The Completeness Property

The order properties discussed in §1.5 are not distinctively characteristic of the *real* numbers, for these properties are also possessed by the rational numbers. However, the property of "completeness," which we are now about to describe, is possessed by the real numbers but not by the system of rational numbers.

If a and b are real numbers, with $a < b$, the set of all real numbers x such that $a < x < b$ is called an *open interval* and is designated (a, b). If $a \leq x \leq b$, the set is a *closed interval* and is designated $[a, b]$. The sets $(2, 3)$ and $[2, 3]$ are respective illustrations of an open and a closed interval, with 2 and 3 as *end points*. Either type of interval is "bounded" by its end points in the sense of the following definition.

Definition. A set S of real numbers is *bounded above* by b (or has b as an *upper bound*), if $x \leq b$ for every x in S. Similarly, S is *bounded below* by a (or has a as a *lower bound*), if $a \leq x$ for every x in S.

If S is the set of all rational numbers x such that $x^2 < 2$, it is clear that $\sqrt{2}$ or any larger number is an upper bound of S, while $-\sqrt{2}$ or any numerically larger negative number is a lower bound. The set N of natural numbers has 1 for a lower bound, but no upper bound exists; and neither an upper nor a lower bound exists for the set of all integers. We have implied, of course, that if a bound exists, this is never a unique number. As a final example, if S is the set of numbers consisting of 1, -2, 3, two upper bounds of S are 4 and 5.5, while two lower bounds are -2 and -3.75.

If c is any real number such that $a < c < b$, the order properties of R require that $a < (a + c)/2 < c < (c + b)/2 < b$. Hence, no c can be either a lower or upper bound of (a, b) or $[a, b]$, a fact that is geometrically evident. Hence b is the "least" upper bound and a is the "greatest" lower bound of either interval, two notions more carefully described by the following definition.

Definition. Let S be a set of real numbers. A lower bound l of S is called a *greatest lower bound* if $a \leq l$, for every lower bound a of S. Similarly, an upper bound u of S is a *least upper bound* if $u \leq b$, for every upper bound b of S.

The left and right end points of an interval are, respectively, the greatest lower bound and the least upper bound of the set of points in the interval (whether open or closed). Moreover, if a greatest lower bound or least upper bound of a set of real numbers exists, this number is unique. (Why?) The following is an important property of the system of real numbers, and is one which is in fact characteristic of R.

Completeness Property. If a nonempty set of real numbers is bounded above, it has a least upper bound; if the set is bounded below, it has a greatest lower bound. In short, any bounded set of real numbers has a greatest lower bound and a least upper bound.

We emphasize that this property is not capable of proof as in a theorem, but it is an intrinsic property of real numbers. The property may be stated in many equivalent forms, some of which involve such concepts as "Dedekind cuts," "nested intervals," and "Cauchy sequences," but the above form in terms of bounds seems to be the most intuitive. As we mentioned earlier, this property is not possessed by the rational numbers. For example, the set of all rational numbers x such that $x^2 < 2$ has no *rational* least upper bound; but $\sqrt{2}$ is a *real* number which is the least upper bound of the set in R. This property of completeness is essential to any critical discussion of length of a nonlinear arc of a curve—to mention but one of its many points of impact with elementary mathematics.

PROBLEMS

1. Find the real least upper bound and greatest lower bound of each of the finite sets whose members are listed: (a) 1, 4, 5, -3; (b) 0, -2, 5, 10; (c) $-\frac{1}{2}$, $-\frac{2}{3}$, $\frac{1}{4}$, 1, 0.

2. Identify the real least upper bound and the greatest lower bound of each of the following intervals: (a) [2, 5]; (b) $(-2, 3)$; (c) $[-1, 1]$; (d) (0, 7).

3. Explain why a least upper bound (or greatest lower bound) is unique, if it exists.

4. Give an example of a set which contains its greatest lower bound, and one which does not.

5. Use the directions of Problem 4 with "least upper bound" replacing "greatest lower bound."

6. Prove that every finite set of real numbers contains both its least upper bound and its greatest lower bound.

7. If $c > 0$, and S is the set of all positive integral multiples of c (i.e., S consists of $c, 2c, 3c, \ldots, nc, \ldots$), prove that S has no upper bound and so no least upper bound.

8. Use Problem 7 to prove the "Archimedean Principle": If c and d are real numbers, $c > 0$, there exists a positive integer n such that $nc > d$.

9. Prove that the least upper bound of the set consisting of $\frac{1}{2}$, $\frac{2}{3}$, $\frac{3}{4}$, $\frac{4}{5}$, $\ldots$, $n/n + 1$, $\ldots$ is 1. [Hint: Use Problem 8.]

10. Use Problem 8 to show that 0 is the greatest lower bound of the set consisting of $\frac{1}{1}$, $\frac{1}{2}$, $\frac{1}{3}$, $\ldots$, $1/n$, $\ldots$.

11. Prove that there always exists a rational number between any two given real numbers. [Hint: Use Problem 8.]

CHAPTER 2

Systems of Equations

2.1 Sets

The notion of a *set* is so basic in mathematics that we shall not attempt any definition and shall accept it as completely intuitive. We used the word several times in Chapter 1, where it was assumed that its meaning in the context was clear. It may help, however, if we remark that the word "set" may be regarded as a synonym for the words "collection" and "class," and these three words may be used interchangeably. For example, we may speak of the "set of real numbers," the "collection of books in your school library," or the "class of native Floridians."

The essential feature of a set is its membership, and if x is a member of a set S, we indicate this by writing $x \in S$. If x is not a member of S, we write $x \notin S$. To illustrate, if $R^\#$ is the set of rational numbers, $\frac{2}{3} \in R^\#$, but $\sqrt{2} \notin R^\#$.

There are two important ways to describe a set. If the set has a finite number of members, it is possible to list its entire membership, the names of the members usually being enclosed in braces. For example, the set whose members are the numbers $1, 3, 5$ may be designated as the set $\{1, 3, 5\}$. In cases where the set is not finite, or where its members are included because of some characteristic property, we may use the "set-builder" symbol $\{x| \quad \}$. The property required of x, if it is to be included in the set, is then described in the space following the vertical bar. Thus, the set of real numbers whose squares exceed 3 may be designated $\{x | x \in R, x^2 > 3\}$. If I is the set of integers, the set of positive integers which are less than 20 may be designated $\{x | x \in I, 1 \leq x < 20\}$.

If every member of a set A is also a member of a set B, we say that A is a *subset* of B and write $A \subseteq B$. The notation $A \subset B$ will be used to indicate that there exists at least one element of B which is not a member of *A,* or that *A* is a *proper* subset of *B.* Two sets *A* and *B* are *equal,* and we write *A* = *B* in case each set is a subset of the other. This will mean that "equal" sets contain the same elements, in agreement with our intuitive notion of equality.

The *empty* set $\varnothing$ is the set with no members, and, even though this may appear to be an unimportant set, it will turn out to be very useful. We consider the set $\varnothing$ to be unique and a subset of every set. Thus, $\varnothing \subseteq S$, for an arbitrary set *S.* If two sets have no elements in common, they are *disjoint,* which is equivalent to the statement that the empty set is their only common subset.

There is an arithmetic, or algebra, of subsets of a given set which has some resemblance to the arithmetic of real numbers. In the analogy between the two systems, the real numbers are replaced by the subsets of the given "universal" set *U.* We have already defined the equality relation for sets, while the operations of addition and multiplication are replaced by the operations of *union* ($\cup$) and *intersection* ($\cap$), respectively, which are defined as follows:

$$X \cup Y = \{x | x \in X \text{ or } x \in Y \text{ or both}\}.$$
$$X \cap Y = \{x | x \in X \text{ and } x \in Y\}.$$

These operations of union and intersection may be considered "binary" because they operate on any *two* subsets of *U* to produce a third subset. In addition to these binary operations, it is convenient to have a further "unary" operation in the algebra of subsets which operates on any one subset to produce a second subset, according to the following definition:

$$X' = \{x | x \in U, x \notin X\}.$$

Thus, *X'*, or the *complement* of *X* in *U,* is the set of elements in *U* which are not members of *X.* This operation of taking complements has no precise analogue in the arithmetic of real numbers. In the system of subsets, the role of 0 is played by the empty set $\varnothing$, since $X \cup \varnothing = \varnothing \cup X = X$, for any $X \subseteq U$. The role of the multiplicative identity 1 is played by the universal set *U,* because $X \cap U = U \cap X = X$, for any $X \subseteq U$. It may be well to point out that the set $\{b\}$, whose single member is the element *b,* is to be distinguished from the element *b.* For example, a mathematics class of one student may be abolished by the registrar, but the student will likely survive to register in another class!

In order to illustrate these operations, consider the universal set $U = \{1, 2, 3, 4, 5, 6, 7, 8, 9\}$, with subsets $X = \{1, 3, 5\}$ and $Y = \{2, 3, 4, 5, 9\}$. Then $X \cup Y = \{1, 2, 3, 4, 5, 9\}$, $X \cap Y = \{3, 5\}$, $X' = \{2, 4, 6, 7, 8, 9\}$, and $Y' = \{1, 6, 7, 8\}$.

The algebra of subsets of a set is an example of *Boolean* algebra, a mathematical discipline which has recently achieved considerable prominence. While we have noted that there are analogies between the system of real numbers and this Boolean algebra of subsets, the student is cautioned not to assume that all the familiar laws of arithmetic continue to hold in the new environment. It is true, however, that many of these do hold, and we shall illustrate this remark with an example. In order to verify the laws of an algebra of subsets, it is convenient to represent the subsets as plane sets of points within some plane figure, the latter to be regarded as the universal set. These diagrams, known as *Venn diagrams,* are of great use in the construction of proofs of propositions in an algebra of sets.

EXAMPLE 1. Use a Venn diagram to verify in an algebra of subsets that:

$$A \cap (B \cup C) = (A \cap B) \cup (A \cap C).$$

PROOF. A careful proof of this distributive law would require that we show that each element of the set represented on the left of the equality sign is in the set represented on the right, and conversely. However, if we represent each of the sets A, B, C by the points within the circles shown in Figure 3, it is easy to see that the shaded portion is a representation of both members of the given equation.

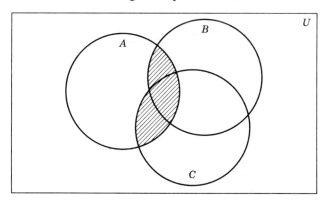

Figure 3

EXAMPLE 2. Use a Venn diagram to show that

$$(A \cup B)' = A' \cap B'.$$

PROOF. In Figure 4 we have represented the sets A and B by the sets of points within the indicated circles, both circles being inside a rectangle as universal set. If we recall that the complement of a set is the subset of points within the universe but not in the given set, the assertion of the equality follows immediately from an inspection of the Venn diagram.

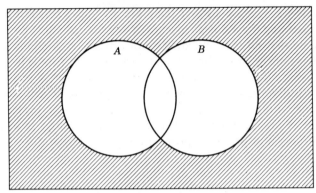

Figure 4

PROBLEMS

1. If A is the set of Boy Scout virtues, which of the following symbolic statements do you consider correct? (a) Rudeness $\in A$; (b) Bravery $\notin A$; (c) Loyalty $\in A$; (d) Uncleanliness $\notin A$; (e) Cheerfulness $\in A$.

2. List the members of the following sets:
   (a) $\{x|x$ is a city in your state with population over $100{,}000\}$.
   (b) $\{x|x$ is the catalogue designation of a course which you are taking$\}$.
   (c) $\{t|t$ is a planet in our solar system$\}$.
   (d) $\{y|y$ is a country in North America$\}$.

3. Let A be the set of universities in the Big Ten football conference, and decide which of the following are members of A: (a) the University of Illinois; (b) the head coach of the football team of Ohio State University; (c) the football team of the University of Wisconsin; (d) Purdue University.

4. Let $A = \{y|y$ is an equilateral triangle$\}$ and $B = \{t|t$ is a triangle with its interior angles equal$\}$. State a theorem from Plane Geometry which has the effect of asserting that $A = B$.

5. If $A = B$, $B = C$, and $C = D$, for sets A, B, C, explain why it must be the case that $A = D$.

6. Explain why $A \cap B = \varnothing$ means that A and B are disjoint sets.

7. Show that $A \cap B \cap C$ has a definite meaning without the use of any parentheses.

8. List all the subsets of $\{1, 3, 7\}$ which have at least two members.

9. The *power set* of a given set A is the set of all subsets of A. Verify that the power set of $\{a, b, c\}$ has eight members, and generalize this result.

10. If A and B are sets such that $A \subset B$, where $B = \{1, 2, 3, 4\}$, list the possibilities for A.

11. If S is the set of people in your state, identify two subsets of S which are: (a) disjoint; (b) not disjoint, but distinct.

12. List the members of $A \cup B$ and of $A \cap B$ for each of the following cases:
    (a) $A = \{1, 2, 3\}$, $B = \{1, 3, 5\}$; (b) $A = \{a, x, t\}$, $B = \{1, a, 2\}$; (c) $A = \{3, x, a\}$, $B = \{3, y, 2\}$.

13. If $A = \{1, 2, 3\}$, $B = \{2, 3, 4\}$, $C = \{3, 4, 5\}$, and $D = \{4, 5, 6\}$, list the

members of each of the following sets: (a) $A \cap B$; (b) $A \cup C$; (c) $(A \cap B) \cup (C \cap D)$; (d) $A \cap (B \cup D)$.

14. Use a Venn diagram to verify that $(A \cap B)' = A' \cup B'$.

15. Use a Venn diagram to verify each of the following laws for an algebra of sets:
(a) $A \cup (B \cup C) = (A \cup B) \cup C$;   (b) $(A \cap B) \cap C = A \cap (B \cap C)$;
(c) $A \cup A' = U$; (d) $A \cap A' = \varnothing$; (e) $A' \cap (A \cup B) = A' \cap B$.

16. Use the set-builder notation to symbolize each of the following sets, designating the integers, rational numbers, and real numbers by I, $R^{\#}$, and R, respectively: (a) the real numbers between 2 and 5, inclusive; (b) the integers between 1 and 25, inclusive; (c) the rational numbers whose squares do not exceed 9; (d) the real numbers which exceed 10 in absolute value.

2.2   Truth or Solution Sets

In its somewhat restricted usage by a mathematician, a *statement*, or *sentence*, is a declaration which is either true or false. The sentence "Florida is south of New York" is true, while the sentence "Chicago is in the State of Ohio" is false. Sentences of this kind always have "truth values": *true* for a true sentence and *false* for a false one. A formal or incomplete sentence such as "_____ is the capital of Michigan" or "X was the first President of the United States" is called an *open sentence* because, as it stands, it is neither true nor false. It is to be noted, however, that the first open sentence becomes false if the blank is filled in with "Flint," while the second is true if X is replaced by "George Washington."

In mathematics, the most common type of open sentence is an *equation* or *inequality*. From our present point of view, $x + 6 = 5$ [or, _____ $+ 6 = 5$] is an open sentence, which is called an *equation*, and is true if x is replaced by -1 and otherwise false. The symbol x plays the role of a "spaceholder" for a numeral, which would convert the equation into either a true or a false statement. Such a symbol is usually known as a *variable*. The *truth set*, or *solution set*, of an equation is the set of replacements which transform the open sentence into a true equality. Of course, we must know what sort of replacements for x are eligible. For example, is a replacement for x required to be a positive integer, a rational number, or a real number? The set of eligible replacements for a variable is called the *universe*, or the *domain U*, of the variable. If U is the set of positive integers, the solution set of the above equation $x + 6 = 5$ is the empty set $\varnothing$, but, if U is the set of integers, the solution set is $\{-1\}$. It is important to realize that the solution set of an equation depends on the universe of the variable as well as on the formal equation. A determination of the solution set of an equation is known as *solving* the equation.

The remarks in the preceding paragraph may also be applied to *inequalities*, or *inequations*. For example, we may wish to find the solution set of the inequality $t - 1 < 4$ in the universe of all real numbers. This solution set is the set of all real numbers less than 5, or, symbolically, $\{x | x \in R, x < 5\}$.

Open sentences are, of course, not restricted to one variable. Equations such as $y = x + 2$ and inequalities such as $x + y < z$ are of common occurrence and are illustrative of the use of more than one variable in an open sentence. While the universes of the variables in a given equation or inequality may be different, usually they are the same. Without an explicit statement to the contrary, we shall always assume that they are the same. Before discussing solution sets of open sentences involving more than one variable, however, it is necessary to introduce the notion of a *Cartesian product* of sets.

In our introduction to sets, it was implicit from our discussion that the order in which the elements of a set are listed is of no importance. For example, $\{1, 3, 5, 7\} = \{3, 5, 1, 7\} = \{7, 1, 5, 3\}$. However, there are times when it *is* important to take notice of the listed order of the elements of a set, and we then have an *ordered set*. If the names of the six prize winners of a contest are listed, the order in which the names occur usually makes quite a difference to the persons involved! It has been said that a recipe for success is "work, play," while the arrangement "play, work" often leads to disastrous results. If the latitude and longitude of a position are recorded as (45, 65), it is of great importance to anyone interested in locating the position to know which of the numbers is latitude and which is longitude. Such a pair of numbers in a prescribed order is called an *ordered pair*; the two numbers in the pair are called its *components*. It is customary to distinguish an ordered pair from an unordered set by the use of parentheses instead of braces. Two ordered sets are *equal* ($=$) if their respective components are equal. Thus $(2, 3) \neq (3, 2)$ but $\{2, 3\} = \{3, 2\}$. If there are three (or n) components of an ordered set, this set is called an *ordered triple* (or *ordered n-tuple*).

If A and B are any two sets (possibly not even distinct), the set of all ordered pairs (a, b), with $a \in A$ and $b \in B$, is called the *Cartesian product* set $A \times B$. Thus, $A \times B = \{(a, b) | a \in A, b \in B\}$. The special case $A \times A$ is frequently called simply the *Cartesian set* of A. By way of illustration, let $A = \{1, 2, 3\}$ and $B = \{-1, 1\}$. Then, $A \times B = \{(1, -1), (2, -1), (3, -1), (1, 1), (2, 1), (3, 1)\}$ and $B \times B = \{(-1, -1), (-1, 1), (1, -1), (1, 1)\}$. There is a very simple way to give a graphical representation in a plane, of a Cartesian product set. We first associate the elements of A with distinct points on a horizontal line, and the elements of B with distinct points on an intersecting vertical line in the plane. If we now draw vertical lines through all points associated with elements of A and horizontal lines through all points associated with elements of B, the points of intersection of these lines may be considered to represent the elements of $A \times B$. For example, the vertical line through $a \in A$ and the horizontal line through $b \in B$ intersect in a point which will represent the ordered pair (a, b). In Figure 5, we have given a graphical representation, or *have drawn a graph*, of $A \times B$, where $A = \{1, 2, 3, 4\}$ and $B = \{a, b, c\}$.

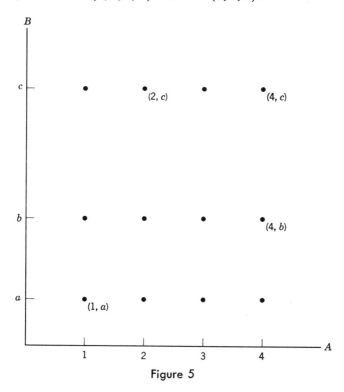

Figure 5

The case of most interest to us here is that in which both A and B are subsets of real numbers. In this case, the horizontal and vertical lines can be regarded as algebraic scales which intersect at their common zero point. We recall that each point of such a scale is associated with a real number, and every real number is associated with a point on an algebraic scale. We have already referred to this fact as the *Fundamental Postulate of Analytic Geometry*. The number scales are constructed so that positive numbers are to the right, or up, while negative numbers are to the left, or down, on the respective scales. A pair of algebraic scales placed in this position constitute a *rectangular coordinate system*. If $A = B = R$, the set of all real numbers, the graph of the Cartesian set $R \times R$ is the set of all points of the plane, while the ordered pair (a, b) associated with a point is called its *coordinate pair.* To illustrate a more restrictive situation, however, if we let $A = \{-1, 1, 2, 3\}$ and $B = \{-2, -1, 0, 1, 2\}$, the graph of the Cartesian product set $A \times B$ is shown in Figure 6.

If A, B, C are three sets, the set $\{(a, b, c) | a \in A, b \in B, c \in C\}$ is defined to be the Cartesian Product $A \times B \times C$, and it is immediate how this notion of product can be extended to involve any number of sets. However, we shall restrict our graphs to cases where the number of sets involved is two.

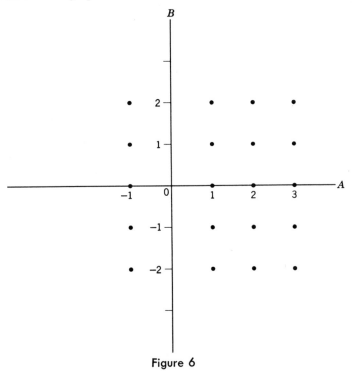

Figure 6

Returning now to the matter of solution sets, consider the equation $y = x + 4$, with x and y variables in the universe R. The equation becomes a true statement if x is replaced by 1 and y is replaced by 5, and so we say that $(1, 5)$ is a solution of the equation. There are, of course, many other solutions, and the complete solution set may be designated as $\{(x, y) | (x, y) \in R \times R, y = x + 4\}$. In stating that $(1, 5)$ is a solution of $y = x + 4$, it is important to understand, of course, that 1 is a replacement for x and 5 is a replacement for y. In general, if we designate an n-tuple as a solution of an equation in n variables, it is necessary to order the variables and to understand that the components of the n-tuple solution are associated with the variables *in the same ordered position.*

The usual methods of solving linear and quadratic equations are reviewed in the Appendix, while we consider the problem for more general polynomial equations in Chapter 9. Most of this chapter is devoted to methods of solving *systems* of linear equations, a subject which we introduce in the following section.

PROBLEMS

1. Paraphrase each of the following statements into a form not involving the symbol x:
   (a) For some integer x, x is divisible by 5.
   (b) For every x, if x is an orange then x is a fruit.
   (c) If x is a student who studies hard, then x will pass his examinations.
   (d) There exists x such that x is a dog and x is dangerous.
2. Decide which of the following are open sentences:
   (a) Abraham Lincoln was a President of the United States.
   (b) The number of prime factors of 12 is x.
   (c) x is an integer less than 10.
   (d) x is an integer which is either odd or the square of an integer.
3. In the universe of natural numbers, decide whether each of the following is an open sentence or a statement:
   (a) t is even. (b) x is a prime between 4 and 18.
   (c) For every x, x is either divisible by 3 or 2. (d) $3 + 5 = 8$.
   (e) $x + y = z$. (f) $2 + 3 < 10$.
4. In the universe of rational numbers, decide whether each of the following open sentences is true of all, a finite number of, or no elements in the universe:
   (a) $x^2 - 25 = (x - 5)(x + 5)$.   (b) $2x - 5 = 7$.
   (c) $x^2 - 5x + 6 = 0$.   (d) $x^2 = 5$.
   (e) $x^2 > -2$.   (f) $x^2 + 2x = x(x + 2)$.
5. List the members of $A \times B$ for each of the following definitions:
   (a) $A = \{1, 2, 3\}$, $B = \{1, 2\}$. (b) $A = \{a, b\}$, $B = \{2, 4, 6\}$.
   (c) $A = \{1, a, c\}$, $B = \{3, x, a\}$. (d) $A = \{1\}$, $B = \{2, 3\}$.
6. List all the members of $A \times A$ where $A = \{2, 4, 6\}$.
7. If A and B are sets which contain 5 and 10 members, respectively, how many members are there in (a) $A \times B$; (b) $A \times A$; (c) $B \times B$?
8. Draw a conclusion from each of the following assertions:
   (a) $(2, x) = (2, y)$; (b) $(x, 1) = (3, y)$; (c) $(x, y) = (y, x)$.
9. Determine the maximum number of ordered pairs which can be formed, using the elements of $\{a, b, c, d\}$ for components.
10. If $A = \{1, 2, 3\}$, determine: (a) all subsets of A with two members; (b) the power set of A (see Problem 9 of §2.1); (c) the Cartesian set of A.
11. Construct a graph of $A \times B$ where (a) $A = \{1, 2\}$, $B = \{1, 2, 3\}$; (b) $A = \{1, 3\}$, $B = \{2, 3\}$; (c) $A = \{2\}$, $B = \{3\}$.
12. Explain why an open sentence always partitions the universe into two disjoint subsets. What is the significance if one of these sets is $\varnothing$?

13. If the truth set of an open sentence is $\varnothing$, what does one conclude?
14. What is the effect on the truth set of an equation if both members of the equation are multiplied by $k \neq 0$? If $k = 0$, what is the effect?
15. Find the truth set of each of the following open sentences in the universe of real numbers:
    (a) $x^2 - 9 = 0$. (b) $x^2 + 6 = 0$. (c) $x^2 - 4x + 4 = 0$.
    (d) $x(x - 2)(x - 3) = 0$. (e) $x + 1 < 6$. (f) $x^2 < 4$.

2.3 Systems of Linear Equations

A compound statement is one which involves more than one assertion. For example, "George Washington was the first President of the United States and Albany is the capital of the State of New York," is the union, or "conjunction," of two statements. Since each of the individual statements is true, the compound statement is also seen to be true. It is easy to think of compound statements involving any number of individual statements, some of them false and some of them true. Of course, each separate statement has its own truth-value, and the compound statement is false if any one of the separate statements is false. For example, "A circle is round and a man has never orbited the earth" is a false statement, due to the falsity of the second part of the double statement.

Just as we have compound statements, so we have compound open sentences which involve one or more variables. An example of this, with one variable, is "x is a capital city and x is a city in the State of California," while a variant of this with two variables would be "x is a capital city and y is a city in the State of California." The universe of x is the set of names of the fifty capital cities, and the universe of y is the set of names of all cities in California. In the case of the first compound sentence, it is clear that there is only one replacement for x which will make the sentence true, and this replacement is "Sacramento." This set of one name is then the truth set of the first open sentence. In the case of the second sentence, there are many elements in its truth set; there are fifty choices for x, while the name of any city in California may replace y.

More generally, suppose T is a compound open sentence made up of the union of n open sentences, each involving the same variable. Then, if $S_1, S_2, \ldots, S_n$ are the truth sets of the n individual sentences, the truth set of T is the intersection $S_1 \cap S_2 \cap \cdots \cap S_n$. In the case of more than one variable, if we order them in some manner and agree to list the separate solutions in the same order, we again have the result that the truth set of a compound sentence is the intersection of the truth sets of the separate sentences. The meaning of this will be clarified in our subsequent discussions.

Before considering the simultaneous solutions of a system of linear equation—the principal topic of this chapter—we digress to introduce some useful notation. An n-tuple $(a_1, a_2, \ldots, a_n)$ is sometimes called a *vector*, or *row vector*. As an ordered set, it is apparent that we may just as well write it as a vertical array:

$$\begin{pmatrix} a_1 \\ a_2 \\ \cdot \\ \cdot \\ \cdot \\ a_n \end{pmatrix},$$

and in this form it may be called a *column vector*. A vector of either kind is a special case of a *matrix*—to be discussed later. For reasons of consistency with matrix practice we *define* the product of a row vector and a column vector, each with the same number of components, as follows:

$$(a_1, a_2, \ldots, a_n) \begin{pmatrix} b_1 \\ b_2 \\ \cdot \\ \cdot \\ \cdot \\ b_n \end{pmatrix} = (a_1 b_1 + a_2 b_2 + \cdots + a_n b_n),$$

and the latter "ordered" 1-tuple need not be distinguished from its single scalar component. The "scalar," or number resulting from this type of product of a row and column vector is also called the "scalar product" of the two vectors. We make the remark, in passing, that the commas are often omitted in writing an n-tuple, another practice due to matrix influence. To illustrate, the scalar product of two vectors,

$$(2 \quad 3 \quad 5) \begin{pmatrix} 1 \\ -1 \\ 2 \end{pmatrix} = (2 - 3 + 10) = (9) = 9.$$

In mathematics, the usual type of open sentence is the equation, and a compound open sentence in this environment is usually a *system* of equations. In this chapter, for the most part, we are interested in systems of linear equations—or "linear systems"—and their simultaneous solutions. A typical linear equation in n "unknowns" or variables $x_1, x_2, \ldots, x_n$ has the form $a_1 x_1 + a_2 x_2 + \cdots + a_n x_n = b$, where $a_1, a_2, \ldots, a_n$, and b are real numbers. If we let

$$\mathbf{F} = (a_1, a_2, \ldots, a_n)$$

and

$$X = \begin{pmatrix} x_1 \\ x_2 \\ \cdot \\ \cdot \\ \cdot \\ x_n \end{pmatrix}$$

this typical equation can now be written in compact form as the scalar product of two vectors: $\mathbf{F}\mathbf{X} = b$. If the domain of each variable is R, the domain of the "vector" variable $\mathbf{X}$ is the Cartesian product $R \times R \times \cdots \times R$, where we think of the elements of this universe of n-tuples as *column vectors*. *In this chapter, unless explicit statement is made to the contrary or the context implies otherwise, we shall always assume the universe of our system of equations is a Cartesian set of R.* The *solution set* of $\mathbf{F}\mathbf{X} = b$ is then the set of all real n-tuples, which, when replacing $\mathbf{X}$ in the equation, result in true equalities. The symbol $\mathbf{X}$ will designate a "column" variable throughout the chapter, except in §2.9 where no use is made of vector equations of the form $\mathbf{F}\mathbf{X} = b$.

Finally, let us consider a system of linear equations, which we may write in the form: $\mathbf{F}_1\mathbf{X} = b_1, \mathbf{F}_2\mathbf{X} = b_2, \ldots, \mathbf{F}_m\mathbf{X} = b_m$. This system consists of m individual equations, whose solution sets may be designated by $S_1, S_2, \ldots, S_m$, respectively. As with general compound sentences, the solution set of the system is then the intersection $S_1 \cap S_2 \cap \cdots \cap S_m$ of the individual solutions sets. For example, consider the linear system:

$$2x_1 - 3x_2 + 4x_3 = 9,$$
$$x_1 + x_2 + x_3 = 1.$$

Then, with $\mathbf{X} = \begin{pmatrix} x_1 \\ x_2 \\ x_3 \end{pmatrix}$, it is easy to see that $\begin{pmatrix} 1 \\ -1 \\ 1 \end{pmatrix}$ is a replacement for $\mathbf{X}$

which makes both equations of the system true and so is a solution of the system. Various methods for obtaining such solutions will be outlined in subsequent sections. To save space, it is often desirable to designate a column vector by the "transpose" (indicated by $^\mathrm{T}$), of the equivalent row vector. The word "transpose" has been borrowed from a more general usage in matrix theory, but in the present context the *transpose* of a row vector is the same ordered set written as a column. In this symbolism, the vector $\begin{pmatrix} x_1 \\ x_2 \\ x_3 \end{pmatrix}$ may then be written as $(x_1 \quad x_2 \quad x_3)^\mathrm{T}$.

PROBLEMS

1. Let p, q, r, s be the indicated statements:

     p: Today is warm. q: It is cloudy.

     r: The air is humid. s: A breeze is blowing.

Write down the statement which is the conjunction of: (a) p and q; (b) q and r; (c) p, q, and r; (d) p, q, and s.

2. Explain why the following statements are not conjunctions of two statements:

(a) John and Bill are good friends.

(b) The sum of 5 and 2 is 7.

(c) Work and play should be accomplished in that order.

(d) Wisconsin and Illinois share a common border.

3. Write each of the following compound statements as the conjunction of two or more statements:

(a) x and y are both even integers.

(b) The problem can be solved by either algebra or arithmetic.

(c) t is an odd number which is larger than 10.

(d) Mary and I had a date and we went to a movie.

(e) The room was hot and crowded but no one opened a window.

(f) The sum of two integers is 15 while their difference is 1.

4. Identify the vectors **F** and **X**, and write each of the following equations in the form $\mathbf{FX} = b$:

(a) $2x_1 + 2x_2 - x_3 = 5$.   (b) $3x - 2y + z = 7$.

(c) $x + y + z = 0$.   (d) $x - y = 2$.

(e) $x_1 - 2x_2 + 3x_3 = 1$.   (f) $2x + 0y + z = 5$.

5. Verify that $(x \; y \; z)$ [or $(x_1 \; x_2 \; x_3)$] = $(1 \; 0 \; -2)$ is a solution of each of the following equations:

(a) $2x - 5y + 4z = -6$.   (b) $x_1 + 2x_2 - 3x_3 = 7$.

(c) $4x + 0y - 2z = 8$.   (d) $0x_1 + 0x_2 - x_3 = 2$.

6. Verify that $(x \; y)$ [or $(x_1 \; x_2)$] = $(-1 \; 2)$ is a solution of each of the following systems of equations:

(a) $x + y = 1$,   (b) $3x_1 - 2x_2 = -7$,

     $2x + y = 0$. $2x_1 + x_2 = \quad 0$,

                              $3x_1 + 4x_2 = \quad 5$.

(c) $x - y = -3$,

     $3x + 2y = \quad 1$,

     $4x - x = -6$.

7. Consider the two equations:

$$2x - 3y + \quad z = 10,$$
$$3x + \quad y - 2z = \quad 5.$$

By actual experimentation, determine two solutions of each equation in $R \times R \times R$. Replace the right member of the second equation by any convenient number, so that exactly one of the solutions obtained for the first equation will also be a solution of the revised second equation.

8. Consider a system of linear equations involving the variable vector $\mathbf{X} = (x_1 \; x_2 \; x_3)^\mathsf{T}$. If $I, R^\#$, and R are, respectively, the sets of integers, rational numbers, and real numbers, explain what it means to determine the solution set of the system in: (a) $R \times R \times R$; (b) $R^{\#} \times R^{\#} \times R^{\#}$; (c) $I \times I \times I$; (d) $R \times I \times I$; (e) $I \times R^{\#} \times R^{\#}$.

2.4   Simple Systems

We now come to the problem of actually determining the solution set of a system of linear equations. The general method is to replace each of the equations by another equation which has the same solution set, so that the conjunction of the new equations has the same solution set as the original system. After a finite number of replacements, we obtain a system of equations whose solutions are immediately evident. If this final solution set is empty, the system has no solution and its equations are *inconsistent*. If there is a single member in the solution set, the system has this member as its *unique* solution, but it may happen that a solution set has infinitely many members. In this section we confine our discussion to systems of two equations in two variables.

Two equations or systems of equations are said to be *equivalent* if their solution sets are the same. Any operation which we can perform on the equations of a system without any change in its solution set is known as an *elementary operation*. There are three such elementary operations in common use:

1. Eliminate any equation which has no nonzero coefficient.
2. Multiply both members of an equation by the same nonzero number.
3. Add any real multiple of the members of one equation to the corresponding members of another equation of the system.

Any one of these operations on an equation of a system transforms the system into an equivalent system, and so does any sequence of such operations. These are the operations which we use to convert a system of equations into its simplest or solved form. We illustrate this "elimination" procedure with an example.

EXAMPLE 1.   Solve the linear system:

$$3x - 2y = 1,$$
$$6x + y = 7.$$

SOLUTION.   If we multiply both members of the second equation by 2, the resulting system is:

$$3x - 2y = 1,$$
$$12x + 2y = 14.$$

On adding the members of the second equation to the corresponding members of the first equation, we obtain:

$$15x = 15,$$
$$12x + 2y = 14.$$

From the first equation it follows that $x = 1$, while the second equation gives $y = 1$. The desired unique solution of the given system of equations is then:

$$X = (x \quad y)^T = (1 \quad 1)^T.$$

Let us now apply the above procedure to the more general pair of equations:

$$a_1 x + b_1 y = c_1,$$
$$a_2 x + b_2 y = c_2,$$

where we assume, for the sake of generality, that $a_1 a_2 \neq 0$ and $b_1 b_2 \neq 0$. On multiplying the members of the first equation by b_2 and those of the second by b_1, the result is the equivalent system

$$a_1 b_2 x + b_1 b_2 y = c_1 b_2,$$
$$a_2 b_1 x + b_2 b_1 y = c_2 b_1.$$

If we subtract the members of the second equation from the corresponding members of the first equation, we obtain:

$$(a_1 b_2 - a_2 b_1)x = c_1 b_2 - c_2 b_1,$$
$$a_2 b_1 x + b_2 b_1 y = c_2 b_1.$$

The first equation of this system now yields $x = (c_1 b_2 - c_2 b_1)/(a_1 b_2 - a_2 b_1)$, provided $a_1 b_2 - a_2 b_1 \neq 0$. If we substitute this solution for x in the second equation and solve the resulting linear equation for y, the result is $y = (a_1 c_2 - a_2 c_1)/(a_1 b_2 - a_2 b_1)$, and our system of equations has been solved.

We now introduce what we shall call for the present a "memory device" for the above solution. If we define the symbol $\begin{vmatrix} a & b \\ c & d \end{vmatrix}$ to represent the number $ad - bc$ (the difference of the products of the diagonal elements in the square array), the solution of the general system above is then $(x \quad y)^T$ where:

$$x = \frac{\begin{vmatrix} c_1 & b_1 \\ c_2 & b_2 \end{vmatrix}}{\begin{vmatrix} a_1 & b_1 \\ a_2 & b_2 \end{vmatrix}} \quad \text{and} \quad y = \frac{\begin{vmatrix} a_1 & c_1 \\ a_2 & c_2 \end{vmatrix}}{\begin{vmatrix} a_1 & b_1 \\ a_2 & b_2 \end{vmatrix}}.$$

Three things should be noted about the above symbolic solution:

1. the denominator, in both cases, involves the array of coefficients as they appear in the left members of the original equations;
2. the numerator, in each case, may be obtained from the denominator by replacing the coefficients of the unknown being determined by the right members of the equations;
3. the method fails to give a solution if $a_1b_2 - a_2b_1 = 0$.

If it happens that $a_1b_2 - a_2b_1 = 0$, the system is either inconsistent (with an empty solution set) or it has infinitely many solutions. These cases will be treated later in more general circumstances, but we shall give a few illuminating examples in this section.

EXAMPLE 2. Solve the linear system:

$$x - 3y = 1,$$
$$2x - 3y = 5.$$

SOLUTION. An application of the above memory device gives us the following results:

$$x = \frac{\begin{vmatrix} 1 & -3 \\ 5 & -3 \end{vmatrix}}{\begin{vmatrix} 1 & -3 \\ 2 & -3 \end{vmatrix}} = \frac{1(-3) - 5(-3)}{1(-3) - 2(-3)} = \frac{-3 + 15}{-3 + 6} = \frac{12}{3} = 4$$

$$y = \frac{\begin{vmatrix} 1 & 1 \\ 2 & 5 \end{vmatrix}}{\begin{vmatrix} 1 & -3 \\ 2 & -3 \end{vmatrix}} = \frac{1(5) - 2(1)}{3} = \frac{5 - 2}{3} = \frac{3}{3} = 1$$

The solution of the system is then $(4 \quad 1)^T$.

EXAMPLE 3. If we consider the equations

$$x - 2y = 5,$$
$$2x - 4y = 10,$$

we discover that $a_1b_2 - a_2b_1 = 0$. The above method is then inapplicable, but we observe that the second equation is obtainable from the first by merely doubling each of its members. Hence the two equations are equivalent as a system to the single equation $x - 2y = 5$. This equation—and so the original pair of equations—has infinitely many solutions for $(x \quad y)^T$. For example, $(7 \quad 1)^T$ and $(3 \quad -1)^T$ are easily seen to be solutions.

EXAMPLE 4. If we consider the system

$$x - 2y = 5,$$
$$2x - 4y = 3,$$

we again note that $a_1b_2 - a_2b_1 = 0$. However, while the left member of the second equation is twice the left member of the first equation, it is not true that 3 is twice 5! Hence no simultaneous solution of these equations is possible, and the system is inconsistent.

PROBLEMS

1. Explain why the solution set of a linear equation is unchanged by an application of any of the elementary operations.

   Use the method developed in this section to investigate the solution set of each of the systems in Problems 2 through 11. If a unique solution is found for any system, check this solution in the system by substitution. In each case, consider $R \times R$ as the universe.

2. $2x + 5y = 12,$
   $x + 3y = 7.$

3. $3x - y = -7,$
   $2x + 3y = 10.$

4. $x - 2y = 2,$
   $3x - 6y = 6.$

5. $x - 2y = 2,$
   $3x - 3y = 9.$

6. $2x + 3y = 1,$
   $8x + 12y = 3.$

7. $x + 2y/3 = 3,$
   $2x + y = 5.$

8. $2/x - 3/y = 3,$
   $3/x + 6/y = 8.$

9. $4/x - 3/y = 3,$
   $2/x + 9/y = -2.$

10. $x/2 + y/3 = 6,$
    $x/4 + y/5 = \frac{7}{2}.$

11. $1.2x + 0.4y = 1.24,$
    $0.2x - 2.2y + 0.02 = 0.$

12. The sum of the digits of a two-digit number is 14, while the number formed by reversing the digits is 18 less than the original number. Determine the number.

13. Determine the quantities of a 5 per cent acid solution which must be mixed with a 20 per cent acid solution in order to produce two gallons of a 15 per cent acid solution.

14. An airplane flies 1,386 miles with a tail wind in $4\frac{1}{2}$ hours. On the return trip, and against the same wind, the time of flight is $5\frac{1}{2}$ hours. Determine the speed of the wind.

2.5   Matrices and Determinants

A *matrix* is a rectangular array of numbers, usually enclosed by parentheses or brackets, the numbers being called the *elements* of the matrix. The following is an illustration of a matrix with integral elements:

$$\begin{bmatrix} 2 & -1 & 4 & 1 \\ 2 & 0 & 3 & 2 \\ -1 & 1 & 2 & 1 \end{bmatrix}.$$

The individual horizontal and vertical arrays of numbers are called, respectively, the *rows* and *columns* of the matrix. If a matrix has m rows and n columns, it is called an "*m* by *n*" matrix. The matrix above is then a "3 by 4" matrix. If $m = 1$, the matrix may be identified with a *row vector*, while a matrix with $n = 1$ is essentially a *column vector*, as discussed in §2.3. In case $m = n$, a matrix is said to be *square* of *order n*, while a square matrix of order 1 need not be distinguished from its one element. For the remainder of this section we shall be concerned only with square matrices.

If we designate a matrix by A, it is convenient to indicate the element at the intersection of the ith row and j^{th} column by a_{ij}. The matrix may then also be designated as $A = [a_{ij}]$ and, in the 3 by 3 case, A takes the following form:

$$\begin{bmatrix} a_{11} & a_{12} & a_{13} \\ a_{21} & a_{22} & a_{23} \\ a_{31} & a_{32} & a_{33} \end{bmatrix}.$$

There is associated with every square matrix $A = [a_{ij}]$ a number called the *determinant* of A, which is designated by $|A|$, or det A. We also write

$$|A| = \begin{vmatrix} a_{11} & a_{12} & a_{13} \\ a_{21} & a_{22} & a_{23} \\ a_{31} & a_{32} & a_{33} \end{vmatrix}$$

to illustrate the 3 by 3 case and refer to the number so indicated as an *evaluation* or *expansion* of the determinant. We shall make a "recursive" definition of the determinant of a matrix of order n in terms of determinants of matrices of order $n - 1$. Then, *if we agree to identify the determinant of a 1 by 1 matrix $A = [a]$ with the number a*, our recursive definition will completely describe how to evaluate any determinant. We first develop some preliminary terminology in anticipation of this definition.

If one row and column of a square matrix are deleted, the resulting array of numbers is a *submatrix* whose determinant is a *minor* of A. (It is possible to give more general definitions of "submatrix" and "minor," but this restrictive definition takes care of our present needs.) We label a minor as M_{ij} if it arises from the deletion of the ith row and j^{th} column of A. The element a_{ij} is at the intersection of the deleted row and column, and $(-1)^{i+j} M_{ij} = A_{ij}$ is a number called the *cofactor* of a_{ij}. If we multiply the elements of any row or column of a matrix by their respective cofactors and add these products, *the resulting sum can be shown to be independent of which row or column was selected.* We shall assume this result, and make the following definition for a matrix A of order n:

Definition. If $A = [a_{ij}]$, det $A = |A| = a_{i1}A_{i1} + a_{i2}A_{i2} + \cdots + a_{in}A_{in}$ $= a_{1j}A_{1j} + a_{2j}A_{2j} + \cdots + a_{nj}A_{nj}$, for any i or j between 1 and n, inclusive.

In practice, in the applications of this definition, it is customary to select either $i = 1$ or $j = 1$, and thereby evaluate the determinant "in terms of" the first row or column of the matrix. An exception to this practice occurs, however, whenever zeros are more numerous in some other row or column, and then this row or column is selected.

EXAMPLE 1.   Show that:

$$\begin{vmatrix} a_{11} & a_{12} \\ a_{21} & a_{22} \end{vmatrix} = a_{11}a_{22} - a_{12}a_{21}.$$

PROOF.   We evaluate the determinant in terms of the elements of the first row. Since $A_{11} = (-1)^2 M_{11} = M_{11} = \det[a_{22}] = a_{22}$, and $A_{12} = (-1)^3 M_{12} = -M_{12} = -a_{21}$, an application of the above definition gives $|A| = a_{11}a_{22} - a_{12}a_{21}$, where we have designated the original matrix by A.

We now see from the result of Example 1 that the "memory device" introduced in the preceding section was in reality a formula for the evaluation of the determinant of a 2 by 2 matrix.

EXAMPLE 2.   Evaluate:

$$\begin{vmatrix} 1 & 2 \\ -1 & 3 \end{vmatrix}.$$

SOLUTION.   By the result of Example 1, we see that the desired determinant is $1(3) - (-1)2 = 3 + 2 = 5$.

EXAMPLE 3.   If $A = [a_{ij}] = \begin{bmatrix} 2 & -1 & 1 \\ 1 & 2 & 2 \\ -3 & 2 & 1 \end{bmatrix}$, determine A_{12} and A_{23}.

SOLUTION.   If we delete the first row and second column of A, we see that

$$M_{12} = \begin{vmatrix} 1 & 2 \\ -3 & 1 \end{vmatrix} = 1 + 6 = 7.$$

Hence,

$$A_{12} = (-1)^3 M_{12} = -7.$$

Similarly, if we delete the second row and third column of A, we find that

$$M_{23} = \begin{vmatrix} 2 & -1 \\ -3 & 2 \end{vmatrix} = 4 - 3 = 1,$$

and so $A_{23} = (-1)^5 M_{23} = -1$.

EXAMPLE 4. Determine $|A|$ if $A = \begin{bmatrix} 2 & 2 & 1 \\ -1 & 1 & 2 \\ 1 & -2 & 3 \end{bmatrix}$.

SOLUTION. We shall evaluate the determinant in terms of the first row of the matrix. Hence, we must first determine A_{11}, A_{12}, and A_{13}.

$$A_{11} = (-1)^2 \begin{vmatrix} 1 & 2 \\ -2 & 3 \end{vmatrix} = 3 - (-4) = 3 + 4 = 7.$$

$$A_{12} = (-1)^3 \begin{vmatrix} -1 & 2 \\ 1 & 3 \end{vmatrix} = (-1)(-3 - 2) = 5.$$

$$A_{13} = (-1)^4 \begin{vmatrix} -1 & 1 \\ 1 & -2 \end{vmatrix} = 2 - 1 = 1.$$

It now follows from the definition that $|A| = 2(7) + 2(5) + 1(1) = 25$.

We conclude this section with the statements of several theorems on determinants. The proofs of these theorems may be found in books which contain a more detailed treatment of determinants, and we shall not give any of these proofs. However, it is easy to check the validity of these theorems for matrices of low orders, and some of the problems of this section suggest checks of this type.

THEOREM 2.51. If each element of a row (or column) of a square matrix is multiplied by a number c, the determinant of the matrix is multiplied by c.

THEOREM 2.52. If two rows (or columns) of a square matrix are interchanged, the determinant of the matrix is changed only in algebraic sign.

COROLLARY. If two rows (or columns) of a matrix are identical, the determinant of the matrix is 0.

PROOF. For it follows from Theorem 2.52 that an interchange of the two identical rows (or columns) would change the sign of the determinant. But since these rows (or columns) are identical, no change would result in the determinant, and so this number must be 0.

THEOREM 2.53. If any multiple of a row (or column) of a matrix is added element by element to another row (or column), the determinant of the matrix is unchanged.

PROBLEMS

1. If $A = [a_{ij}] = \begin{bmatrix} 1 & 3 & -1 & 1 \\ 2 & 0 & 1 & -1 \\ -1 & 2 & 1 & 2 \end{bmatrix}$ is designated as an m by n matrix,

identify: (a) m and n; (b) $a_{21}, a_{11}, a_{32}, a_{34}$.

2. List the elements of the second column and the elements of the third row of the matrix in Problem 1.

3. If $A = \begin{bmatrix} -1 & 2 & 1 \\ 1 & 2 & 5 \\ 0 & -1 & 4 \end{bmatrix}$, determine: (a) M_{12}; (b) M_{13}; (c) M_{22}.

4. Use the results of Problem 3 to determine the cofactor: (a) A_{12}; (b) A_{13}; (c) A_{22}.

5. With A given in Problem 3, evaluate det A in terms of the: (a) second row; (b) first column; (c) third column.

6. If $B = \begin{bmatrix} 2 & -1 & 1 & 2 \\ 3 & 8 & 4 & 0 \\ 0 & 7 & -2 & 4 \\ 1 & 1 & 8 & 1 \end{bmatrix}$, determine the cofactor: (a) B_{21}; (b) B_{13}.

7. Determine det B, for the matrix B of Problem 6, and check your answer by using a different row or column as the basis for the expansion.

8. Expand each of the following determinants:

(a) $\begin{vmatrix} x & 1-x \\ 2 & 5 \end{vmatrix}$; (b) $\begin{vmatrix} 1-x & -2 \\ 1 & 1+x \end{vmatrix}$; (c) $\begin{vmatrix} -1 & 2x \\ x & -1 \end{vmatrix}$.

9. Expand each of the following determinants:

(a) $\begin{vmatrix} 1 & x & 1 \\ 2 & -x & x \\ 3 & y & y \end{vmatrix}$; (b) $\begin{vmatrix} 1 & x & x^2 \\ 1 & y & y^2 \\ 1 & z & z^2 \end{vmatrix}$.

10. Prove Theorem 2.52 for a general matrix of order 3.
11. Prove Theorem 2.51 for a general matrix of order 3.
12. Verify the Corollary to Theorem 2.52 for the case of a third order matrix which has two identical columns.

2.6   Linear Systems and Cramer's Rule

It is possible to use some of the results of §2.5 on matrices to generalize the method of solution given in §2.4. Instead of a pair of equations, we could consider a general system of n linear equations in n variables. However, the method becomes awkward if $n > 3$, and so we shall confine our discussion to the case of three equations in three variables.

The general system under consideration may be expressed in the following form:

$$a_{11}x + a_{12}y + a_{13}z = k_1,$$
$$a_{21}x + a_{22}y + a_{23}z = k_2,$$
$$a_{31}x + a_{32}y + a_{33}z = k_3.$$

The *coefficient matrix A* of the system is the matrix $\begin{bmatrix} a_{11} & a_{12} & a_{13} \\ a_{21} & a_{22} & a_{23} \\ a_{31} & a_{32} & a_{33} \end{bmatrix}$. In the above system x, y, z are to be considered real variables, while the coefficients a_{11}, a_{12}, a_{13}, a_{21}, a_{22}, a_{23}, a_{31}, a_{32}, a_{33} and k_1, k_2, k_3 are arbitrary real numbers—which are assumed to be known. We shall have found a solution to the system when we have determined $x = c_1$, $y = c_2$, $z = c_3$ to satisfy each of the equations of the system. If we think of $X = (x \quad y \quad z)^T$ as the variable of the system, with universe $R \times R \times R$, the triple $(c_1 \quad c_2 \quad c_3)^T$ is then a solution of the system of equations. The set of all such solutions is, of course, the solution set of the system.

The following is the key theorem of this section which leads to the method known as Cramer's Rule.

THEOREM 2.61.   If the elements of any row (or column) of a matrix are multiplied by the cofactors of the corresponding elements of *another* row (or column), the sum of the products is 0.

PROOF.   Let us multiply the elements of the ith row by the corresponding cofactors of the elements of the jth row. If we were to replace the elements of the jth row by the elements of the ith row, it is apparent that the cofactors of the elements of the "new" j^{th} row would be the same as for the original j^{th} row. However, two rows of the matrix are now identical, and so its determinant is 0 by the Corollary to Theorem 2.52. The expansion of this determinant in terms of the elements of the "new" j^{th} row is precisely the same as the sum of the products of the elements of the ith row by the cofactors of the elements of the jth row. Hence, this latter sum is 0, and the proof is complete.

In order to use this theorem for the desired purpose, we introduce the following notation:

$$D = \begin{vmatrix} a_{11} & a_{12} & a_{13} \\ a_{21} & a_{22} & a_{23} \\ a_{31} & a_{32} & a_{33} \end{vmatrix}, \qquad K_1 = \begin{vmatrix} k_1 & a_{12} & a_{13} \\ k_2 & a_{22} & a_{23} \\ k_3 & a_{32} & a_{33} \end{vmatrix},$$

$$K_2 = \begin{vmatrix} a_{11} & k_1 & a_{13} \\ a_{21} & k_2 & a_{23} \\ a_{31} & k_3 & a_{33} \end{vmatrix}, \qquad K_3 = \begin{vmatrix} a_{11} & a_{12} & k_1 \\ a_{21} & a_{22} & k_2 \\ a_{31} & a_{32} & k_3 \end{vmatrix}.$$

As usual, we let A_{ij} designate the cofactor of the element a_{ij} in the coefficient matrix A. If we multiply both members of the first equation of the system by A_{11}, both members of the second equation by A_{21}, and both members of the third equation by A_{31}, and add the corresponding members of each transformed equation, the result is:

$$(a_{11}A_{11} + a_{21}A_{21} + a_{31}A_{31})x + (a_{12}A_{11} + a_{22}A_{21} + a_{32}A_{31})y + (a_{13}A_{11}$$
$$+ a_{23}A_{21} + a_{33}A_{31})z = k_1 A_{11} + k_2 A_{21} + k_3 A_{31}.$$

It follows from the above theorem that the coefficients of y and z are 0, while the coefficient of x is the determinant D of the coefficient matrix. Moreover, the right member of this equation may be seen to be an evaluation of the determinant K_1 in terms of the elements of the first column of the associated matrix. The equation we have obtained may then be written in the simple form $Dx = K_1$, from which we get

$$x = \frac{K_1}{D}.$$

A similar analysis yields $y = K_2/D$ and $z = K_3/D$. This result, known as *Cramer's Rule*, may be used if $D \neq 0$. It may be noted that the method developed in §2.4 is the simplest case of Cramer's Rule, adapted to two equations in two variables.

EXAMPLE. Use Cramer's Rule to solve the following system of equations:

$$3x + y + 3z = 8,$$
$$x - 2y - z = 1,$$
$$2x + 5y + 2z = 1.$$

SOLUTION. We must first determine D, K_1, K_2, and K_3 for this system of equations:

$$D = \begin{vmatrix} 3 & 1 & 3 \\ 1 & -2 & -1 \\ 2 & 5 & 2 \end{vmatrix} = 26, \qquad K_1 = \begin{vmatrix} 8 & 1 & 3 \\ 1 & -2 & -1 \\ 1 & 5 & 2 \end{vmatrix} = 26,$$

$$K_2 = \begin{vmatrix} 3 & 8 & 3 \\ 1 & 1 & -1 \\ 2 & 1 & 2 \end{vmatrix} = -26, \qquad K_3 = \begin{vmatrix} 3 & 1 & 8 \\ 1 & -2 & 1 \\ 2 & 5 & 1 \end{vmatrix} = 52.$$

With these results, it follows from Cramer's Rule that $x = K_1/D = 1$, $y = K_2/D = -1$, $z = K_3/D = 2$. It is easy to check that $(1 \quad -1 \quad 2)^\mathrm{T}$ is a solution of the system for $X = (x \quad y \quad z)^\mathrm{T}$.

In applications of Cramer's Rule, it is often easier to solve for the final variable by substitution in one of the equations. For instance, in the preceding example we could determine $x = 1$ and $y = -1$ by Cramer's

Rule and then substitute these solutions in, say, the first equation. The result is $3 - 1 + 3z = 8$, from which we obtain $3z = 6$ and $z = 2$. The remaining equations may then be used for purposes of checking.

The method of Cramer's Rule is very useful in solving systems of linear equations, and we have noted that the method can be generalized to more than three equations. However, the method has certain limitations, which we list:

1. The method may be used only if $D \neq 0$.
2. The computation of the determinants can be very laborious if there are more than three equations.
3. The method is applicable only if there are the same number of equations as there are variables.

In §2.7 we shall outline a method of solving linear systems of equations by means of matrices, which is free of these undesirable features.

PROBLEMS

Use Cramer's Rule to solve each of the systems of equations given in Problems 1 through 8.

1. $3x - 2y + z = 5,$
$\quad x + y - 2z = -2,$
$\quad 2x - 2y + 4z = 8.$

2. $3x + 4y = 6,$
$\quad 2x - 5y = -19.$

3. $x - 4y + 3z = -10,$
$\quad 2x - y + z = -4,$
$\quad 4x - 3y + z = -12.$

4. $2x - y = 0,$
$\quad 4x - y + z = \frac{1}{2},$
$\quad x + 4z = -\frac{3}{2}.$

5. $5x - 7y + z = 4,$
$\quad x + 3y - 5z = -14,$
$\quad 2x + y - z = -5.$

6. $2x - y = 0,$
$\quad x + 4z = -\frac{1}{2},$
$\quad 4y - z = \frac{17}{4}.$

7. $4/x - 2/y + 1/z = 11,$
$\quad 3/x - 1/y - 1/z = 9,$
$\quad 1/x + 2/y - 1/z = -1.$

8. $4x + 5z = 6,$
$\quad y - 6z = -2,$
$\quad 3x + 4z = 3.$

9. Write down an arbitrary matrix of order 3 with integral elements. Then check the truth of the theorem of this section by applying it to: (a) the elements of the first column and the cofactors of the elements of the third column; (b) the elements of the second row and the cofactors of the elements of the first row.

10. What conclusion does Cramer's Rule allow us to draw for a system of three equations in which $k_1 = k_2 = k_3 = 0$? Such a system of equations is called a *homogeneous* system.

11. Derive the part of Cramer's Rule pertaining to y and z, using the given general system of three equations.

12. The sum of the digits of a three-digit number is 13, and the middle digit is five less than the sum of the other two digits. If the last two digits are reversed in order, the resulting number is 27 larger than the original number. Determine the original number.

13. Determine the condition on a, b, c if the following system of equations is to have a unique solution:

$$ax \quad + 3z = 2,$$
$$by - 2z = 1,$$
$$x \quad + cz = 2.$$

2.7   Matrices in Echelon Form

In this section we describe a method of reducing a matrix which will be very useful in determining the set of solutions of any system of linear equations. There are three *elementary row* operations which we shall use in this reduction procedure. It may be noted that these are quite similar to the row operations for equations as discussed in §2.4.

1. The interchange of any two rows of the matrix.
2. The multiplication of all elements of any row of the matrix by a nonzero number.
3. The addition of a nonzero multiple of the elements of any row of the matrix to the corresponding elements of another row.

If we perform any finite sequence of operations of these types on a given matrix A, the final matrix—as well as any intermediate matrix—is said to be *row-equivalent* to A.

For example, suppose $A = \begin{bmatrix} 1 & -1 & 2 & 3 \\ 2 & 3 & 8 & -1 \\ 0 & 1 & 5 & -1 \end{bmatrix}$. If we interchange the second and third rows of A, we obtain $A_1 = \begin{bmatrix} 1 & -1 & 2 & 3 \\ 0 & 1 & 5 & -1 \\ 2 & 3 & 8 & -1 \end{bmatrix}$. If we now add three times the elements of the first row of A_1 to the elements of its second row, the result is $A_2 = \begin{bmatrix} 1 & -1 & 2 & 3 \\ 3 & -2 & 11 & 8 \\ 2 & 3 & 8 & -1 \end{bmatrix}$. Finally, we can multiply each element of the first row of A_2 by two and obtain $A_3 = \begin{bmatrix} 2 & -2 & 4 & 6 \\ 3 & -2 & 11 & 8 \\ 2 & 3 & 8 & -1 \end{bmatrix}$. It is a consequence of our definition above that the matrix A_3, as well as A_2 and A_1, is row-equivalent to A.

The above illustration shows that row-equivalent matrices may be very different in their outward appearances. However, if we use a proper sequence of elementary row operations, it can be shown that any given matrix can be transformed into an "invariant" form. We mean by this that the same final matrix will always be obtained, although there may be a great variety of sequences of operations involved in the various processes of reduction. Such an invariant form is often said to be *canonical*. A description of one of these canonical forms for matrices with integral elements is now given.

If we read the elements of a row from left to right, let us call the first nonzero element its *leading* element. A matrix of integral elements will be said to be in *echelon form* if the following conditions are satisfied:
1. The only integral factor of all elements of any row is 1.
2. The column which contains the leading element of any row has 0 for all of its other elements.
3. The leading element of any nonzero row (i.e., not all of its elements are zero) is positive.
4. If the leading element of the ith row appears in the t_ith column, then $t_1 < t_2 < \cdots < t_r$, where r is the number of nonzero rows.

The following are examples of matrices in echelon form:

$$\begin{bmatrix} 1 & 0 & 0 \\ 0 & 8 & 0 \\ 0 & 0 & 1 \end{bmatrix}, \begin{bmatrix} 2 & 0 & 1 & 0 \\ 0 & 7 & 0 & -2 \\ 0 & 0 & 0 & 0 \end{bmatrix}, \begin{bmatrix} 3 & 8 & 0 & 0 & 0 & 0 \\ 0 & 0 & 2 & 0 & 0 & -1 \\ 0 & 0 & 0 & 1 & 0 & 2 \\ 0 & 0 & 0 & 0 & 2 & 1 \end{bmatrix}, \begin{bmatrix} 3 & 0 & 5 & 7 \\ 0 & 4 & 0 & 0 \\ 0 & 0 & 0 & 0 \\ 0 & 0 & 0 & 0 \\ 0 & 0 & 0 & 0 \end{bmatrix}.$$

We now state the important theorem of this section.

THEOREM 2.71.   Any matrix with integral elements is row-equivalent to a matrix with integral elements in echelon form.

We shall not give a formal proof of this theorem. Instead, two illustrations will be given of how a reduction to echelon form can actually be carried out. In the reduction process, we shall refer to the first row as (1), the second row as (2), and so on.

EXAMPLE 1.   Reduce the following matrix to echelon form with integral elements:

$$\begin{bmatrix} 3 & 1 & -1 & 2 \\ 2 & 0 & 3 & 4 \\ 1 & 1 & 5 & 7 \end{bmatrix}.$$

SOLUTION

$$\begin{bmatrix} 3 & 1 & -1 & 2 \\ 2 & 0 & 3 & 4 \\ 1 & 1 & 5 & 7 \end{bmatrix} \xrightarrow{\text{interchange (1) and (3)}} \begin{bmatrix} 1 & 1 & 5 & 7 \\ 2 & 0 & 3 & 4 \\ 3 & 1 & -1 & 2 \end{bmatrix},$$

$$\xrightarrow{\text{subtract 2(1) from (2)}} \begin{bmatrix} 1 & 1 & 5 & 7 \\ 0 & -2 & -7 & -10 \\ 3 & 1 & -1 & 2 \end{bmatrix} \xrightarrow{\text{subtract 3(1) from (3)}} \begin{bmatrix} 1 & 1 & 5 & 7 \\ 0 & -2 & -7 & -10 \\ 0 & -2 & -16 & -19 \end{bmatrix},$$

multiply (2) and (3) by —1
$$\longrightarrow \begin{bmatrix} 1 & 1 & 5 & 7 \\ 0 & 2 & 7 & 10 \\ 0 & 2 & 16 & 19 \end{bmatrix}$$
subtract (2) from (3)
$$\longrightarrow \begin{bmatrix} 1 & 1 & 5 & 7 \\ 0 & 2 & 7 & 10 \\ 0 & 0 & 9 & 9 \end{bmatrix},$$

multiply (1) by 2
$$\longrightarrow \begin{bmatrix} 2 & 2 & 10 & 14 \\ 0 & 2 & 7 & 10 \\ 0 & 0 & 9 & 9 \end{bmatrix}$$
subtract (2) from (1)
$$\longrightarrow \begin{bmatrix} 2 & 0 & 3 & 4 \\ 0 & 2 & 7 & 10 \\ 0 & 0 & 9 & 9 \end{bmatrix},$$

divide (3) by 9
$$\longrightarrow \begin{bmatrix} 2 & 0 & 3 & 4 \\ 0 & 2 & 7 & 10 \\ 0 & 0 & 1 & 1 \end{bmatrix}$$
subtract 3(3) from (1)
$$\longrightarrow \begin{bmatrix} 2 & 0 & 0 & 1 \\ 0 & 2 & 7 & 10 \\ 0 & 0 & 1 & 1 \end{bmatrix},$$

subtract 7(3) from (2)
$$\longrightarrow \begin{bmatrix} 2 & 0 & 0 & 1 \\ 0 & 2 & 0 & 3 \\ 0 & 0 & 1 & 1 \end{bmatrix}.$$

This final matrix is in the desired echelon form.

EXAMPLE 2. Reduce the following matrix to echelon form:

$$\begin{bmatrix} -2 & 3 & -6 \\ 1 & -2 & 3 \\ 2 & -4 & 7 \end{bmatrix}.$$

SOLUTION

$$\begin{bmatrix} -2 & 3 & -6 \\ 1 & -2 & 3 \\ 2 & -4 & 7 \end{bmatrix}$$
interchange (1) and (2)
$$\longrightarrow \begin{bmatrix} 1 & -2 & 3 \\ -2 & 3 & -6 \\ 2 & -4 & 7 \end{bmatrix},$$

add 2(1) to (2)
$$\longrightarrow \begin{bmatrix} 1 & -2 & 3 \\ 0 & -1 & 0 \\ 2 & -4 & 7 \end{bmatrix}$$
subtract 2(1) from (3)
$$\longrightarrow \begin{bmatrix} 1 & -2 & 3 \\ 0 & -1 & 0 \\ 0 & 0 & 1 \end{bmatrix},$$

multiply (2) by —1
$$\longrightarrow \begin{bmatrix} 1 & -2 & 3 \\ 0 & 1 & 0 \\ 0 & 0 & 1 \end{bmatrix}$$
add 2(2) to (1)
$$\longrightarrow \begin{bmatrix} 1 & 0 & 3 \\ 0 & 1 & 0 \\ 0 & 0 & 1 \end{bmatrix},$$

subtract 3(3) from (1)
$$\longrightarrow \begin{bmatrix} 1 & 0 & 0 \\ 0 & 1 & 0 \\ 0 & 0 & 1 \end{bmatrix}.$$

This final matrix is in echelon form, as desired.

There is no fixed sequence of operations which are necessary to make the reduction of a matrix with integral elements to echelon form. However, the following list of suggestions may be of use as a general guide in this process.

1. If the first column contains an element 1, interchange the necessary rows to put this element in the upper left hand corner of the matrix.
2. After the position of the leading element of any row has been established, reduce by subtraction to 0 all other elements of the column in which this leading element occurs.
3. Proceed in a systematic way with the reduction from the left to the right side of the matrix.
4. If at any stage of the reduction all elements of any row have a common factor different from 1, and it is apparent that this factor is not needed for subsequent reductions, divide each element of this row by this factor.

PROBLEMS

Reduce each of the following matrices to echelon form with integral elements.

1. $\begin{bmatrix} 3 & -1 & 2 \\ 1 & 4 & -2 \\ 4 & -2 & 0 \end{bmatrix}$
2. $\begin{bmatrix} 4 & -1 & 5 & 0 \\ 1 & -1 & 5 & 2 \\ 4 & -2 & 15 & 4 \\ 5 & -2 & 25 & 10 \end{bmatrix}$
3. $\begin{bmatrix} 0 & 1 & 0 & -2 \\ 2 & 2 & 3 & 0 \\ 5 & 3 & -1 & 7 \end{bmatrix}$

4. $\begin{bmatrix} 0 & -1 & -4 & 12 & 19 \\ 6 & 3 & 0 & 3 & 12 \\ 2 & 1 & 4 & 0 & 4 \\ -6 & -3 & 0 & 9 & 12 \end{bmatrix}$
5. $\begin{bmatrix} 4 & 2 & -1 & 2 \\ 4 & 3 & 0 & 1 \\ 2 & 5 & 3 & 2 \\ 1 & 1 & 1 & 2 \end{bmatrix}$
6. $\begin{bmatrix} 4 & 5 & -6 \\ 2 & -4 & 3 \\ 7 & -1 & 0 \end{bmatrix}$

7. $\begin{bmatrix} 3 & 5 & 7 & 1 & 1 \\ 2 & 5 & -1 & 0 & 0 \\ 0 & 0 & 1 & -2 & 5 \end{bmatrix}$
8. $\begin{bmatrix} -1 & 1 & 4 & 2 \\ 2 & 5 & -2 & 5 \\ 1 & 4 & 2 & 6 \\ 0 & -2 & 1 & 5 \end{bmatrix}$
9. $\begin{bmatrix} 0 & 0 & 1 & -4 \\ 2 & 5 & -2 & 6 \\ 1 & 1 & -1 & 5 \\ 0 & 0 & 1 & 0 \end{bmatrix}$

2.8 Use of Matrices in Solving Linear Systems

We now return to the problem of obtaining simultaneous solutions of a system of linear equations. While the method of this section does not eliminate the usefulness of the determinant method, it does not have any of the defects of this latter method as listed in §2.6.

The *coefficient matrix* of a linear system of equations has already been defined. If we include the right-hand members of the equations as an extra column of the coefficient matrix, we have what is called the *augmented matrix* of the system. Every system of linear equations has a uniquely associated augmented matrix, and every matrix can be considered the unique augmented matrix of a linear system. *Let us first suppose that the augmented matrix of a system of linear equations is in echelon form.* The solution possibilities for the system then fall into three categories, each of which we shall discuss in some detail.

1. *The number of nonzero rows of the augmented matrix is also the number of variables in the equations of the system.*

For example, let us suppose we have a linear system with three variables x, y, z, and that the augmented matrix is:

$$\begin{bmatrix} 4 & 0 & 0 & 3 \\ 0 & 1 & 0 & -3 \\ 0 & 0 & 5 & 2 \end{bmatrix}.$$

The equations associated with this matrix are:

$$\begin{aligned} 4x \quad\quad &= \quad 3, \\ y \quad &= -3, \\ 5z &= \quad 2, \end{aligned}$$

or, to use the vector notation previously introduced,

$$\begin{aligned} (4 \quad 0 \quad 0)X &= \quad 3, \\ (0 \quad 1 \quad 0)X &= -3, \\ (0 \quad 0 \quad 5)X &= \quad 2, \end{aligned}$$

where $X = (x \quad y \quad z)^{\mathrm{T}}$.

It is apparent, from an examination of the equations, that $x = \frac{3}{4}$, $y = -3$, $z = \frac{2}{5}$. The only solution of the system is then $(\frac{3}{4} \quad -3 \quad \frac{2}{5})^{\mathrm{T}}$, and we add that uniqueness of solution is a characteristic of systems whose augmented matrix is in this first category.

2. *The number of nonzero rows of the augmented matrix is less than the number of variables in the equations of the system.*

For example, let us suppose we have a linear system with four variables x, y, z, w and that the augmented matrix of the system is:

$$\begin{bmatrix} 3 & 0 & 0 & 1 & -6 \\ 0 & 2 & -4 & 1 & 5 \\ 0 & 0 & 0 & 0 & 0 \\ 0 & 0 & 0 & 0 & 0 \end{bmatrix}.$$

The two bottom rows of the matrix have no significance for equations, but if we "translate" the other two rows into equations we obtain:

$$\begin{aligned} 3x \quad\quad\quad\quad + w &= -6, \\ 2y - 4z + w &= \quad 5, \end{aligned}$$

or, in vector notation,

$$\begin{aligned} (3 \quad 0 \quad 0 \quad 1)X &= -6, \\ (0 \quad 2 \quad -4 \quad 1)X &= \quad 5, \end{aligned}$$

where $X = (x \quad y \quad z \quad w)^T$. It is now possible to determine solutions for the "beginner" variables x and y for arbitrary choices of z and w. Thus, if $z = \alpha$ and $w = \beta$, we obtain:

$$3x = -6 - \beta,$$
$$2y = \quad 5 - \beta + 4\alpha,$$

or, more simply:

$$x = -2 + (-\tfrac{1}{3})\beta,$$
$$y = \tfrac{5}{2} + (-\tfrac{1}{2})\beta + 2\alpha.$$

The general solution of the system may then be expressed in the form:

$$x = -2 \quad\quad + (-\tfrac{1}{3})\beta,$$
$$y = \tfrac{5}{2} + 2\alpha + (-\tfrac{1}{2})\beta,$$
$$z = \quad\quad\quad \alpha,$$
$$w = \quad\quad\quad\quad\quad \beta.$$

As stated previously, α and β are arbitrary real numbers. For example, if $\alpha = \beta = 0$, we obtain $x = -2$, $y = \tfrac{5}{2}$, $z = 0$, $w = 0$, and so $(-2 \quad \tfrac{5}{2} \quad 0 \quad 0)^T$ is one of the infinitude of solutions of the given system. An infinitude of solutions will always characterize a system in this category.

The general solution of a system in this category can be expressed in somewhat neater form, if we introduce the operations of addition and multiplication by a scalar for vectors. Both of these operations are accomplished componentwise, and so for the column case we have the following:

$$\begin{pmatrix} a_1 \\ a_2 \\ \cdot \\ \cdot \\ \cdot \\ a_n \end{pmatrix} + \begin{pmatrix} b_1 \\ b_2 \\ \cdot \\ \cdot \\ \cdot \\ b_n \end{pmatrix} = \begin{pmatrix} a_1 + b_1 \\ a_2 + b_2 \\ \cdot \\ \cdot \\ \cdot \\ a_n + b_n \end{pmatrix} \text{ and } c\begin{pmatrix} a_1 \\ a_2 \\ \cdot \\ \cdot \\ \cdot \\ a_n \end{pmatrix} = \begin{pmatrix} ca_1 \\ ca_2 \\ \cdot \\ \cdot \\ \cdot \\ ca_n \end{pmatrix},$$

for real number or "scalar" c. With these definitions, the general solution of the above system can now be put in the following convenient form:

$$X = \begin{pmatrix} x \\ y \\ z \\ w \end{pmatrix} = \begin{pmatrix} -2 \\ \tfrac{5}{2} \\ 0 \\ 0 \end{pmatrix} + \alpha\begin{pmatrix} 0 \\ 2 \\ 1 \\ 0 \end{pmatrix} + \beta\begin{pmatrix} -\tfrac{1}{3} \\ -\tfrac{1}{2} \\ 0 \\ 1 \end{pmatrix}.$$

An alternate form for this would be:

$$X = (x \quad y \quad z \quad w)^T = (-2 \quad \tfrac{5}{2} \quad 0 \quad 0)^T + \alpha(0 \quad 2 \quad 1 \quad 0)^T + \beta(-\tfrac{1}{3} \quad -\tfrac{1}{2} \quad 0 \quad 1)^T.$$

3. *The number of nonzero rows of the augmented matrix exceeds the number of variables in the equations of the system.*

To illustrate this situation, let us suppose the variables are x, y, z and the augmented matrix of the system is

$$\begin{bmatrix} 1 & 0 & 0 & 0 \\ 0 & 1 & 0 & 0 \\ 0 & 0 & 1 & 0 \\ 0 & 0 & 0 & 1 \\ 0 & 0 & 0 & 0 \end{bmatrix}.$$

If we interpret the rows of this matrix as equations, the result is:

$$x = 0,$$
$$y = 0,$$
$$z = 0,$$
$$0 = 1,$$
$$0 = 0.$$

Since the statement $0 = 1$ is not true for any choice of x, y, z, the given system of equations has no solution. The absence of a solution is characteristic of this type of system.

It must be recalled, of course, that in the above discussions *the augmented matrices were all assumed to be in echelon form.* Our analysis then shows that, if the augmented matrix of a system is in echelon form, we are able to tell by inspection whether there is a unique solution, no solution, or an infinitude of solutions to the system. Moreover, one can determine all solutions immediately from the augmented matrix. The problem of solving a system of linear equations is then one of reducing its augmented matrix to echelon form—but without altering the solutions of the system. A little reflection will reveal that the following operations on a system of equations will not alter its set of solutions:

1. The interchange of any two equations of the system.
2. The multiplication of both members of any equation of the system by a nonzero real number.
3. The addition of any real multiple of both members of any equation of the system to the corresponding members of another equation.

A quick check of these allowable operations with the elementary operations for matrices in §2.7 shows us that the two are essentially the same, with the notions of "row of a matrix" and "equation" playing parallel roles. The following theorem is then an immediate consequence of theorem 2.71.

THEOREM 2.81. If the augmented matrix of a system of linear equations is reduced to echelon form by elementary row operations, the solutions of the system of equations associated with this echelon matrix are the same as the solutions of the original system.

We have already seen how easy it is to solve a linear system with an augmented matrix in echelon form, and so this theorem gives us the following procedure for solving any such system:

By means of elementary row operations, reduce the augmented matrix of the given system to echelon form and solve the system associated with the echelon matrix.

EXAMPLE. Obtain simultaneous solutions for the following system of equations:

$$\begin{aligned} 3x + y - z &= 2, \\ 2x \quad + 3z &= 4, \\ x + y + 5z &= 7. \end{aligned}$$

SOLUTION.   The augmented matrix of the system is

$$\begin{bmatrix} 3 & 1 & -1 & 2 \\ 2 & 0 & 3 & 4 \\ 1 & 1 & 5 & 7 \end{bmatrix},$$

and we saw in Example 1 of §2.7 that the associated echelon matrix is

$$\begin{bmatrix} 2 & 0 & 0 & 1 \\ 0 & 2 & 0 & 3 \\ 0 & 0 & 1 & 1 \end{bmatrix}.$$

But then $2x = 1$, $2y = 3$, and $z = 1$, so that $x = \frac{1}{2}$, $y = \frac{3}{2}$, and $z = 1$. If $X = (x \quad y \quad z)^T$ is then regarded as the variable of the system of equations, the unique solution is $(\frac{1}{2} \quad \frac{3}{2} \quad 1)^T$.

The examples given for systems whose augmented matrices are in echelon form will serve to illustrate the other different possibilities which may arise. For the procedure is merely to reduce the matrix to echelon form and then solve the associated reduced system of equations. Another matrix method for solving a linear system is known as *matrix inversion,* and we have included a very brief informal discussion of this in Appendix B.

PROBLEMS

1. The following are the augmented matrices of a system of linear equations in x, y, z. Determine all solutions of each system.

(a) $\begin{bmatrix} 2 & 0 & 0 & 5 \\ 0 & 5 & 0 & -6 \\ 0 & 0 & 4 & 1 \end{bmatrix}$
(b) $\begin{bmatrix} 4 & 0 & 0 & -3 \\ 0 & 2 & 0 & 5 \\ 0 & 0 & 1 & -1 \end{bmatrix}$

2. The following are the echelon matrices of the augmented matrices of systems of linear equations in x, y, z. Determine all solutions of each system.

(a) $\begin{bmatrix} 1 & 0 & 0 & 2 \\ 0 & 3 & 0 & 4 \\ 0 & 0 & 1 & 5 \\ 0 & 0 & 0 & 2 \\ 0 & 0 & 0 & 0 \end{bmatrix}$ (b) $\begin{bmatrix} 2 & 0 & 0 & 7 \\ 0 & 1 & 0 & -6 \\ 0 & 0 & 0 & 0 \\ 0 & 0 & 0 & 0 \\ 0 & 0 & 0 & 0 \end{bmatrix}$

3. Each of the following matrices is the augmented matrix of a system of linear equations in x, y, z [and w in the case of (c)]. Solve each system completely.

(a) $\begin{bmatrix} 1 & 2 & 1 & 4 \\ 3 & -1 & 2 & -1 \\ 4 & 2 & 3 & 3 \end{bmatrix}$ (b) $\begin{bmatrix} 2 & -1 & 3 & 2 \\ 1 & 0 & 2 & -1 \\ 5 & -2 & 8 & 3 \end{bmatrix}$ (c) $\begin{bmatrix} 2 & 0 & 0 & 0 & -5 \\ 0 & 5 & -1 & 0 & 8 \\ 0 & 0 & 0 & 4 & 7 \end{bmatrix}$

In Problems 4 through 9 use the matrix method to determine the complete solution set of each system of equations.

4. $2x + 3y + 4z = 0,$
$3x + 4y + 5z = 0,$
$5x + 7y + 9z = 0.$

5. $4x - 3y + 5z = 1,$
$2x + 5y + 2z = -5,$
$3x - 7y + 4z = 2.$

6. $x + 2y - z = 1,$
$-x + 2y + 2z = 2,$
$2x - 3y - 3z = -3.$

7. $x - 2y + 3z = -3,$
$3x - y - 2z = -4,$
$x + y - 2z = 0.$

8. $2x + 3y - z - t = 0,$
$x - y - 2z - 4t = 0,$
$3x + 3y \quad - 7t = 0.$

9. $2x - y + 4z = 1,$
$x + 3y - z = -1,$
$2x + 3y - 4z = 2.$

10. Determine k if the following system of equations is to be solvable:

$$x + y = 1,$$
$$ky + z = 1,$$
$$z + x = 1.$$

11. Use an example to verify that it is possible for a nonhomogeneous system of linear equations to be unsolvable, even though there are more variables than equations. [Cf. Category 2 of this section.]

12. Prove that if two linear equations—not identically zero—have the same solution set, one is a nonzero multiple of the other.

13. There are fifty coins in a bag, made up of nickles, dimes, and quarters of total value $5. Should you believe an assertion that there are four times as many nickels as dimes?

2.9 Systems Involving Quadratic Equations

There are times when it is necessary to solve a system of equations in which one or more of the equations is not linear. A general method for solving such a system would be very complicated and will not be attempted here. Instead, we shall consider examples of a few isolated types that occur rather commonly. Only equations with two variables will be discussed, and we shall designate the general variable X of each system and its solutions as *row* vectors.

EXAMPLE 1.   Solve for $X = (x, y)$ in $R \times R$ the system:

$$3x^2 + y^2 = 4,$$
$$2x - y = 1.$$

SOLUTION.   We first solve the linear equation for y in terms of x, and obtain $y = 2x - 1$. On substituting $2x - 1$ for y in the first equation the result is:

$$3x^2 + (2x - 1)^2 = 4 \quad \text{or} \quad 7x^2 - 4x - 3 = 0.$$

Hence,

$$(7x + 3)(x - 1) = 0 \quad \text{and} \quad x = -\tfrac{3}{7} \text{ or } x = 1.$$

If $x = -\tfrac{3}{7}$, $y = 2(-\tfrac{3}{7}) - 1 = -\tfrac{13}{7}$; if $x = 1$, $y = 2(1) - 1 = 2 - 1 = 1$.

The solution set of the equation is then:

$$\{(1, 1), (-\tfrac{3}{7}, -\tfrac{13}{7})\}.$$

The method of substitution, as used in Example 1, may also be used successfully on occasion when neither equation is linear.

EXAMPLE 2.   Solve for $X = (x, y)$ in $R \times R$ the system:

$$x^2 + 2y^2 = 33,$$
$$xy = 10.$$

SOLUTION.   From the second equation we obtain $y = 10/x$, and, on substituting $10/x$ for y in the first equation, we obtain:

$$x^2 + 2\left(\frac{100}{x^2}\right) = 33.$$

Then

$$x^4 - 33x^2 + 200 = 0 \quad \text{or} \quad (x^2 - 25)(x^2 - 8) = 0,$$

and so

$$x = \pm 5 \quad \text{or} \quad x = \pm 2\sqrt{2}.$$

The corresponding solutions for y are ± 2 and $\pm 5\sqrt{2}/2$, and so the solution set of the system is:

$$\left\{(5, 2), (-5, -2), \left(2\sqrt{2}, \frac{5\sqrt{2}}{2}\right), \left(-2\sqrt{2}, \frac{-5\sqrt{2}}{2}\right)\right\}.$$

It sometimes happens that two quadratic equations are "linear" in the squares of the variables, and then the methods of linear systems are applicable.

EXAMPLE 3.   Solve for $X = (x, y)$ in $R \times R$ the system:

$$2x^2 + 3y^2 = 7,$$
$$x^2 - y^2 = 1.$$

SOLUTION.   If we let $x^2 = u$ and $y^2 = v$, the equations become:

$$2u + 3v = 7,$$
$$u - v = 1.$$

The unique solution for u and v in this linear system is easily found to be: $u = 2$, $v = 1$. Hence, the complete solution of the original system is: $\{(\sqrt{2}, 1), (\sqrt{2}, -1), (-\sqrt{2}, 1), (-\sqrt{2}, -1)\}$.

NOTE: We should warn at this point that before a "solution" is accepted, it should be checked by substitution in *each* equation of the system. There are, in general, many solutions of one equation of a system which may not be solutions of another.

It is sometimes possible to solve a quadratic system by some special device peculiar to the given system.

EXAMPLE 4.   Solve for $X = (x, y)$ in $R \times R$ the system:

$$9x^2 + 4y^2 = 10,$$
$$3xy - 2y^2 = -2.$$

SOLUTION.   If we multiply the members of the second equation by 5 and add them to the corresponding members of the first equation, the result is: $9x^2 + 15xy - 6y^2 = 0$ or $3x^2 + 5xy - 2y^2 = 0$. Hence, $(3x - y)(x + 2y) = 0$, so that $y = 3x$ or $x = -2y$.

(a) If $y = 3x$, the first equation becomes $9x^2 + 36x^2 = 10$ so that $x^2 = \frac{2}{9}$. Hence, $x = \pm\sqrt{2/3}$, and solutions are $(\sqrt{2}/3, \sqrt{2})$ and $(-\sqrt{2}/3, -\sqrt{2})$.

(b) If $x = -2y$, the first equation becomes $36y^2 + 4y^2 = 10$ or $y^2 = \frac{1}{4}$. Hence, $y = \pm\frac{1}{2}$, and solutions are $(1, -\frac{1}{2})$ and $(-1, \frac{1}{2})$.

The complete solution set of the given system is then:

$$\left\{ \left(\frac{\sqrt{2}}{3}, \sqrt{2} \right), \left(\frac{-\sqrt{2}}{3}, -\sqrt{2} \right), (1, -\tfrac{1}{2}), (-1, \tfrac{1}{2}) \right\}.$$

That these are all solutions of the system may be verified by substitution in the second equation.

The methods which we have given are by no means exhaustive for nonlinear systems, but we prefer not to pursue the matter any further.

PROBLEMS

In Problems 1 through 8, solve each of the given systems for $\mathbf{X} = (x, y)$ in $R \times R$.

1. $4x^2 - 3y^2 = 9,$
$5x^2 - 8y^2 = -27.$

2. $x^2 + y^2 = 25,$
$x - 7y + 25 = 0.$

3. $3x + 2y - 6 = 0,$
$xy + 12 = 0.$

4. $xy + 1 = a^2,$
$x - y = 2.$

5. $x^2 + xy = 3,$
$xy + 2y^2 = 2.$

6. $4x^2 + 9y^2 = 36,$
$3x^2 - 5y^2 = 27.$

7. $xy + 4y^2 = 0,$
$2xy + x^2 - 4y^2 = 0.$

8. $2x^2 - 3xy = 5,$
$2xy - 3y^2 = 2.$

9. Each page of a book is to have a one-inch margin on all four sides. The pages are to have individual areas of 54 square inches, with 28 square inches of each devoted to printing. What must be the dimensions of each page?

10. A box is to be constructed by cutting one-inch squares from each corner of a rectangular sheet of cardboard, and folding it up. If the volume of the box is to be 36 cubic inches, and the perimeter of the base is to be 24 inches, determine the dimensions of the sheet of cardboard.

11. Three rational numbers a, b, c are so related that $b - a = c - b$. If their sum is 25 and the difference between the smallest and largest is 2 less than twice the middle number, determine the numbers.

12. Two cars are racing in the same direction around a circular one-mile track. If one car makes the circuit in six seconds less time than the other, and passes the other car every three minutes, determine the speeds of the cars.

CHAPTER 3

Inequalities

3.1 Simple Inequalities

One of the most important properties of real numbers—and one we discussed briefly in §1.5—is that they are *ordered*. That is, given any two distinct real numbers a and b, either $a < b$ or $b < a$. If we include the possibility that $a = b$, these statements of inequality should be written $a \leq b$ and $b \leq a$.

A statement of inequality (or an "inequation") is very similar in external appearance to an equation, the only essential difference being that one of the above-mentioned symbols ($<, >, \leq, \geq$) appear in an inequality instead of the equality symbol ($=$). An inequality which involves variables is an instance of an open sentence, as discussed in Chapter 2, the "domain" of each variable being its universe. The *solution set* of an inequality is then the set of replacements of the variables, each from its own domain, so that the open inequality becomes a true statement. As is the case with equations, the domain of a variable may be a subset of integers, rational numbers, or real numbers, *but in the absence of any statement to the contrary or if the context does not dictate otherwise, we shall always assume the domain of each variable to be R.*

In the symbolism of Chapter 2, this means in general that we are to be concerned with solution sets of inequalities of the form $\mathbf{F}\mathbf{X} < b$, $\mathbf{F}\mathbf{X} > b$, $\mathbf{F}\mathbf{X} \leq b$, or $\mathbf{F}\mathbf{X} \geq b$. In this symbolism, we recall that b is a real number, $\mathbf{F}$ is a horizontal n-tuple, or vector, with given real number components, while $\mathbf{X}$ is a vertical n-tuple, or vector, whose components are the variables of the inequality. An illustration of this would be the inequality $2x + 3y - 5z < 6$, which we may write in vector form as $(2 \quad 3 \quad -5)\mathbf{X} < 6$, where $\mathbf{X} = (x \quad y \quad z)^{\mathrm{T}}$. Since $2(1) + 3(-2) - 5(-1) = 1 < 6$, it is clear that

$(1 \quad -2 \quad -1)^T$ is a solution, but there are many more solutions in the universe $R \times R \times R$ of the inequality!

In very general terms, the procedure for solving an inequality is much like that for solving an equation. That is, we use various kinds of operations to reduce the inequality to a simpler form, from which the solution set is immediately evident. The permissible operations for inequalities are the same as for equations, but with one notable exception: *If each member of an inequality is multiplied or divided by the same negative number, the sense of the inequality is reversed.* Thus, any multiplication by a negative number requires that $<$ ($>$) be replaced by $>$ ($<$) in the inequality.

In the first two sections of this chapter, we shall be concerned with inequalities involving only one variable, and so the vector variable **X** may be considered a scalar or real variable in these sections.

EXAMPLE 1. Solve $3x - 2 < 5x + 3$ for x.

SOLUTION

$$
\begin{array}{ll}
3x - 5x < 2 + 3, & \text{[adding } 2 - 5x \text{ to both members]} \\
-2x < 5, & \text{[combining terms]} \\
2x > -5, & \text{[multiplying both members by } -1\text{]} \\
x > -\tfrac{5}{2}. & \text{[dividing both members by 2]}
\end{array}
$$

Any real number greater than $-\tfrac{5}{2}$ is then a solution of the given inequality, and the desired solution set is $\{x \mid x \in R, x > -\tfrac{5}{2}\}$.

If $x \geq a$ and $x \leq b$, it is often convenient to condense these two inequalities into the compact form $a \leq x \leq b$. This means, of course, that x is any real number between a and b inclusive, i.e., $x \in [a, b]$.

EXAMPLE 2. Solve $|2x + 1| \leq 3$, where the universe of x is (a) the set of integers; (b) R.

SOLUTION. The given inequality is equivalent (i.e., same solution set) to $-3 \leq 2x + 1 \leq 3$ (cf. Problem 19, §1.5). On adding -1 to each member of this inequality, we obtain $-4 \leq 2x \leq 2$ or, more simply, $-2 \leq x \leq 1$.

  (a) If a replacement for x must be an integer, the solution set is then $\{-2, -1, 0, 1\}$.
  (b) If a replacement for x may be any real number, the solution set of the inequality is the interval $[-2, 1]$.

EXAMPLE 3. Solve $x^2 - 2x < 3$ for real x.

       SOLUTION.   The given inequality is equivalent to $x^2 - 2x - 3 < 0$

or

$$(x + 1)(x - 3) < 0.$$

We know that the equation $(x - 3)(x + 1) = 0$ has 3 and -1 for its real solutions, and these two points partition the real line into three subintervals, as shown in Figure 7.

Figure 7

The three subintervals are $\{x \mid x \in R,\ x < -1\}, [-1, 3]$, and $\{x \mid x \in R,\ x > 3\}$, where we note that two of them are of infinite extent. It is a characteristic, though *admittedly intuitive*, property of the real numbers that the algebraic sign of $(x + 1)(x - 3)$ is invariant (i.e., always the same) for points in any one of its associated subintervals. (This is actually a property of "continuity," a topic we do not wish to discuss here.) It is now a simple matter to check the sign of the left member of the simplified inequality at some arbitrary point of each subinterval. For example, we could proceed as follows:

$$
\begin{aligned}
\text{If } x = -2, (x + 1)(x - 3) &= (-1)(-5) = \quad 5 > 0. \\
\text{If } x = 0, (x + 1)(x - 3) &= (1)(-3) = -3 < 0. \\
\text{If } x = 4, (x + 1)(x - 3) &= (5)(1) = \quad 5 > 0.
\end{aligned}
$$

Hence the solution set of the given inequality is the open interval $(-1, 3)$.

      By these examples we have illustrated methods of solving some of the simpler types of linear and quadratic inequalities.

PROBLEMS

Solve each of the following inequalities for x, in the universe R of real numbers, except as indicated otherwise.

1. $3x - 2 < x + 5.$ **2.** $x - 5 \le 3x + 4.$

3. $5x - 2 \ge 5 + x.$ **4.** $|2x - 1| \le 4.$

5. $|x + 4| \le 4$, where the universe of x is the set of: (a) integers; (b) real numbers.

6. $|2x - 4| \ge 4$, where the universe of x is the set of: (a) integers; (b) real numbers.

7. $|3x| < -1.$ **8.** $|3x| > 1.$

9. $-1 \le 2x + 1 < 87.$ **10.** $x^2 - 2x + 1 > 0.$

11. $2x^2 - 4x + 1 \leq 0$, where the universe of x is the set of: (a) integers; (b) real numbers.

12. $x^2 - 3x + 2 \geq 0$, where the universe of x is the set of: (a) integers; (b) real numbers.

13. $3x^2 - 2x + 1 \leq 0$.

14. $-2 < (2x + 1)/5 \leq 4$.

15. $-3x^2 + 4x < 1$.

16. $|x - 1| \leq |x| + 1$.

17. $|x - 3| \leq 3x - 1 < \frac{2}{3}$.

18. $-4 \leq 1 - 2x \leq 8$.

19. $-2 < 3x - 1 < \frac{2}{3}$.

20. $1/(3x) < 2$.

21. $1/x - 1 < k$, where $0 < k < 1$.

22. $x^2 - 16 < k$, where $k > 0$.

3.2 More on Inequalities

In solving an inequality, if each member is multiplied by an expression involving a variable, it is necessary to exercise extreme caution. If the universe of such a variable comprises both positive and negative numbers, any multiplication by this expression becomes subject to the exception as cautioned in §3.1. Under these circumstances, there is no way of knowing in advance whether the sense of the inequality should then be reversed or should remain the same. Example 1 is illustrative of this difficulty, and we shall give two slightly different methods of attack, each method being the best suited for a particular situation. But first it is helpful to establish an elementary theorem.

THEOREM 3.21.   If $a < b$, then

$$(1) \ \frac{1}{a} > \frac{1}{b} \qquad \text{if } ab > 0,$$

$$(2) \ \frac{1}{a} < \frac{1}{b} \qquad \text{if } ab < 0.$$

PROOF
(1) If $ab > 0$, and we multiply both members of the given inequality by $1/(ab)$, the result is $1/b < 1/a$ by property O_4 in §1.5.

(2) If $ab < 0$, and we multiply both members of the given inequality by $1/(ab)$, the result $1/a < 1/b$ follows from Example 2 of §1.5.

As a consequence of this theorem, it should be noted that $a < b < c$ does *not* necessarily imply that $1/c < 1/b < 1/a$. The truth or falsity of this latter assertion depends on the algebraic signs of a, b, c.

EXAMPLE 1.   Solve the inequality $-1 < \dfrac{10}{10 + x} < 1$ for x.

SOLUTION 1.   We consider two cases: $10 + x > 0$ and $10 + x < 0$.

(a) If $10 + x > 0$, we may multiply all members of the inequality by $10 + x$ and obtain $-10 - x < 10 < 10 + x$. On adding 10 to each member, the result is $-x < 20 < 20 + x$, and this is seen to be true for any replacement of x which is *positive*.

(b) If $10 + x < 0$, we may multiply all members of the inequality by $10 + x$ and obtain $-10 - x > 10 > 10 + x$, which may also be written $10 + x < 10 < -10 - x$. On adding -10 to each member of this inequality, the result is $x < 0 < -20 - x$, which is seen to be true for any replacement of x where $x < -20$.

The complete solution set of the given inequality is then

$$\{x|x \in R, x < -20 \quad \text{or} \quad x > 0\}.$$

SOLUTION 2.   We make use of the above theorem and again consider two cases: $10 + x > 0$ and $10 + x < 0$. In addition, we break up the given inequality into two inequalities with two members each:

$$-1 < \frac{10}{10 + x}, \quad \frac{10}{10 + x} < 1.$$

(a) If $10 + x > 0$, we may multiply through by $10 + x$ and obtain:

$$-10 - x < 10, \quad 10 < 10 + x.$$

These may be seen to be equivalent to $x > -20$ and $x > 0$, and *both* conditions are satisfied if $x > 0$.

(b) If $10 + x < 0$, we may multiply through by $10 + x$ and obtain:

$$-10 - x > 10, \quad 10 > 10 + x.$$

These may be seen to be equivalent to $x < -20$ and $x < 0$, and *both* conditions are satisfied if $x < -20$.

As before, the solution set of the given inequality is

$$\{x|x \in R, x < -20 \quad \text{or} \quad x > 0\}.$$

If the variable of an inequality occurs in the denominator of a member, it is possible to "clear fractions" without reversing the sense by multiplying through by the *square* of the least common denominator. However, this procedure usually increases the degree of the inequality. For example, if we multiply through by x^2, the inequality $-3/x < 1 < 5/x$ becomes the second-degree inequality $-3x < x^2 < 5x$.

The next example illustrates two useful techniques for solving more complicated inequalities.

EXAMPLE 2.   Solve $\dfrac{(x - 1)(x + 2)}{x - 3} < 0$ for x.

SOLUTION 1.   This method of solution is essentially the method used in Example 3 of §3.1. If we set each factor, occurring in either numerator or denominator, equal to 0, we obtain the three "critical points" $x = -2$, $x = 1$, and $x = 3$. These points partition the real line into four subintervals, two of infinite extent. Again we use the *intuitive fact* that the sign of the left member of the given inequality is the same for all points in any one of these subintervals. We then check the sign for an arbitrary point in each of the subintervals, as shown in Figure 8, and we have our solution.

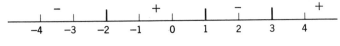

Figure 8

For example, if $x = -3$,

$$\frac{(x-1)(x+2)}{x-3} = \frac{(-4)(-1)}{-6} = -\tfrac{2}{3};$$

if $x = 0$,

$$\frac{(x-1)(x+2)}{x-3} = \frac{(-1)(2)}{-3} = \tfrac{2}{3};$$

if $x = 2$,

$$\frac{(x-1)(x+2)}{x-3} = \frac{(1)(4)}{-1} = -4;$$

if $x = 4$,

$$\frac{(x-1)(x+2)}{x-3} = \frac{(3)(6)}{1} = 18.$$

It follows that

$$\frac{(x-1)(x+2)}{x-3}$$

is negative in both the first and third subintervals, and so the solution set of the given inequality is:

$$\{x \mid x < -2 \quad \text{or} \quad 1 < x < 3\}.$$

SOLUTION 2.   This method is slightly more geometric and requires that we draw an algebraic scale corresponding to each component of the left member of the inequality and place them horizontally so that their scale readings are in vertical alignment. For the factors $x - 1$, $x + 2$, and $x - 3$ in this problem, the scales are shown in Figure 9.

On each scale we designate the sets of real numbers for which the

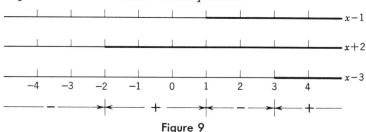

Figure 9

associated factor is undefined by means of a wavy line and those for which the factor is positive by means of a heavy line, and we leave the rest of the scale unchanged. We now recall that the product or quotient of an even number of negative numbers is positive, while an odd number of negative numbers results in a negative number. It is then possible to tell at a glance those portions of the real line for which the given expression is negative. The desired solution set is easily found from Figure 9 to be $\{x|x < -2$ or $1 < x < 3\}$.

Example 2 did not illustrate the case where one or more of the component factors is undefined for certain ranges of x. This situation gives no trouble, however, if we simply note that an expression is undefined for any replacement of x which results in *any one* of its component factors being undefined. For example, the factor $\sqrt{x-1}$ is undefined for $x < 1$, and its associated algebraic scale would be shown as in Figure 10.

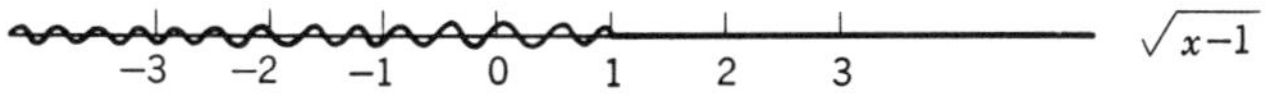

$$\text{───────────────}\sqrt{x-1}$$
$$\quad -3 \quad -2 \quad -1 \quad 0 \quad 1 \quad 2 \quad 3$$

Figure 10

PROBLEMS

Solve each of the inequalities in Problems 1–16 for x.

1. $|2x + 1| < 2$.   2. $|3x + 4| > 2$.
3. $|x/(1 - x)| < 2$.   4. $|2x/(x + 1)| > 1$.
5. $-1 \le x/(x + 2) < 3$.   6. $-3 \le x/(x + 2) \le 5$.
7. $x^2 - 5x + 6 < 0$.   8. $x^2 - x - 12 \ge 0$.
9. $(x + 1)(x - 2)(x + 5) < 0$.   10. $x(x - 2)(x + 3)(x - 5) > 0$.
11. $x(x^2 + 1)(x^4 + 1) < 0$.   12. $x(x + 1)/(x - 2) < 0$.
13. $x^2(x + 1)(x - 1)/(x - 2) < 0$.   14. $x^2(x + 1)\sqrt{1 + x} > 0$.
15. $x\sqrt[3]{1 - x^2} > 0$.   16. $(x - 1)/\sqrt{1 + x} > 0$.
17. If $a < b < c$, formulate a theorem which relates the reciprocals $1/a$, $1/b$, $1/c$.
18. Solve $(2x - 1)|x| \ge 0$ for x.
19. Solve $(2x + 1)|x| \le 0$ for x.
20. Solve $\sqrt{x - 1}|x| < 0$ for x.

3.3   Convex Sets

The subject matter of this and the following sections is to be largely centered around a geometric approach to linear inequalities in two variables. An example of this type of inequality is $2x - 3y - 4 < 0$, or, in equivalent form, $2x - 3y < 4$. In the vector notation which we have introduced earlier, this latter form may also be written as $(2 \quad -3)X < 4$, where $X = \begin{pmatrix} x \\ y \end{pmatrix}$. The set of all real replacements for X, which make the inequality a true statement, is the truth or solution set of the inequality in $R \times R$. In §2.2 we described a Cartesian coordinate system for a plane, which associated with each ordered pair of real numbers (written in either horizontal or vertical form) a point of the plane. It is traditional in geometry to refer to the set of real points associated in this way with the solution set of an equation or inequality in two variables as the *locus* of the equation or inequality. This locus is also referred to as the *graph* of the given equation or inequality.

It is shown in a study of geometry that the graph of a linear equation in two variables is a straight line. For example, the graph of $2x - 3y = 4$, or $(2 \quad -3)X = 4$, is the straight line shown in Figure 11. The (column) coordinate pairs are given for a few points of the linear graph. For instance,

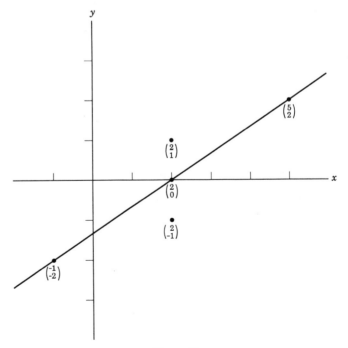

Figure 11

the point $\begin{pmatrix} -1 \\ -2 \end{pmatrix}$ is on the locus because $2(-1) - 3(-2) = -2 + 6 = 4$.

Any straight line in a plane partitions the plane into two *half planes* which may or may not include the line itself. If the line is included, the half plane is said to be *closed*, while a half plane which does not include its boundary line is said to be *open*. Let us now consider the five open mathematical statements given below:

(a) $2x - 3y = 4$ or $(2 \quad -3)X = 4$.
(b) $2x - 3y < 4$ or $(2 \quad -3)X < 4$.
(c) $2x - 3y > 4$ or $(2 \quad -3)X > 4$.
(d) $2x - 3y \le 4$ or $(2 \quad -3)X \le 4$.
(e) $2x - 3y \ge 4$ or $(2 \quad -3)X \ge 4$.

If we replace X by $\begin{pmatrix} 2 \\ 1 \end{pmatrix}$ in (b), we find that $(2 \quad -3)\begin{pmatrix} 2 \\ 1 \end{pmatrix} = 2(2) - 3(1) =$ $4 - 3 = 1 < 4$ is a true statement. Hence, the point $\begin{pmatrix} 2 \\ 1 \end{pmatrix}$ is on the locus of (b). We note that this point is *above* the straight line locus of (a), and *it is true* that the complete locus of (b) is the set of all points *above* the line and so is the open half plane above this line. Similarly, a replacement of X in (c) by $\begin{pmatrix} 2 \\ -1 \end{pmatrix}$ results in $(2 \quad -3)\begin{pmatrix} 2 \\ -1 \end{pmatrix} = 2(2) - 3(-1) = 4 + 3 =$ $7 > 4$, a true statement. Hence, the point $\begin{pmatrix} 2 \\ -1 \end{pmatrix}$, and likewise all other points *below* the line lie on the locus of (c) and comprise the open half plane below this line. The solution set of (d) is the union of the solution sets of (a) and (b), and so its graph is the closed half plane *above* the line. Similarly, the solution set of (e) is the union of the solution sets of (a) and (c), and the graph of this set is the closed half plane *below* the line.

In general, the locus of any linear equation $ax + by = c$, with a and b real numbers, is a straight line, while the graphs of $ax + by < c$ and $ax + by > c$ are the open half planes on either side of the line. *We have not given a proof of this remark*, but a proof is suggested in Problem 18. By merely checking any point not on the line, it is easy to decide which side of the line is the graph of either inequality. If $<$ or $>$ are replaced by $\le$ or $\ge$, of course, the half planes become closed.

The problem of solving a *system* of inequalities now arises, and we consider the simultaneous solutions of such a system. For example, let us examine the system

$$2x + 3y \le 6,$$
$$x - y \le 0,$$
$$x \quad\quad \ge 0.$$

As usual, with $\mathbf{X} = \begin{pmatrix} x \\ y \end{pmatrix}$, the vector representation of this system is:

$$(2 \quad 3)\mathbf{X} \le 6,$$
$$(1 \quad -1)\mathbf{X} \le 0,$$
$$(1 \quad 0)\mathbf{X} \ge 0.$$

The solution, or truth, set of this system is the intersection of the solution sets of the individual inequalities. Since each of these solution sets is a closed half plane, the desired solution set is the intersection of these three half planes. The checking of a few points will show, in this case, that the solution set of the given system is the set of points within and on the finite triangle shown in Figure 12.

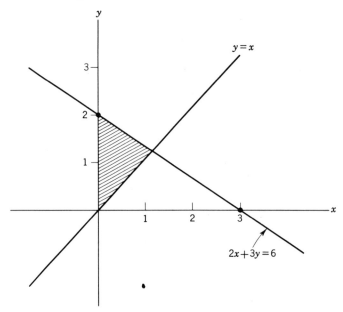

Figure 12

Definition. A plane set is said to be *convex* if whenever two planar points belong to the set so do all points of the line segment joining the two points.

It is intuitively evident that *the intersection of any finite number of closed half planes is a convex set*, this kind being referred to as a *polygonal convex set*. This deduction is capable of formal proof, and we indicate the proof in some of the problems following.

Since the solution set of any linear inequality in two variables, which involves $\le$ or $\ge$, is a closed half plane, it is apparent that the common solutions of any such system of inequalities comprise a polygonal convex set. This convex set may be of finite extent—as in Figure 12—or it may be of infinite extent as for the system:

$$x \geq 0,$$
$$y \geq 0.$$

EXAMPLE. A boy is allowed to spend up to $24 for records and paperbacks. If paperbacks cost $2 each and records cost $3 each, use a system of inequalities to investigate the possibilities.

SOLUTION. Let us suppose that the boy buys x paperbacks and y records. The requirements of the purchase may then be represented by the following system of inequalities:

$$2x + 3y \leq 24,$$
$$x \quad\quad \geq 0,$$
$$y \quad\quad \geq 0.$$

The latter two inequalities hold, of course, because it is impossible to buy a negative number of records or paperbacks. We also observe that the context of the problem requires that the domain of both variables x and y be the set of nonnegative integers. [The vector form of the system of inequalities is: $(2 \quad 3)X \leq 24, (1 \quad 0)X \geq 0, (0 \quad 1)X \geq 0$, where, as usual, $X = (x \quad y)^T$.] If we make a graph of the system, we obtain the convex set shown in Figure 13. We note in passing that if we replace x and y by 0

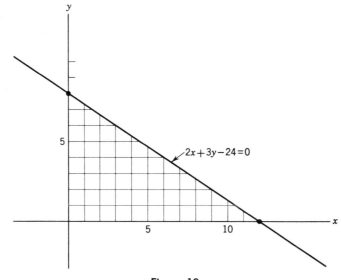

Figure 13

[or X by (0 0)^T] in the first inequality, we obtain $2(0) + 3(0) = 0 \leq 24$ and observe that this is a true statement. Hence, the point (0 0)^T—and hence all points below the line—satisfy this inequality. Within the universe of non-negative integers, any point $\begin{pmatrix} x \\ y \end{pmatrix}$ with integral coordinates and within or on the boundary of the triangle, provides us with a solution to the problem. For example, one solution would be $\begin{pmatrix} 5 \\ 4 \end{pmatrix}$, and the boy could purchase 5 paperbacks and 4 records.

PROBLEMS

In Problems 1 through 6, draw the general polygonal convex sets which represent the solutions of the given systems of inequalities.

1. $x \geq 2,$
$y \leq 5,$
$2x - 3y \leq 0.$

2. $3x + 2y \leq 5,$
$x + y \leq 2,$
$x - y \geq 0.$

3. $x \leq 3,$
$x \geq -3,$
$y \leq 2,$
$y \geq -2.$

4. $x - 2y \geq -2,$
$x + 2y \leq 0,$
$y \geq 0.$

5. $(2 \quad -1)X \leq -1$ where $X = \begin{pmatrix} x \\ y \end{pmatrix},$
$(1 \quad 2)X \geq -2,$
$(2 \quad -3)X \leq 0,$
$(1 \quad 0)X \geq 0.$

6. $(1 \quad 1)X \leq 0$ where $X = \begin{pmatrix} x \\ y \end{pmatrix},$
$(-2 \quad 1)X \geq 1,$
$(0 \quad 1)X \leq 0,$
$(1 \quad 0)X \geq 2.$

7. Prove that the intersection of two or more convex sets is a convex set. (Use the definition of a convex set.)
8. Prove that any half plane—either open or closed—is a convex set. (Use the definition of a convex set.)
9. Deduce from Problems 7 and 8 that the intersection of any number of half planes is a convex set.
10. Modify the diagram of the example, if there are only three available paperbacks of any interest to the boy.
11. Modify the diagram of the example, if there are only six records available and of any interest to the boy.
12. If the boy in the example is to buy at least twice as many paperbacks as records, make an appropriate modification of the diagram.
13. If the boy in the example is to spend $12 on records, make an appropriate modification of the diagram.
14. A farmer wishes to spend not over $300 for young pigs and lambs. If lambs cost $10 each and pigs cost $5 each, draw the polygonal convex set to represent the different possibilities for the farmer.
15. Modify the diagram of Problem 14 if the farmer must buy at least six pigs and ten lambs.

16. A manufacturer of fruit cocktail wishes to produce a fruit mixture which will cost not over 20¢ per pint. To the main body of the mixture, which costs 15¢ per pint, he will add some special kinds of red and green cherries. Each pint is to have at least 5 cherries of each kind. If the red cherries cost 0.2¢ while the green ones cost 0.1¢ each, use a diagram to represent the possible number of red and green cherries in each pint of the cocktail.

17. If each pint of the cocktail in Problem 16 is to have twice as many red as green cherries, modify the diagram of that problem.

18. Consider the coordinates of the points $\mathbf{X} = \begin{pmatrix} x \\ y \end{pmatrix}$ to verify the following rule:

The half plane which represents the solutions of the inequality $(a \quad b)\mathbf{X} < c$ lies *below* the line graph of $(a \quad b)\mathbf{X} = c$ if and only if $b > 0$.

19. Use the result of Problem 18 to describe the solutions of the following inequalities:

(a) $2x - 3y + 2 < 0$.   (b) $3x - 2y > 7$.
(c) $x + 3y < -3$.   (d) $2x + 5y > 8$.

3.4   Linear Programming

In previous sections we have discussed methods of finding the solution set of a system of linear equations or inequalities. Reduced to its fundamentals, this involved the checking of elements from the replacement sets or universes of the variables in an open sentence and observing whether the resulting statements were true or false. We now consider a slightly different but related problem, involving maximum or minimum values. We introduce this type of problem with an example.

A small furniture manufacturer makes tables and chairs, each of these items requiring the use of three machines, which we shall refer to as A, B, and C. The manufacture of a table requires the use of A for four hours, B for two hours and C for one hour; for a chair, two hours are needed on A, one hour on B and three hours on C. Let us suppose that the profit on the sale of a table is $15 and the profit on the sale of a chair is $10, while we further assume that sales of either article are unlimited. The following question now arises: How many of each article should be manufactured per day for maximal profit, if only one each of the three machines is available but 24 hour daily operation is permitted?

Let us suppose that x tables and y chairs are turned out each day. Since one table takes four hours of time on A, and one chair takes two hours of time on A, the total hours needed on A for x tables and y chairs is $4x + 2y$. Since a day is limited by 24 hours, the following inequality must be satisfied:

$$4x + 2y < 24.$$

If we examine the time requirements on machine B in a similar way, we obtain another inequality:

$$2x + y \leq 24.$$

Similarly, an analysis of C gives us the following:

$$x + 3y \leq 24.$$

The context of the problem demands that $x \geq 0$ and $y \geq 0$. Therefore, any solution for x and y is subject to these five inequalities. If we replace x and y in each of the inequalities by 0, the resulting inequalities are seen to be true. From our discussion in §3.3, it then follows that the solution set of each inequality is the associated closed half plane which contains the origin, and the solution set of the system is the intersection of these half planes. The graph of this solution set is shown in Figure 14.

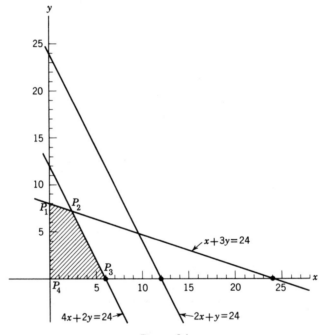

Figure 14

Any point in this solution set is a "solution" in the sense that the various time requirements on the machines are satisfied; but no mention of profit has been made up to this stage. However, if there is to be a daily profit of P in the business, the conditions of the problem give us the following equation:

$$P = 15x + 10y.$$

Any expression of the form $ax + by + c$ is often referred to as a linear polynomial in x and y, the "coefficients" a, b, c being arbitrary real numbers. The representation above for P is then a polynomial in x and y. If x and y are replaced by "permissible" real numbers, these real numbers may be considered the "replacement set" of the polynomial—to generalize a notion previously used in connection with open sentences or statements. We shall now state without proof the basic theorem of this section.

THEOREM 3.41. If the replacement set of a polynomial in two variables x and y is a convex polygon, the polynomial assumes its largest and smallest values when x and y are replaced by the coordinates of a vertex (possibly not unique) of the polygon.

The convex polygon, which comprises the solution set of the system of inequalities previously introduced, is labeled $P_1P_2P_3P_4$ in Figure 14. The coordinate pairs of the vertices of the polygon, in the order of listing are as follows: $(0, 8)$, $(\frac{12}{5}, \frac{36}{5})$, $(6, 0)$, $(0, 0)$. If we now replace x and y by the coordinates of these points, in order, in the polygon $15x + 10y$, we obtain: $80, 108, 90, 0$. It then follows from the above theorem that the maximum value of P, for any replacement of x and y as coordinates of points within or on the polygon, occurs at the point $(\frac{12}{5}, \frac{36}{5})$. This means that maximal daily profit results for the manufacturer, if the output per day is $2\frac{2}{5}$ tables and $7\frac{1}{5}$ chairs, and in this event the daily profit is \$108. Expressed on the basis of a five-day week, the output per week should be 12 tables and 36 chairs, which would then result in a weekly profit of \$540.

The above problem is typical of a relatively new mathematical discipline known as *linear programming*. In general, the problems are such that one wishes to maximize or minimize a linear polynomial which is subjected to certain conditions, or "constraints." In the example we have worked out, the polynomial was the expression for P, i.e., $15x + 10y$, while the constraints were the inequalities. It is to be noted that our method of solution was largely intuitive. However, a theoretical treatment of the mathematics involved would entail a study of "linear functions on a vector space," a subject somewhat beyond the scope of this book.

PROBLEMS

1. A convex polygon is defined by the inequalities: $x - 2y \leq 0$, $x + 3y \leq 0$, $2x - 3y + 6 \geq 0$. Using the points of the polygon as the replacement set, determine the maximum and minimum values of each of the following polynomials: (a) $2x - 3y$; (b) $x + 2y$; (c) $3x - y$; (d) $x + 3y$.
2. Use the same polygonal replacement set as in Problem 1, and find the maximum and minimum values of each of the following polynomials: (a) $x - 2y + 2$; (b) $2x - 5y + 5$; (c) $2x - 3y + 6$.

3. Determine the maximum and minimum values of the polynomial $5x + 3y - 6$, using as the replacement set the polygon defined in: (a) Problem 1; (b) Problem 3; (c) Problem 4 of §3.3.

4. The owner of a truck, with a capacity of 800 gallons, hauls gasoline and fuel oil. On a certain trip he must haul at least 300 gallons of gasoline and at least 100 gallons of fuel oil for his regular customers. He has also found from experience that he can never dispose of more than four times as much gasoline as fuel oil. If profits on gasoline and fuel oil are 3¢ and 1¢ per gallon, respectively, how should the truck be loaded for maximum profit?

5. If the trucker in Problem 4 must haul at least 200 gallons of each liquid for his regular customers, how should his truck be loaded for maximum profit?

6. If not more than 100 gallons of fuel oil can be used, how would the trucker in Problem 4 make up his load for maximum profit?

7. The profit per unit of time in producing x units of one product and y units of another is known to be $3x + 4y$ dollars. Let us suppose that conditions of manufacture are such that the following constraints must be met: $x - y \geq 2$, $3x + y \leq 14$, $x + 6y \geq 10$. Determine the number of units of each product to be produced for maximum profit.

8. Use the constraints of Problem 7 and determine the maximum profit if profit in dollars is expressible in the form $2x + 6y - 12$.

9. With reference to the example worked out in this section, let us suppose that the price of tables takes a drop to $12 per table. Determine the output of chairs and tables for maximum profit.

10. With reference to the example worked out in this section, let us suppose that the profit on a chair is the same as for a table. What should the output be for maximum profit?

11. Joe and Pete are in partnership in the manufacture of two novelty items A and B. Each item requires two hours of Joe's time, while Pete needs two hours on item A and three hours on item B. Joe can work six hours per day, while Pete can work eight hours each day. If the profit on each A item is $3 and each B item is $4, determine the most profitable number to produce of each type of item in a day.

CHAPTER 4

Functions

4.1 The Function Concept

In earlier chapters, we have seen examples of relations between the elements of a set. The order relation ($<$), as defined in the set of real numbers, was one notable example of this concept, and there have been others. Quite frequently in mathematics, the elements of *two* sets are related in some way, and this kind of "relation" will be of interest to us in this chapter. Of course, the two sets may on occasion be the same, but they are more often different. For example, the set of articles in a store and the set of prices of these articles are in an obvious relationship to each other. In order to determine the price associated with a given article, one has merely to inquire of a clerk in the store or look at the price tag on the article. It is important to note that while many articles may have the same price, there is nevertheless a well-defined price for each and every article. As another example of a relationship between two sets, consider the set of telephone subscribers in your city and the set of telephone numbers in your city directory. In order to get the correct association between the elements of these two sets, it is merely necessary to consult the directory. In this case, the correspondence between the two sets is more nearly—but perhaps not exactly—one-to-one. There may be more than one person or firm listed under the same number, and one person or firm may have more than one telephone number listed. So in this example, it is possible that neither the telephone number nor the name of a subscriber is determined by the other, in the same sense as the price was determined by the article in the previous example.

More generally, let S and T be two sets which, for the convenience of a diagram, we shall designate as point sets in Figure 15. If each point of S is associated with a well-defined point of T, we say that a *function* has been

71

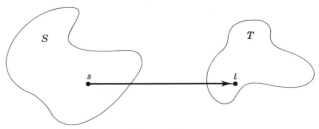

Figure 15

defined *on S to T*. It should be understood, of course, that the notion of a function on *S* to *T* implies that some rule has been given which allows us to associate an arbitrary $s \in S$ with some $t \in T$. A more exact definition of a function will be given in the next section, but for the present we shall be content with this somewhat intuitive description.

If *S* is a finite set, it is possible to give a complete representation of the function by explicitly listing the associated elements. For example, if $S = \{1, 2, 3, 4, 5\}$ and $T = \{0, 1, 2\}$, a function on *S* to *T* can be completely defined by the following diagrammatic associations:

$$1 \rightarrow 1, 2 \rightarrow 0, 3 \rightarrow 1, 4 \rightarrow 0, 5 \rightarrow 1.$$

It is often more convenient, and sometimes necessary, to use a rule to describe the association between the elements of two sets. For example, if *S* is the set of all real numbers and *T* is the subset of nonnegative real numbers, an association of the elements of *S* with elements of *T* can be accomplished by the following rule: $s \rightarrow t$, for any $s \in S$, where $t = s^2 \in T$. This rule of correspondence then defines a function on *S* to *T*. We note in passing that the definition of a function on *S* to *T*, as in this example, requires that each element of *S* be associated with some element of *T*, but every element of *T* does not have to be so associated.

The basic ingredients of what we are loosely referring to as a "function" are the *set S*, the *set T*, and the *rule* of association between each $s \in S$ and some $t \in T$. If we use *f* to designate such a function, it is convenient and customary to use $f(s)$ to designate the element of *T* which corresponds to $s \in S$. The number $f(s)$ is also known as the *value* of *f* at *s*, and it is common practice to state that the equation $t = f(s)$ defines *t* as "a function of *s*." For example, if *F* is the function discussed in the preceding paragraph, $F(s) = s^2$, for each real number *s*. If *g* is the function described two paragraphs previously, we may write: $g(1) = 1$, $g(2) = 0$, $g(3) = 1$, $g(4) = 0$, $g(5) = 1$. If *f* is a function on *S* to *T*, the set *S* is called the *domain* of *f*, while the set $\{f(s)|s \in S\}$ is a subset of *T* called the *range* of *f*. The domain of the function *g* above is $\{1, 2, 3, 4, 5\}$ and its range is $\{0, 1\}$; the domain and range of F are, respectively, the set R and the subset of all nonnegative real numbers.

In the great majority of cases occurring in elementary mathematics, both the domains and ranges of the functions are subsets of real numbers, and a function is completely defined if we know its domain and rule of correspondence. If it happens that the domain consists of all real numbers for which the rule makes sense, it is common practice in most books of an elementary nature not to make any specific mention of the domain and to consider that the function has been adequately defined by its rule of correspondence. For example, it is quite traditional that x and y are corresponding elements of the domain and range, respectively, and so it has become customary to speak of functions such as "the function $y = x^2$," without further comment on the domain or range. It is to be understood for this function that the domain is the set R, with the range the set of nonnegative real numbers. In the discussions of this book, however, we shall try to be explicit and state what is to be considered the domain in each case.

EXAMPLE 1. If $S = \{1, 2, 3, 4, 5\}$, describe the function f on S defined by $f(x) = x^2$.

SOLUTION. The domain is finite in this case, and the complete function is described by the indicated correspondences:

$$1 \to 1, 2 \to 4, 3 \to 9, 4 \to 16, 5 \to 25.$$

EXAMPLE 2. A function f is defined on the set of real numbers $x \neq 1$ by $y = 1/(x - 1)$, where $y = f(x)$. Determine $f(0), f(2),$ and $f(-1)$.

SOLUTION. Since $f(x) = y = 1/(x - 1)$, it is immediate on replacing x by the appropriate number that: $f(0) = 1/(0 - 1) = -1$; $f(2) = 1/(2 - 1) = 1$; $f(-1) = 1/(-1 - 1) = -\frac{1}{2}$.

EXAMPLE 3. A body falls 64 feet from a ledge to the ground below. If we assume the ideal conditions of a vacuum, and that the body falls d feet in t seconds where $d = 16t^2$, describe the function defined here by this equation.

SOLUTION. The equation defines a function whose domain is the (time) interval $[0, 2]$ and whose range is the (distance) interval $[0, 64]$. The "rule" $d = 16t^2$ allows us to calculate the distance d that the body falls in any time $t \in [0, 2]$. For instance, if $t = 1, d = 16$; if $t = \frac{3}{2}, d = 36$; etc.

PROBLEMS

1. Consider the correspondences discussed in the first paragraph of this section (in connection with the store and telephone directory), and decide whether a function has been defined in either case.

2. If $-1, 0, 1, 2$ are elements in the domain of a function f defined by $f(x) = 2x^2 - 1$, determine $f(-1)$, $f(0)$, $f(1)$, and $f(2)$.

3. A function F is completely defined by the following table.

x	1	2	3	4	5
$F(x)$	-1	0	1	2	3

(a) What are $F(2)$ and $F(3)$? (b) Describe the domain and range of F.

4. If $A = \{-2, 3, 5, 6\}$ and f is the function defined on A by $f(x) = x^2 + 1$, describe the range of f.

5. If f is the function defined on $\{1, 2, 3, 4, 5, 6\}$ by $f(x) = x^2 + 1$, determine: (a) $f(2)$, $f(3)$, $f(6)$; (b) $f(2) - 2f(3)$; (c) $2f(1) + 3f(2)$.

6. If f is the function defined on R by $f(x) = 1 - 2x + x^2$, determine the value of f at each of the following real numbers: (a) 1; (b) -2; (c) $\frac{1}{2}$; (d) 0.

7. A function F is defined by $F(x) = \dfrac{2x}{(x - 1)(x + 1)}$ on the subset of R for which the rule has meaning. (a) Describe the domain of F. (b) Determine $F(0)$ and $F(-2)$.

8. Describe the range of each of the following functions whose domain D and rule of association is given: (a) D = set of integers, $f(x) = x^2 + 1$; (b) D = set of nonzero integers, $f(x) = 2/x$; (c) D = set of all odd integers, $f(x) = 2x$; (d) $D = R$, $f(x) = 2x$.

9. The symbol $[x]$ denotes the largest integer not exceeding x. If f is the function defined on the set of positive real numbers by $f(x) = [x]$, describe the range of f.

4.2   Graphs of Functions

If f is a function on S to T, instead of stating that $f(s) = t$ or writing $s \rightarrow t$ to indicate the association of s with t, we can agree to use the ordered pair (s, t). By this pair, we must understand that $s \in S$ and $t \in T$, and that s corresponds to t by the rule of correspondence of the function. With this understanding, the function f is completely described by the collection of all such ordered pairs, and for some purposes it is convenient to identify f with the set $\{(s, t) | t = f(s)\}$. This leads us to the formal definition of a function.

Definition.   Let S and T be arbitrary sets. Then a function *on S to T* is a set of ordered pairs $\{(s, t) | s \in S, t \in T\}$, such that each element of S occurs once and only once as a first component.

The condition on the ordered pairs in the definition is equivalent to the statement that $(s, t_1) = (s, t_2)$ implies $t_1 = t_2$. Moreover, the definition identifies a function on S to T with a subset of the Cartesian product set $S \times T$, but it should be observed that every subset of $S \times T$ is not a function.

For example, consider the function f defined on $\{1, 2, 3\}$ by $f(s) = s + 2$. As a consequence of the definition, f is a subset of $S \times T$ where $S = \{1, 2, 3\}$ and $T = \{3, 4, 5\}$, and $f = \{(1, 3), (2, 4), (3, 5)\}$. On the other hand, the set $\{(1, 2), (1, 3), (2, 5)\}$ does not define a function on $\{1, 2\}$, because the condition on the ordered pairs which define a function is violated by the inclusion of two pairs $(1, 2)$ and $(1, 3)$ with the same first component.

The matter of constructing a graph of a Cartesian product set or a subset thereof was considered in §2.2. It then follows that we can construct the graph of a function by graphing the subset of ordered pairs which we have identified with the function. For example, the graph of the function f described in the preceding paragraph is shown in Figure 16. We illustrate the graphical aspect of a function with further examples.

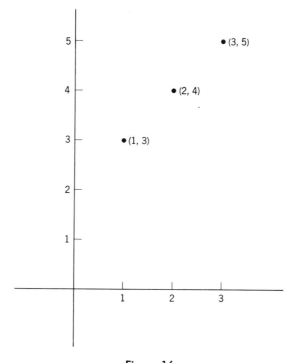

Figure 16

EXAMPLE 1.   Graph the function F defined on $\{-2, -1, 0, 1, 2\}$ by $f(x) = x^2$.

SOLUTION. From the definition, we may write the following equality:

$$F = \{(-2, 4), (-1, 1), (0, 0), (1, 1), (2, 4)\}.$$

The graph of F is then the five distinguished points shown in Figure 17a.

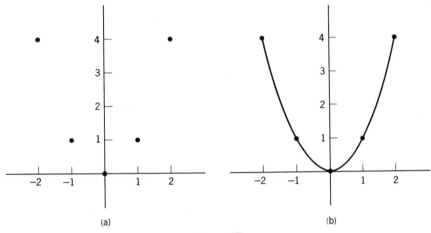

(a)   (b)

Figure 17

In cases where the domain of a function contains an infinite number of elements, or when the domain is of infinite extent on an algebraic scale, it is possible to graph only a representative set of points of the function. If the domain happens to be an interval $[a, b]$, it is *very often* quite proper that these representative points be then joined with a smooth curve. However, we must emphasize that the graph is *not* a curve unless the domain is such an interval, and even with a domain of this kind common sense must decide whether a smooth curve should be drawn. The property of a function which guarantees a graph which is smooth is "continuity," a topic which is discussed in a first course in analysis.

EXAMPLE 3.   Graph the function f defined on the interval $[-2, 2]$ by $f(x) = x^2$.

SOLUTION.   In this case, we reproduce the graph of Example 1, and then join these points with a smooth curve, since it is intuitive that intermediate points of the domain will be associated with intermediate points of the range. The graph is shown as the solid curve in Figure 17b.

Inasmuch as most functions which occur in mathematics have subsets of real numbers for both domain and range, it is usually the case that the graph of a mathematical function is the graph of a subset of $R \times R$.

PROBLEMS

1. Each of the following tables gives a complete definition of a function f, for which $y = f(x)$. Make a graph of each function.

(a)

x	1	2	3
y	0	1	2

(b)

x	-1	0	2	-3
y	-2	1	3	4

(c)

x	1	2	3	4
y	2	2	2	2

2. If $A = \{-2, -1, 1, 2, 3\}$, make a graph of the function f defined on A by $f(x) = 2x^2 - 1$.

3. Make a graph of the function F defined on S by $F(x) = x^2 - 2$, where: (a) $S = \{0, 1, 2, 3, 4\}$; (b) $S = \{-2, -1, 0, 1, 2, 3, 4\}$.

4. A function G consists of the following set of ordered pairs:
$$\{(-2, 6), (1, 3), (2, 3), (3, -2)\}.$$
(a) Determine $G(2)$ and $G(1)$.
(b) Determine $[G(-2) + 2G(3)]/G(1)$.
(c) Make a graph of the function G.

5. If S is the interval $[-2, 2]$, graph the function f on S defined by: (a) $f(x) = 2x + 1$; (b) $f(x) = 3x^2 - 1$; (c) $f(x) = x^3$.

6. Let S be a subset of A. Then the *characteristic function* of the subset S is the function on A defined as follows: $f(x) = 1$, if $x \in S$; $f(x) = 0$, if $x \notin S$. Let $A = [0, 5]$, and construct a graph of f if (a) $S = \{0, 1, 2, 3, 4, 5\}$; (b) $S = [0, 3]$; (c) $S = [0, 2] \cup [3, 5]$.

7. Refer to Problem 6 for the definition, and describe the characteristic function of S on A, if $A = R$ and S is the subset of rational numbers. Could you construct a graph of f in this case?

8. Graph the function F defined on $[-2, 2]$ by $F(x) = |x|$.

9. Graph the function f defined on $[-3, 3]$ by $f(x) = [x]$, where $[x]$ is the number defined in Problem 9 of §4.1.

10. Construct a graph of the function f defined on $[-3, 3]$ by: (a) $f(x) = |x| - x$; (b) $f(x) = |x| + x$; (c) $f(x) = |x| + x$ if $x > 0$, $f(x) = |x| - x$ if $x \leq 0$.

11. With $[x]$ defined as in Problem 9 of §4.1, construct a graph of the function f on $[-2, 2]$ by $f(x) = [2x]$.

12. If I amperes of current flow in a long wire, a magnetic field of H gauss is established at a point r centimeters from the wire, where $H = 2I/r$. Let $I = 10$, and graph the function defined for $2 \leq r \leq 10$.

4.3 Polynomial Functions

A general polynomial in a variable x is an expression of the form $a_0 x^n + a_1 x^{n-1} + \cdots + a_{n-1} x + a_n$, with n a positive integer. For the cases of

interest to us, the "coefficients" $a_0, a_1, \ldots, a_{n-1}, a_n$ are to be regarded as
real numbers, while the universe of x is R. If $a_0 \neq 0$, the *degree* of the
above polynomial is n. Any function f whose rule of correspondence is
$y = f(x)$, where $f(x)$ is a polynomial in x, is known as a *polynomial function*.
We are to be concerned here principally with two special cases, $n = 1$ and
$n = 2$. In the case $n = 1$, both the polynomial and function are said to be
linear, while in the case $n = 2$, they are said to be *quadratic*. There is some
difference of opinion as to whether a function defined by a polynomial of
the first degree should be called "linear" unless the term independent of x
(i.e., the "constant" term) is 0. However, we shall follow the usual practice
of referring to *all* polynomial functions of the first degree as linear. The
reason for this practice will become apparent from the graphs of these
functions. We now consider the graphs of linear and quadratic functions.

If f is a polynomial function of the first degree, $f(x) = ax + b$ for real
numbers a, b and every x in the domain of f, it then follows from the "set"
definition of a function as given in §4.2 that f is the same as the *solution set*
of the equation $y = ax + b$, where we are to understand that the universes
of the variables x and y are, respectively, the domain of f and the set R of
real numbers. We noted—without proof—in §3.3 that the graph of the
solution set of any first degree equation, whose variables have universe R,
is a straight line, and so the graph of any linear function on R is also a
straight line. More generally, the graph of any linear function defined on
an interval $[a, b]$ is a line *segment*. This explains the usage of the word
"linear" as applied to a function. Any linear equation of the form $y = ax + b$
defines a function f *explicitly* where $y = f(x) = ax + b$. If the linear equation has the form $ax + by + c = 0$, its solution set in any universe comprises a function which is said to have been defined *implicitly* by the
equation. If $b \neq 0$, the equation can be written in equivalent form as
$y = (-a/b)x - c/b$, and this equation defines the same function explicitly.

Since the graph of a linear function is a portion of a straight line, it
can be constructed from two (or three, if a check point is desired) ordered
pairs of the function. All other points of the graph must lie on the straight
line through these points which have been determined. If the domain
is an interval, the graph is the complete segment joining its two endpoints.

EXAMPLE 1.   Graph the linear function f defined on $[-3, 3]$ by
$2x - 3y + 6 = 0$, where $y = f(x)$.

SOLUTION.   Three ordered pairs of the function are easily found
to be: $(0, 2), (-3, 0), (3, 4)$. If we plot these points on a Cartesian plane,
it is a simple matter to complete the linear graph as shown in Figure 18.

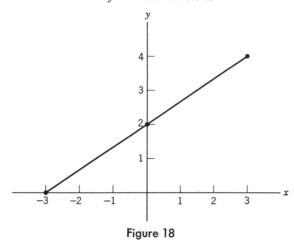

Figure 18

The general *quadratic*, or "second degree," polynomial in x has the form $ax^2 + bx + c$, where a, b, c are real numbers, and a function f so defined that $f(x) = ax^2 + bx + c$, for each x in its domain, is called a *quadratic function*. Any section of an infinite right circular cone cut by a plane parallel to one of its generating elements, is a geometric curve known as a *parabola*. It can be shown that the graph of any quadratic function consists of points which lie on a parabola, but we leave the verification of this fact to books on analytic geometry. The graphing of a few selected points will indicate the probable truth of the assertion, however. When graphed in the usual way with horizontal and vertical coordinate axes, the underlying parabola opens "upward" if $a > 0$, and "downward" if $a < 0$. When the domain of a quadratic function is an interval of real numbers, the graph of f will be an actual segment of a parabola.

EXAMPLE 2. Graph the quadratic function f defined on $\{-2, -1, 0, 1, 2\}$ by $y = 2x^2 + x - 1$, where $y = f(x)$.

SOLUTION. The elements of the function are as follows: $(-2, 5)$, $(-1, 0)$, $(0, -1)$, $(1, 2)$, $(2, 9)$. The graph is shown in Figure 19, where it may be observed that the points of the function lie on a segment of a parabola.

EXAMPLE 3. Graph the function f defined on $[-3, 2]$ by $f(x) = -x^2 + x + 10$.

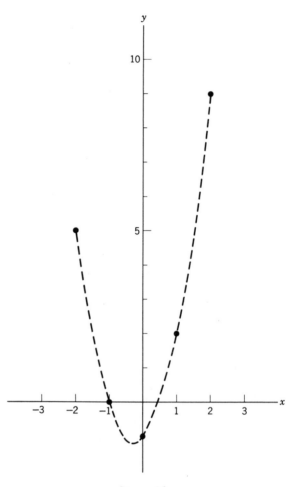

Figure 19

SOLUTION.   A representative collection of points of the function may be seen to be: $(-3, -2), (-2, 4), (-1, 8), (0, 10), (1, 10), (2, 8)$. The complete graph of the function is shown in Figure 20, the points being located on a segment of a parabola opening downward.

The graph of any polynomial function of degree greater than 2 can be obtained in a similar way, but there are very few graphical features common to all such graphs. It is a fact, however, that if the domain of any polynomial function is an interval, its graph is a "smooth" curve, and the number of times that the curve changes direction increases with the degree

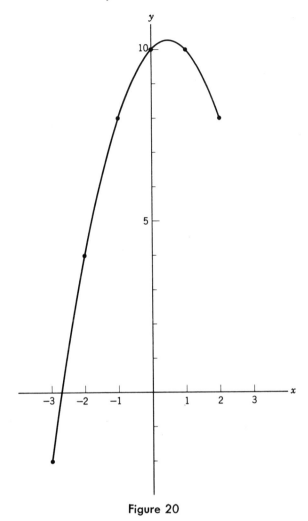

Figure 20

of the polynomial. We do not wish to dwell further on this topic of "curves of higher degree," but will content ourselves with an example.

EXAMPLE 4.   Graph the function f defined on $[-2, 2]$ by $f(x) = 2x^3 - 8x$.

SOLUTION.   A representative set of points of the graph may be obtained as follows: $(0, 0), (-1, 6), (-2, 0), (1, -6), (2, 0)$. The complete graph is then the smooth curve drawn through these points as shown in Figure 21.

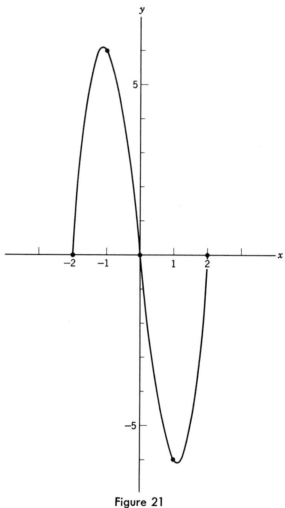

Figure 21

PROBLEMS

Sketch the graph of each of the functions, whose rules of correspondence and domains are given below.

1. $f(x) = 2x - 5$, $[-2, 2]$.

2. $f(x) = x - 2$, $[-3, 3]$.

3. $2x + 3y - 5 = 0$, $[-1, 3]$.

4. $3x - 2y + 6 = 0$, $[-3, 2]$.

5. $3x^2 - 2x = y$, $[-1, 1]$.

6. $2x^2 + 3x - 4 = y$, $[-2, 2]$.

7. $2x - y + 1 = 0$, $\{-2, -1, 0, 1, 2, 3\}$.

8. $x + y - 2 = 0$, $\{0, 1, 2, 3\}$.

9. $f(x) = 3x^2$, $\{-3, -2, -1, 1, 2\}$.

10. $f(x) = -2x^2 + x - 1$, $\{-1, 3, 5, 7\}$.

11. $f(x) = 2x^2, \{-\frac{3}{2}, -1, -\frac{1}{2}, 0, 1, \frac{1}{2}, \frac{3}{2}\}$.
12. $f(x) = -3x^2, \{-\frac{3}{2}, -1, -\frac{1}{2}, 0, 1, \frac{1}{2}, \frac{3}{2}\}$.
13. $f(x) = x^3 + 2x, [-2, 2]$.   **14.** $f(x) = x^4 - 2x^2 - 2, [-2, 2]$.

4.4   An Algebra of Functions

If S is a set of functions, *each with the same domain D*, it is possible to define operations of addition and multiplication in S and obtain an "algebra" (or "arithmetic") of functions quite similar to the system of rational numbers. We proceed to these definitions.

Definitions.   If $f \in S$ and $g \in S$, then:

1. $f + g$ is a function on D, called the "sum" of f and g, such that $(f + g)(x) = f(x) + g(x)$, for each $x \in D$.
2. $f \cdot g$ is a function on D, called the "product" of f and g, such that $(f \cdot g)(x) = f(x) \cdot g(x)$, for each $x \in D$.

These definitions then define the sum and product of two functions by merely adding and multiplying the corresponding functional values.

EXAMPLE 1.   If f and g are functions on $[0, 2]$ defined so that $f(x) = 2x^2$ and $g(x) = 3x - 1$, describe $f + g$ and $f \cdot g$. In particular, determine $(f + g)(1)$ and $(f \cdot g)(1)$.

SOLUTION.   By the above definitions, $f + g$ and $f \cdot g$ are defined on $[0, 2]$ as follows:

$$(f + g)(x) = f(x) + g(x) = 2x^2 + 3x - 1,$$
$$(f \cdot g)(x) = f(x) \cdot g(x) = 2x^2(3x - 1).$$

Hence,

$$(f + g)(1) = 2 + 3 - 1 = 4 \text{ and } (f \cdot g)(1) = 2(3 - 1) = 4.$$

If we are to develop an algebra of functions similar to the rational numbers, we must define a "zero" function and additive inverse or "negative" functions. This is done according to the following definitions.

Definitions
3. The *zero* function on D is a function, designated 0, such that $0(x) = 0$, for each $x \in D$.
4. If f is a function on D, $-f$ is the function on D such that $(-f)(x) = -f(x)$, for each $x \in D$.

The zero function on any domain is then so defined that its value at any point of the domain is 0. The same symbol 0 will be used to designate any zero function, regardless of its domain, for the context will remove any ambiguity. The context will also distinguish between the real number 0 and a zero function. It is quite possible, of course, that the function 0 is not contained in the set S. It follows from (4) that $[f + (-f)](x) = f(x) + (-f)(x) = f(x) + [-f(x)] = f(x) - f(x) = 0$, for any $x \in D$, and so $f + (-f)$ is the 0 function on D. We define $f - g$ to be the same as $f + (-g)$, and so the *subtraction* of two functions is accomplished by subtracting their functional values. In particular, $f - f = 0$.

EXAMPLE 2. Describe the zero function on $[0, 2]$ and the function $-f$, where f is the function given in Example 1.

SOLUTION. The zero function on $[0, 2]$ is the function 0, such that $0(x) = 0$ for each $x \in [0, 2]$. By our definition 4, $-f$ is the function on $[0, 2]$ such that $(-f)(x) = -2x^2$, for each $x \in [0, 2]$.

The function 0 on any domain D is a special case of a whole class of "constant" functions, whose values are constant at any point of D. It is then convenient to extend the usage of 0 to include any real number c, where c is regarded as a function whose value at any point of its domain is c. For example, we may refer to "the function 1" or "the function 2," and so on. The context again will distinguish the real number from the constant function which it may designate.

Finally, we wish to introduce the idea of division for two suitable functions. We do this by means of "reciprocal" functions.

Definition
5. Let f be a function defined on D such that $f(x) \neq 0$, for $x \in D$. Then the *reciprocal* function $1/f$ is the function on D such that $(1/f)(x) = 1/f(x)$, for each $x \in D$.

It follows from Definition 5 that $f(x)[1/f(x)] = 1$, for any $x \in D$, and so $f(1/f) = 1$. Moreover, if we define f/g to be identical with $f(1/g)$, *we are identifying division by g with multiplication by the reciprocal of g.* This rule of division and the earlier rule of subtraction are in harmony with the corresponding rules for rational numbers, and it may be seen that the requirement for the existence of $1/f$ that $f(x) \neq 0$, for $x \in D$, corresponds to the arithmetic rule which forbids division by 0.

EXAMPLE 3. Describe f/g, where f and g are functions defined on $[0, 2]$ by $f(x) = 3x^2$ and $g(x) = 2x + 1$. Determine $(f/g)(1)$.

SOLUTION.   By our definition of division, $(f/g)(x) = f(x)/g(x) = 3x^2/(2x + 1)$, for each $x \in [0, 2]$. In particular, $(f/g)(1) = \frac{3}{3} = 1$.

It is easy to see that the associative, commutative, and distributive properties of the real numbers are inherited by real-valued functions. That is, $f + (g + h) = (f + g) + h$, $f \cdot (g \cdot h) = (f \cdot g) \cdot h$, $f + g = g + f$, $f \cdot g = g \cdot f$, and $f \cdot (g + h) = f \cdot g + f \cdot h$, for any functions f, g, h with common domain D. We shall prove the associative law of addition and leave the verification of the rest to the student.

THEOREM 4.41. $f + (g + h) = (f + g) + h$,   for any functions f, g, h on D.

PROOF.   Let $x \in D$. Then,

$$[f + (g + h)](x) = f(x) + [g(x) + h(x)] = [f(x) + g(x)] + h(x)$$
$$= [f + g](x) + h(x) = [(f + g) + h](x).$$

Hence, $f + (g + h) = (f + g) + h$, as desired.

A slight variation is sometimes made in the definitions of $f + g$, $f - g$, fg, and f/g in an algebra of functions. If D_f and D_g are the respective domains of f and g, we are simply to understand that the domain of $f + g$, $f - g$, and fg is D where $D = D_f \cap D_g$, while the domain of f/g is $\{x \mid x \in D, g(x) \neq 0\}$. The two definitions are essentially the same, however. If a set S of functions is closed under the operations of addition and multiplication, contains the constant functions 0 and 1, and also the functions $-f$ and $1/f$ whenever it contains $f(\neq 0)$, the set S possesses all the usual properties of the system of rational numbers. It would then be appropriate to refer to S as a "field" of functions. A further extension of function symbolism is given in Problem 23.

PROBLEMS

1. Is it correct to state that all zero functions are the same? Explain.
2. Is it correct to assume that the constant function c is the same on every occurrence?
3. Prove the commutative laws of addition and multiplication for real-valued functions.
4. Prove the distributive law for real-valued functions.

For Problems 5 through 10, assume f and g defined on $[-2, 2]$. Describe each indicated function where $f(x) = 3x^2 + 1$, $g(x) = 2x + 7$.
5. $f + g$. 6. $f \cdot g$. 7. f/g. 8. $1/f$. 9. $1/g$. 10. $f + 1/f$.

For Problems 11 and 12, the domains of f and g are the maximal subsets of real numbers for which the defining rules make sense.

11. If $f(x) = 1/x + 2/(x - 2)$ and $g(x) = 3x$, describe $f + g$, on a suitable domain.

12. If $f(x) = 1/(x - 1)$ and $g(x) = 1/(x - 2)^2$, describe $f \cdot g$, on a suitable domain.

13. $f(x) = 2/x, x \neq -1, 0, 1$ $g(x) = 2/[(x - 1)(x + 1)], x \neq -1, 0, 1$
    $= 15, x = 1.$ $= 10, x = 1.$

    Use the above definitions of f and g and describe $f + g$ and $f \cdot g$.

14. With f and g as in Problem 11, describe $f - g$ and f/g on a suitable domain.

15. With f and g as in Problem 12, describe $f - g$ and f/g on a suitable domain.

16. Let $f(x) = 2$ and $g(x) = [x]$, for each $x \in [0, 5]$, construct the graph of $f + g$. [See Problem 9 of §4.1 for the definition of $[x]$].

17. Refer to Problem 16 and describe $f \cdot g$ and $f - g$.

18. Let $f(x) = |x|$ and $g(x) = x$, for each $x \in [-3, 3]$. Construct graphs of the functions $f + g$, $g - f$, and $f \cdot g$.

19. With f and g defined in Problem 18, describe the function f/g, on a suitable domain.

20. Take any real number x and perform in order the following sequence of operations on x: Add 3; double the result; subtract 4; divide result by 6; multiply by 3; subtract the original number. If $f(x)$ is the resulting number, describe the function f.

21. Let f be the characteristic function (See Problem 6 of §4.2) of a subset A of B, and let $g(x) = 1$ for every $x \in B$. Prove that $g - f$ is the characteristic function of A', where A' is the complement of A in B.

22. The functions f, g are completely defined on $\{-1, 0, 1\}$ by the following table:

x	$f(x)$	$g(x)$
-1	2	3
0	-1	-3
1	5	6

    Construct a similar table for the function: (a) $f + g$; (b) $f - g$; (c) $f \cdot g$; (d) f/g.

23. If α is a real number and f is a function, let us define the function αf by the rule that $(\alpha f)(x) = \alpha f(x)$, for each x in the domain of f. Then refer to Problem 22 and construct a table for the function (a) $2f$; (b) $3f + 2g$; (c) $4f^2$, where $f^2 = f \cdot f$; (d) $2f + 3g - 1$; (e) $4g^2 + 3f - 2$, where $g^2 = g \cdot g$.

4.5   Composite and Inverse Functions

It is possible to define the product of two functions in an entirely different way from that given in §4.4 and thereby obtain a different algebra of functions. For suitable functions f and g, the new product—which we shall call the "composite" of f by g—will be designated fg.

Definition. Let f and g be two functions so related that the range of g is a subset of the domain of f. Then the *composite fg* of f by g is a function defined on the domain D of g such that $(fg)(x) = f[g(x)]$, for every $x \in D$.

It is convenient to use $g(D)$ to refer to the range of g. If we think of a function as essentially a *mapping* of the elements of its domain onto its range, a composite fg is a sequence of two such mappings, first by g and then by f. Thus, if g maps D onto $g(D)$, and f maps $g(D)$ onto $f[g(D)]$, the function fg maps D directly onto $f[g(D)]$. These mappings are shown pictorially in Figure 22. In particular, an arbitrary element $x \in D$ is mapped

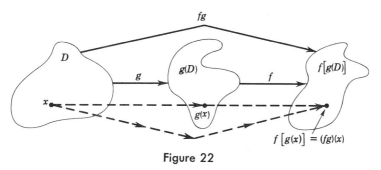

Figure 22

by g onto $g(x)$, while this element is then mapped by f onto $f[g(x)]$. By definition of fg, the element x is mapped by fg onto $f[g(x)]$.

EXAMPLE 1. If f is defined on R by $f(x) = 2x - 1$, and g is defined on $[-2, 2]$ by $g(x) = x^2$, describe and graph the function fg.

SOLUTION. The domain of fg is $[-2, 2]$, and for each x in this domain $(fg)(x) = f[g(x)] = f(x^2) = 2x^2 - 1$. The graph of fg, as shown in Figure 23, may be seen to be a segment of a parabola.

It should have been observed in §4.4 that our definitions of the constant functions 0 and 1 cause them to play roles in function theory quite similar to those played by their real number counterparts in ordinary arithmetic. In ordinary arithmetic, $a + 0 = 0 + a$, $a - a = 0$; and $a(1) = (1)a = a$, $a(1/a) = (1/a)a = 1$ if $a \neq 0$, for a real number a. In function theory, $f + 0 = 0 + f = f$, $f - f = 0$; and $f \cdot 1 = 1 \cdot f = f$, $f \cdot (1/f) = (1/f) \cdot f = 1$, provided $1/f$ exists, for a real-valued function f. We now define an *identity* function I and, for certain functions f, an *inverse* function, where I plays the role formerly played by 1 and f^{-1} replaces the reciprocal function $1/f$.

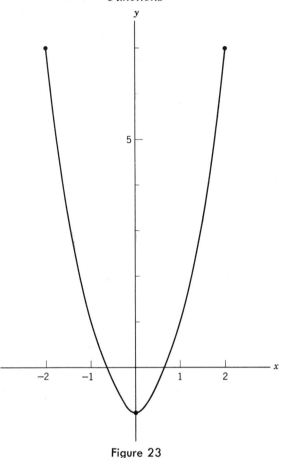

Figure 23

Definition.   The *identity* function *I* on a domain *D* is defined so that $I(x) = x$ for any $x \in D$.

In other words, the identity function *I* maps every element of its domain onto itself. As was the case for the constant function 1, we shall use the symbol *I* to designate *any* identity function regardless of its domain. It then follows immediately that $fI = If = f$, for any real-valued function *f*.

   If we think of a function *f* as a mapping of its domain onto its range, the function which is "inverse" to *f* reverses the mapping due to *f*. Hence the following definition is appropriate.

Definition.   Let *f* be a function with domain *D* and range *f(D)*. Then the function f^{-1} (if it exists) is defined on *f(D)* so that $f^{-1}(y) = x$ if $f(x) = y$.

That is, if f maps the element x onto y, the function f^{-1} maps y onto x. Since each of these functions reverses the mapping of the other, it follows that $ff^{-1} = f^{-1}f = I$, provided we interpret I in its most general sense. (See Problems.)

We have implied that it is possible that f^{-1} does not exist and in this respect is similar to the reciprocal $1/f$. In fact, f^{-1} cannot exist if $f(x) = f(y)$, with $x \neq y$, because any attempted definition of $f^{-1}(x)$ or $f^{-1}(y)$ would be ambiguous. A function f is *one-to-one* if there is a one-to-one correspondence between the elements of the domain and range of f, and so $f(x) = f(y)$ would imply that $x = y$. Since a reverse mapping of a one-to-one function may be defined unambiguously, *the necessary and sufficient condition for the existence of the function f^{-1} is that f be one-to-one.* It should be understood that while the domains of a function and its reciprocal (if it exists) are the same, the domains of a function and its inverse (if it exists) are in general different.

EXAMPLE 2. If f is the function defined on $[-2, 2]$ by $f(x) = 2x - 3$, describe f^{-1} and graph both f and f^{-1}.

SOLUTION. Let $y = 2x - 3$, so that $f(x) = y$. If $2a - 3 = 2b - 3$, it follows that $a = b$, and so the function f is one-to-one. Hence f^{-1} exists and is defined so that $f^{-1}(y) = x$. But $x = (y + 3)/2$, and so $f^{-1}(y) = (y + 3)/2$, for each y in $f[-2, 2]$, i.e., in $[-7, 1]$. If we now replace y by the usual "domain variable" x, the definition of f^{-1} is as follows: $f^{-1}(x) = (x + 3)/2$, for each $x \in [-7, 1]$. On checking ff^{-1} and $f^{-1}f$, we find that $(f^{-1}f)(x) = f^{-1}[f(x)] = f^{-1}(2x - 3) = (2x - 3 + 3)/2 = x$, for each $x \in [-2, 2]$; and also $(ff^{-1})(x) = f[f^{-1}(x)] = f[(x + 3)/2] = 2(x + 3)/2 - 3 = x$, for each $x \in [-7, 1]$. Hence, $f^{-1}f = ff^{-1} = I$, which is the characterizing equation for inverses. The graphs of f and f^{-1} are shown in Figure 24.

If we think of a function as a set of ordered pairs, our definition of f^{-1} implies that $(a, b) \in f$ if and only if $(b, a) \in f^{-1}$. The geometric effect of this is that the graphs of inverse functions are the geometric reflections of each other in the diagonal line drawn through the first and third quadrants. We may observe that the line segments in Figure 24 have this property.

EXAMPLE 3. If f is completely defined by the following table, construct a similar table for f^{-1} and graph both functions.

x	0	1	2	3	4
$f(x)$	2	-2	3	0	-5

Functions

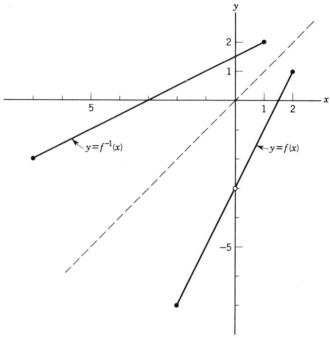

Figure 24

SOLUTION.   We first note that each functional value occurs only once, and so f^{-1} exists. The function table for f^{-1} then follows from the reverse mapping.

x	-5	-2	0	2	3
$f^{-1}(x)$	4	1	3	0	2

Both graphs are shown in Figure 25.

A function f is said to be *strictly increasing* if $f(x) < f(y)$ if and only if $x < y$, for elements x, y in the domain of f. If $f(x) > f(y)$ if and only if $x < y$, the function is said to be *strictly decreasing*. It is a geometrically intuitive fact that the inverse f^{-1} of a function f defined on an interval $[a, b]$ exists if and only if f is either strictly increasing or strictly decreasing. For the increasing case, the domain of f^{-1} is then the interval $[f(a), f(b)]$, while for the decreasing case the domain of f^{-1} is $[f(b), f(a)]$. We used this intuitive fact in Example 2 without comment.

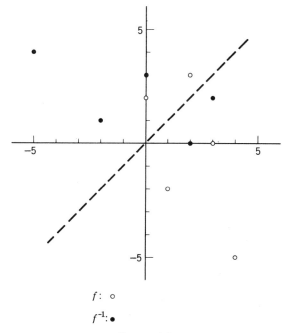

f: ○

f^{-1}: ●

Figure 25

PROBLEMS

1. If f^{-1} exists, explain why $ff^{-1} = f^{-1}f = I$. Is this equality completely accurate? Explain.

2. If f and g are defined on R by $f(x) = 2x^2 - 1$ and $g(x) = 3x - 2$, describe fg and gf.

3. If f and g are defined on R by $f(x) = 3x - 2$ and $g(x) = 3x^3$, describe fg and gf.

4. If $f(x) = 2x^2 + 1$, for each $x \in R$, and $g(x) = 2x - 3$ for each $x \in [0, 2]$, describe and graph fg. Does gf exist as a function on R?

5. If $f(x) = 2/x$ for each $x \in [2, 4]$, and $g(x) = 3x - 1$ for each $x \in R$, describe and graph gf. Does fg exist as a function on R?

6. Each of the following rules defines a function whose domain is the maximal subset of real numbers for which the rule makes sense. Decide which function has an inverse: (a) $f(x) = 2x^2$; (b) $f(x) = 3x + 2$; (c) $f(x) = 2/x$; (d) $f(x) = x^3$.

7. Use the directions of Problem 6 for the functions defined below: (a) $f(x) = \sqrt{1 - x}$; (b) $f(x) = 2x^2 + 1$; (c) $f(x) = 2/(x^2 + 1)$; (d) $f(x) = 1 - 1/x$.

8. The following table defines a function f. Construct a similar table for f^{-1} and graph both functions.

x	-2	-1	0	1	2	3
$f(x)$	3	1	-2	2	-1	4

9. Give an example of a function which is neither strictly increasing nor strictly decreasing but which has an inverse.

10. If f and g are functions defined on R by $f(x) = x^2 + 1$ and $g(x) = 2x - 1$, illustrate the difference between $f \cdot g$ and fg.

11. Use the function f of Problem 10 to illustrate the difference between f^2, regarded as the product $f \cdot f$, and f^2 regarded as the composite ff.

12. If f and g are defined on R by $f(x) = |x|$ and $g(x) = |x| + 1$, describe both fg and gf.

13. If $f(x) = |x|$ and $g(x) = [x]$ (with $[x]$ defined in Problem 9 of §4.1), describe fg and gf.

14. Explain why neither function f nor g of Problem 13 has an inverse.

15. Justify the validity of the following rule: A function f has an inverse if and only if every horizontal straight line intersects the graph of f in not more than one point. Would it be appropriate to replace "not more than" by "precisely?" Explain.

16. If f^{-1} is the inverse of f, is it proper to refer to f as the inverse of f^{-1}. Is it true that $(f^{-1})^{-1} = f$, if f^{-1} exists?

17. If f is defined on $[-2, 3]$ by $f(x) = 3x - 2$, describe the function f^{-1}.

18. If g is defined on the set of non-negative real numbers by $g(x) = (2 + x)/(3 + x)$, describe the function g^{-1}.

19. Let the function f be defined on R by $f(x) = x^2$. Restrict the domain of f in some manner to obtain a new function, defined by the same rule, but which possesses an inverse. Are there more than one such new functions?

20. Describe a function with domain D, range F, and state whether it possesses an inverse if: (a) $D = \{1, 2, 3\}$, $F = \{2, 4, 5\}$; (b) $D =$ set of integers, $F =$ set of even integers; (c) $D = R$, $F = R$.

21. If f and g are constant functions on D, prove that the solution set of $f(x) = g(x)$, for $x \in D$, is either D or $\emptyset$.

CHAPTER 5

Exponential and Logarithmic Functions

5.1 The Meaning of Exponents

If n real numbers, each equal to a, are multiplied together, an easy extension of the associative law of multiplication shows that this product is independent of the order in which the numbers are grouped. The product which is common to all the groupings is denoted by a^n, and is called the nth *power of a* where the natural number n is called an *exponent*. Thus $a^n = (a)(a) \cdots (a)$, where the factor a occurs n times, and the exponent n in a^n tells how many times the "base" number a occurs as a factor. Clearly, this notion of an exponent has meaning only if n is a natural number. For example, 3^4 is a short symbolism for $(3)(3)(3)(3)$, the exponent 4 indicating that the base 3 has been used 4 times as a factor. On many occasions we have already used this type of natural number exponent without comment.

The *Laws of Exponents*, which we now state, follow immediately from the primitive concept we have just reviewed, and we shall omit any proof for them. In the statement of these laws, a and b may designate arbitrary real numbers, but for the present the exponents m and n are natural numbers or positive integers.

LAWS OF EXPONENTS

1. $a^m a^n = a^{m+n}$.
2. $(a^m)^n = a^{mn}$.
3. $(ab)^m = a^m b^m$.
4. $a^m/a^n = a^{m-n}$, if $m > n$
   $\qquad\quad = 1/a^{n-m}$ if $m < n$
   $\qquad\quad = 1$ if $m = n$.

93

While it is possible to *prove* the above laws from the primitive concept of an exponent and the properties of real numbers, the extension of the exponent concept beyond the positive integers is a matter of *definition*. However, these definitions are not made in an arbitrary fashion, but rather with the following guiding principle in mind: *We wish the Laws of Exponents to continue to hold for any extension of the exponent concept.*

As a first application of this principle, consider a^n/a^n for any positive integer n. If the "subtraction" rule for the fourth law of exponents is to hold, this extended rule would require that $a^{n-n} = a^0 = 1$. Hence the following definition is forced upon us.

Definition. $a^0 = 1$, for any real number $a \neq 0$.

The operation which is "inverse" to raising a number to the nth power is a determination of its "n^{th} root." For example, 2 and -2 are 4th roots of 16, because $2^4 = (-2)^4 = 16$; -3 is a "3th," or cube, root of -27, because $(-3)^3 = -27$; and both 5 and -5 are "2th," or square, roots of 25, because $5^2 = (-5)^2 = 25$. If a is a positive real number, it is a fact that there is *exactly one* n^{th} root of a which is positive; while if a is negative, there is a real n^{th} root of a only if n is odd, and this real root is also unique. In either of these cases we refer to this unique real n^{th} root as the *principal* n^{th} *root* of a, and designate it as $\sqrt[n]{a}$, with n omitted in case $n = 2$. As a special application of this definition, it is instructive to point out that $\sqrt{x^2} = |x|$ and so, for example, $\sqrt{(-2)^2} = 2$. On the other hand, $\sqrt[3]{x^3} = x$ regardless of the algebraic sign of x. We call attention to the fact that $\sqrt[n]{a}$ has not been defined if a is negative and n is an even integer. For example, $\sqrt{4} = 2$, and $\sqrt[3]{-8} = -2$, but $\sqrt{-9}$ has not been defined as a real number. In a later part of this chapter we shall discover how to compute any n^{th} roots which have been defined, but for the present we are concerned only with the *meanings* of the symbols. We are now in a position to extend the exponent concept to include both positive and negative rational numbers.

If m and n are positive integers, and $a^{m/n}$ is to be a number which obeys the second, or "multiplication," law of exponents, it must be true that $(a^{m/n})^n = a^m$. Hence, $a^{m/n}$ must be an nth root of a^m, and it may be seen that the following definition is appropriate.

Definition. $a^{m/n} = \sqrt[n]{a^m}$, provided m/n is a rational fraction reduced to lowest terms, and $\sqrt[n]{a^m}$ is defined. If $r/s = m/n$, $a^{r/s} = a^{m/n}$, provided $a^{m/n}$ is defined.

If $\sqrt[n]{a}$ is defined, we must have $(\sqrt[n]{a})^m = (\sqrt[n]{a^1})^m = (a^{1/n})^m = a^{m/n}$, in accordance with the second law of exponents, and so $a^{m/n} = \sqrt[n]{a^m} = (\sqrt[n]{a})^m$. Hence, $\sqrt[n]{a^m} = (\sqrt[n]{a})^m$, whenever these numbers are defined, and it may happen that one of these forms is easier to compute than the other. For example, $\sqrt[5]{32^3} = (\sqrt[5]{32})^3$, and it is easily seen from the second form of this number that $\sqrt[5]{32^3} = 2^3 = 8$.

Finally, if the first law of exponents is to hold for a "number" a^{-r}, where r is a positive rational number, we must have $(a^r)\,(a^{-r}) = a^0 = 1$. This suggests our extension of the exponent concept to include negative rational numbers.

Definition. $a^{-r} = 1/a^r$, for any real number a and an arbitrary rational number r, provided a^r has been defined and $a^r \neq 0$.

For example, this definition requires that $3^{-2} = 1/3^2 = 1/9$, and $2^{-2/3} = 1/2^r = 1/\sqrt[3]{4}$.

To sum up: If a is a positive real number, a^r has been defined for any rational number r; if a is negative, $a|$ has been defined for a rational number r only if the reduced fractional form of r has an odd integer for denominator. It is beyond the scope of this book to consider a further extension of the exponent concept to include irrational numbers. For example, we have not given nor will we give any meaning to such a symbolic number as $2^{\sqrt{3}}$, although such numbers can be defined. In Chapter 8, however, with the introduction of complex numbers, we shall give meaning to certain symbols which until then will remain undefined.

The definitions we have given in this section have been motivated by the Laws of Exponents, and we have indicated how this motivation was given. But this is not sufficient reason for us to be satisfied now that all the Laws of Exponents continue to hold with the enlarged concept of an exponent. However, it is possible to verify that these laws do hold in the more general environment, and we are going to assume this without further proof. We note that the fourth law of exponents can be more simply written now in the form: $a^m/a^n = a^{m-n} = 1/a^{n-m}$ (regardless of the ordering of m and n), provided only that a^m and a^n are real numbers.

We have seen that any "radical" of the form $\sqrt[n]{a}$, if it is defined, can be expressed in exponential form as $a^{1/n}$. Hence, in view of the easy application of the laws of exponents, it is usually desirable to change any simplification problem involving radicals into a problem which involves exponents.

EXAMPLE. Simplify each of the following, where x and y are nonzero real numbers:

(a) $\dfrac{x^{-1} + y^{-1}}{(x + y)^{-2}};$ (b) $(3^{-2} + 4^{-2})^{1/2};$ (c) $\dfrac{\sqrt[3]{x}\,\sqrt[4]{x^3}}{\sqrt{x}},$ $x > 0.$

SOLUTION

(a) $\dfrac{x^{-1} + y^{-1}}{(x + y)^{-2}} = \dfrac{1/x + 1/y}{1/(x + y)^2} = \dfrac{x + y}{xy} \cdot \dfrac{(x + y)^2}{1} = \dfrac{(x + y)^3}{xy}.$

(b) $(3^{-2} + 4^{-2})^{1/2} = \left(\dfrac{1}{9} + \dfrac{1}{16}\right)^{1/2} = \left(\dfrac{25}{144}\right)^{1/2} = \dfrac{5}{12}.$

(c) $\dfrac{\sqrt[3]{x}\ \sqrt[4]{x^3}}{\sqrt{x}} = \dfrac{x^{1/3} \cdot x^{3/4}}{x^{1/2}} = x^{1/3 + 3/4 - 1/2} = x^{7/12} = \sqrt[12]{x^7}.$

PROBLEMS

1. Represent each of the indicated numbers in simplest form: (a) $64^{2/3}$; (b) $-4^{2/3}$; (c) $3/3^0$; (d) $16^{3/2}$; (e) $1/2^{-2}$.

2. Express each of the indicated numbers in radical form: (a) $4^{2/3}$; (b) $6^{3/4}$; (c) $(-4)^{2/3}$; (d) $(-5)^{-3/5}$.

3. Express each of the following numbers in radical form: (a) $2^{3 \cdot 2}$; (b) $3^{1 \cdot 52}$; (c) $5^{2 \cdot 14}$; (d) $10^{0 \cdot 0012}$.

4. Express each of the indicated numbers in a form not involving a radical: (a) $\sqrt[4]{4x^2}$; (b) $\sqrt{1/9}$; (c) $\sqrt[3]{3x^3}$; (d) $\sqrt[4]{(-3/2)^2}$.

5. Give appropriate answers to (a) and (c) of Problem 4 if: (a) $x > 0$; (b) $x < 0$.

6. Designate which of the following real numbers are negative: (a) $(-2)^0$; (b) -2^0; (c) $5^{2/3}$; (d) $5^{-2/3}$; (e) $(-2)^{3/5}$; (f) $(-2)^{-3}$; (g) $4^{-1/2}$.

7. Simplify each of the following expressions: (a) $a^2b^3a^3b^5$; (b) $(a^2)^3/a^3$; (c) $(2 \cdot 3)^3 2^2 3^4$; (d) $(xy)^4/x^3$; (e) $1/(x^{-1} + y^{-1})$.

8. Simplify $\sqrt{(x - 1)^2}$ if: (a) $x > 1$; (b) $x < 1$.

9. Write each of the following numbers in fractional form with denominator 1: (a) $ab^3c/a^2b^2c^2$; (b) $3x^{-2}y^3/2xy^3$; (c) $1/x + 2/y$.

10. Simplify each of the following expressions: (a) $x^{-3}y^2/x^{-1}y^{-4}$; (b) $xy^{-2}z^{-3}/3x^3yz^5$; (c) $[2x^{-1}y^3/x^2y^3]^{1/2}$, where $x > 0$.

11. Assume all letters designate positive numbers, and reduce each of the following to a form involving a single radical:

(a) $\dfrac{\sqrt[3]{x}\ \sqrt[5]{x^4}}{\sqrt{x^5}}$; (b) $\sqrt{a}\ \sqrt[3]{2ab^2}\ \sqrt{3a^2b}$; (c) $\sqrt[4]{24x^5/y^2}\ \sqrt[3]{y^3/(3x)}$;

(d) $\sqrt{3\sqrt{3}\ \sqrt{3}}$.

12. Eliminate all negative exponents and simplify the results:

(a) $\dfrac{x^{-1} + y^{-2}}{x^{-2} + y^{-2}}$; (b) $\dfrac{a^{-3}b^{-3}}{a^{-3} + b^{-3}}$; (c) $\dfrac{(x^2 - y^2)^{-1}}{(x - y)^{-3}}$.

13. Determine all real solutions for x from the equation $\sqrt{(x - 1)^2} = 5$.

14. Determine the real solutions for each of the following inequalities:

(a) $|x - 1| < 2^{-1}$; (b) $|x|^{-1} > 2^{-3}$; (c) $(x + 1)^0 \le x + 2$.

5.2   Exponential Functions

We noted in Chapter 4 that a function is completely defined if we know its *domain* and the *rule* of correspondence between its domain and range. Any function f with a domain of real numbers, whose rule of correspondence for some real number $a > 0$ is $y = a^x$, with $y = f(x)$, is called an *exponential function*.

EXAMPLE 1.   Describe and graph the exponential function f which is defined on $\{-2, -1, 0, 1, 2\}$ by $f(x) = 2^x$.

SOLUTION.   The function f consists of the following ordered pairs: $(-2, \frac{1}{4}), (-1, \frac{1}{2}), (0, 1), (1, 2), (2, 4)$. In Figure 26 we have shown the complete graph of the function.

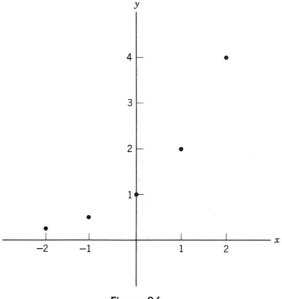

Figure 26

In most instances where exponential functions occur, the domain is an *interval* of real numbers. This raises a difficulty, because every interval of real numbers contains irrational numbers, and we have not given a meaning to a^x if x is irrational. However, we can overcome the difficulty with a bit of intuition! Any irrational number can be expressed as an infinite decimal, while any terminating decimal is a representation of a rational number. Hence, if we are willing to accept the intuitively evident (and true) assertion that any infinite decimal can be approximated to any desired degree of accuracy by a terminating decimal, it is possible to approximate a^x, where x is irrational, by replacing x by one of its rational approximations. We shall accept this fact here without attempt at proof. For example, while we have not defined $3^{\sqrt{2}}$, this "number" can be approximated by $3^{1.4}$, $3^{1.41}$, $3^{1.414}$, etc., the radical form of these approximations being $\sqrt[5]{3^7}$, $\sqrt[100]{3^{141}}$, $\sqrt[500]{3^{707}}$, and so on. While numbers such as these may seem to be extremely difficult to express in decimal form at this time, we have at least given meaning to these symbols, and their computation can be accomplished later. Hence, at least theoretically, it is possible to determine a^x, for $a > 0$ and any real number x, and so the function defined on an interval by an equation $y = a^x$ is well defined.

The graph of an exponential function, as of any other function, is merely the graph of all ordered pairs of the function. In practice, we construct such a graph by plotting a sufficient number of points which can be easily determined, and joining them with a smooth curve if the domain of the function is an interval. The validity of the "smooth curve" feature of the graph is a consequence (known as "continuity") of our assumption that a^{x_1} and a^{x_2} will differ by an arbitrary small amount if $|x_1 - x_2|$ is sufficiently close to 0. We illustrate this graphing procedure with two examples.

EXAMPLE 2.   Graph the function f defined on $[-2, 2]$ by $f(x) = 2^x$.

SOLUTION.   We use the points, as shown in Figure 26, and join them with a smooth curve. The result is shown in Figure 27.

EXAMPLE 3.   Graph the function g defined on $[-2, 2]$ by $g(x) = (\frac{1}{2})^x$.

SOLUTION.   A collection of elements of the function are: $(-2, 4)$, $(-1, 2)$, $(0, 1)$, $(1, \frac{1}{2})$, $(2, \frac{1}{4})$. The graph of g is shown in Figure 28.

The graphs shown in Figures 27 and 28 are illustrative of all exponential functions (except the constant function defined by $y = 1^x$). Figure 27 is typical of a function defined by $y = a^x$, if $a > 1$, while Figure 28 is typical when $0 < a < 1$. We also draw attention to the fact that the point $(0, 1)$ is common to the graphs of all exponential functions defined by $y = a^x$, provided only that 0 is in the domain of the function. The graph of any exponential function lies entirely above the x-axis (i.e., the "domain" axis), even if its domain is the set R of all real numbers.

It is an interesting feature of exponential functions that if x_1, x_2 and $x_1 + x_2$ are in the domain of such a function f, then $f(x_1 + x_2) = f(x_1) \cdot f(x_2)$. This is an immediate consequence of the first law of exponents (§5.1), because if $f(x) = a^x$, it follows that $f(x_1 + x_2) = a^{x_1+x_2} = a^{x_1} \cdot a^{x_2} = f(x_1) \cdot f(x_2)$.

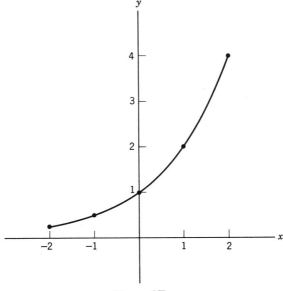

Figure 27

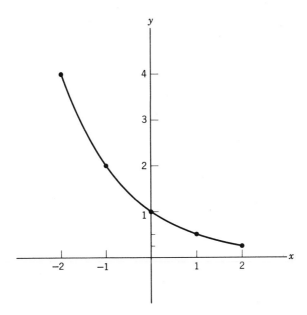

Figure 28

While a "basic" exponential function is defined by an equation of the form $y = a^x$, any equation $y = ca^{kx}$, where c and k are real numbers, defines a function "of the exponential type" and are also frequently referred to as "exponential" functions. If we accept the graphically intuitive fact that any real number $a > 0$ can be expressed in the form $a = b^k$, for some real k and any $b(\neq 1) > 0$, the base of an exponential function can be varied at will. For then $a^x = (b^k)^x = b^{kx}$, and so the defining rule $y = a^x$ of an exponential function can be replaced by $y = b^{kx}$, both rules defining an exponential function in our more general usage of the term.

Functions of exponential type occur quite frequently in descriptions of natural phenomena and, in particular, whenever the rate of change of the amount of a substance at a given time is proportional to the amount present at that time. An example of this occurs in radioactivity, where the rate of decomposition of a radioactive substance is proportional to the amount of the substance present. The law of growth of a bacteria culture under ideal conditions is another example of the occurrence of an exponential function.

EXAMPLE 4. The half life of radium is approximately 1,600 years (i.e., any given amount of radium will be reduced to one-half in 1,600 years). If we assume an exponential-type relationship between the amount of radium and time elapsed, determine how much of 200 milligrams of radium will remain after 6,400 years.

SOLUTION. If f designates the function, our assumption is that $f(t) = 200 \cdot 2^{kt}$, for $t \geq 0$, where k is a real number to be determined and we have selected the base 2 for convenience. When $t = 1,600$, $f(t) = 100$ and so $\frac{1}{2} = 2^{k(1,600)} = 2^{-1}$. Hence $1,600k = -1$ and $k = \frac{-1}{1,600}$, so that $f(t) = 200 \cdot 2^{-t/1,600}$. When $t = 6,400$, $f(t) = 200 \cdot 2^{-4} = \frac{200}{16} = 12.5$, and so 12.5 milligrams of radium will be left in 6,400 years.

PROBLEMS

1. Explain why it is graphically evident that, if $a > 0$ and $b > 0$, there exists a real number k such that $a = b^k$. Is this true if $a \leq 0$? Explain.
2. Explain why it is necessary in the environment of this chapter to require the base number a to be positive in the definition of an exponential function.
3. Approximate the irrational number $\sqrt{3}$ by rational numbers with: (a) two decimal places; (b) three decimal places; (c) four decimal places. Repeat for the irrational number π.
4. Construct a careful graph of f on [0, 4], where $f(x) = 2^x$, and use the graph to obtain an approximation for: (a) $2^{\sqrt{2}}$; (b) $2^{\sqrt{3}}$; (c) $2^{3/5}$; (d) $\sqrt[5]{4}$; (e) 2^π.
5. Use a careful graph of an appropriate function to obtain approximations for: (a) $3^{\sqrt{2}}$; (b) 3^π; (c) $\sqrt[7]{9}$.

6. Use a single pair of coordinate axes to graph the functions f, g, h defined on $[-2, 2]$ by $f(x) = 2^x$, $g(x) = 3^x$, $h(x) = 4^x$.

7. Use a single pair of coordinate axes to graph the functions f, g, h defined on $[-2, 2]$ by $f(x) = (\frac{1}{2})^x$, $g(x) = (\frac{1}{3})^x$, $h(x) = (\frac{1}{4})^x$.

8. The graph of an exponential function defined by $y = a^x$ contains the point $(3, 27)$. What is the number a?

9. If the graph of an exponential function defined by $y = ca^x$ contains the points $(1, 6)$ and $(2, 18)$, determine c and a.

10. The half life of a radioactive material is 1,200 years. Refer to Example 4 and determine how much of 500 milligrams of the material will remain after 6,000 years.

11. Let us assume that the population of a town increases exponentially so that the population p in t years is given by $p = c(\frac{3}{2})^t$, for some real number c. In how many years would the population of the town increase from 8,000 to 27,000?

12. Let us assume that the population of a bacteria culture increases exponentially so that the population p of the culture in t hours is $p = c(5)^t$. In how many hours would a culture of 2,000 bacteria increase to 250,000?

13. If an exponential function f is defined by $f(x) = ca^x$, for some real number $c \neq 1$, is it true that $f(x_1 + x_2) = f(x_1) \cdot f(x_2)$, whenever x_1, x_2, and $x_1 + x_2$ are in the domain of f? Explain.

14. Graph the function f defined on $\{-2, -\frac{3}{2}, -1, -\frac{1}{2}, 0, \frac{1}{2}, 1, \frac{3}{2}, 2\}$ by $f(x) = 2^x$. Use the same coordinate axes to graph the inverse function f^{-1}.

15. Show that a function f defined by $f(x) = 3^{2-x}$ is an exponential function whose value for any x has the form ca^{kx}, for real numbers c, k, and $a > 0$.

16. Assume the intuitive fact that an exponential function is either strictly increasing or strictly decreasing, according as $a > 1$ or $a < 1$, where a is the base, and prove that if $0 < a < b$ then: (a) $a^x < b^x$, $x > 0$; (b) $a^x > b^x$, $x < 0$.

5.3   Logarithmic Functions

If one considers the graph of an exponential function, it is intuitively evident that a horizontal line through a point on the positive y-axis intersects the graph in not more than one point. Hence, for arbitrary base $a \neq 1$, this means that $a^{x_1} = a^{x_2}$ if and only if $x_1 = x_2$, and so any exponential function defines a one-to-one mapping. It then follows from the discussion of §4.5 that such a function has an inverse, and this leads us to the following definition.

Definition. A function which is the inverse of an exponential function is called a *logarithmic* function. Moreover, if the rule which defines the exponential function is $y = a^x$, x is the *logarithm of y to base a*, and we write $x = \log_a y$.

If the domain of an exponential function is R, any horizontal line through a point on the positive y-axis will intersect the graph of the function in one—and precisely one—point. This means that the equation $a^x = N$, for an arbitrary real number N, $a(\neq 1) > 0$, has a unique solution which we indicate $\log_a N$. We recall that the domain of the function which is inverse to a function f is always the range of f, and since the values of any exponential function are positive, the domain of a logarithmic function must be a subset of positive real numbers. In case f is the exponential function defined on R by $f(x) = a^x$, the domain of the inverse logarithmic function is the set of all positive real numbers. Hence, if $f(x) = a^x = y$, for any real number x, $f^{-1}(y) = \log_a y = x$, where $y > 0$. *We remark that $\log_a y$ is not defined as a real number if $y < 0$.*

We have noted in §4.5 that one of the important relationships between a function f and its inverse f^{-1} is that $ff^{-1} = I$ and $f^{-1}f = I$, the former I being the identity function on the range of f and the latter I being the identity function on the domain of f. If f is an exponential function with f^{-1} its logarithmic inverse, these relationships take the form:

$$a^{\log_a y} = y \text{ and } \log_a a^x = x.$$

These two equations, along with the equivalence of $y = a^x$ with $x = \log_a y$, are the most important and useful relationships between exponential and logarithmic functions. Since $a = a^1$, for any real a, it is an immediate consequence that:

$$\log_a a = 1, \text{ for } a > 0.$$

EXAMPLE 1.   Determine $\log_2 16$ and $\log_{10} 0.001$.

SOLUTION.   We know that $\log_2 16$ is the solution of the equation $2^x = 16$, and so $x = 4 = \log_2 16$. Similarly, $\log_{10} 0.001$ is the solution of $10^x = 0.001$, and, since $0.001 = 10^{-3}$, it follows that $x = -3 = \log_{10} 0.001$.

EXAMPLE 2.   If $\log_4 N = \frac{1}{2}$, determine N.

SOLUTION.   The equation $\log_4 N = \frac{1}{2}$ is equivalent to the equation $4^{1/2} = N$, and hence $N = 2$.

EXAMPLE 3.   Determine $\log_4 \frac{1}{32}$.

SOLUTION.   We know that $\log_4 \frac{1}{32}$ is the solution of $4^x = \frac{1}{32}$, i.e., of $2^{2x} = 2^{-5}$. Hence, $2x = -5$ and $x = -\frac{5}{2} = -2.5$.

EXAMPLE 4.   Express 3^x as a power of 10.

SOLUTION.   Since $3 = 10^{\log_{10} 3}$, it follows that $3^x = (10^{\log_{10} 3})^x = 10^{x \log_{10} 3}$.

In view of the inverse relationship between exponential and logarithmic functions, it is instructive to remember the relationship between the graphs of a function and its inverse. We recall that a point $(b, a) \in f^{-1}$ if and only if $(a, b) \in f$, and that the graphs of f and f^{-1} are then geometric reflections of each other in the diagonal line through quadrants I and III. In Figure 29 we have drawn graphs of functions f and g $(= f^{-1})$, where f is defined on $[-2, 2]$ by $f(x) = 2^x$ and g is defined on $[\frac{1}{4}, 4]$ by $g(x) = \log_2 x$.

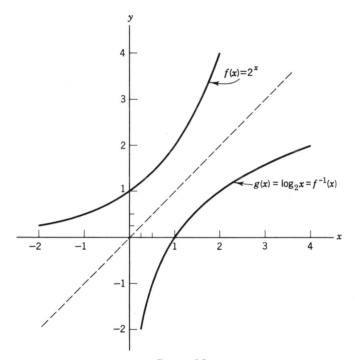

Figure 29

These two graphs are typical of inverse exponential and logarithmic functions, but it must be understood, of course, that the domain of f might be a finite set or even the complete set R of real numbers. In our discussion of logarithmic functions, we shall always assume that the base $a > 1$, so that our logarithmic graphs always have a "concave downwards" appearance.

There are several useful conclusions which we can deduce from a graphical comparison like Figure 29:

1. Whereas $a^x > 0$, for any x, $\log_a x > 0$ if $x > 1$, and $\log_a x < 0$ if $x < 1$.
2. $\log_a x_1 < \log_a x_2$ if and only if $0 < x_1 < x_2$ (assuming $a > 1$).
3. The graph of f, where $f(x) = a^x$, is "steeper" as a increases; hence, the graph of g, where $g(x) = \log_a x$, is "flatter" as a increases.

PROBLEMS

1. Write each of the following in equivalent logarithmic form: (a) $2^4 = 16$; (b) $10^3 = 1,000$; (c) $10^0 = 1$; (d) $3^3 = 27$; (e) $25^{1/2} = 5$.
2. Write each of the following in equivalent exponential form: (a) $2 = \log_3 9$; (b) $-2 = \log_{10} 0.01$; (c) $4 = \log_4 256$; (d) $\frac{3}{2} = \log_4 8$.
3. Write each of the following equations in equivalent logarithmic form: (a) $x^5 = 12$; (b) $5^x = 7$; (c) $6^7 = x$; (d) $10^x = 55$.
4. Write each of the following equations in equivalent exponential form: (a) $5 = \log_3 x$; (b) $x = \log_2 15$; (c) $13 = \log_x 5$; (d) $\frac{8}{3} = \log_x 2$.
5. Determine by inspection the real solution to each of the following equations: (a) $\log_3 x = 2$; (b) $\log_4 x = \frac{2}{3}$; (c) $\log_x 32 = 4$; (d) $\log_4 8 = x$; (e) $\log_9 3 = x$.
6. Explain why it is always true that: (a) $\log_a 1 = 0$, for any $a > 0$; (b) $a^{\log_a 8} = 8$; (c) $\log_a a = 1$, $a > 0$.
7. Use the graph of Figure 29 to determine an approximation for: (a) $\log_2 2.5$; (b) $\log_2 3$; (c) $\log_2 3.5$.
8. Express 3^{2x} as a power of: (a) 5; (b) 10.
9. Determine x from each of the following equations: (a) $3^{\log_3 x} = 7$; (b) $x^{\log_3 8} = 8$; (c) $\log_{10} 10^x = -2$; (d) $\log_x x = 1$; (e) $\log_x 1 = 0$.
10. Construct a graph of the function f, where f is defined on $\{-2, -1, 0, 1, 2\}$ by $f(x) = 3^x$.
11. Use the graph constructed in Problem 10 to graph the function g defined on $[\frac{1}{9}, 9]$ by $g(x) = \log_3 x$. From this graph approximate: (a) $\log_3 2$; (b) $\log_3 4$; (c) $\log_3 7$.
12. Use one pair of coordinate axes to sketch graphs of the logarithmic functions f and g, defined on $[\frac{1}{2}, 10]$ by $f(x) = \log_3 x$ and $g(x) = \log_{10} x$.
13. Let f be a logarithmic function defined on its domain by $f(x) = \log_a x$. Determine the base a if: (a) $f(3) = 1$; (b) the graph of f contains the point $(32, 5)$.
14. What is the logarithmic equivalent of the statement for an exponential function f that $f(x_1 + x_2) = f(x_1) \cdot f(x_2)$?

5.4   The Laws of Logarithms

In view of the inverse relationship existing between exponential and logarithmic functions, it might seem that a study of both kinds of functions would involve a great quantity of what are essentially duplications. While this is true, there are, nonetheless, good reasons for studying both kinds, because some relationships occur naturally in logarithmic form while others are more natural in terms of exponential functions. In addition, logarithms are useful in computational work and, although they are not as important as they were before the advent of electronic computers, we shall devote the later sections of this chapter to this topic. By a logarithmic "base" we shall always mean a positive number different from 1.

We have already noted the important fact, which is intuitive graphically, that for any base a there is a one-to-one correspondence $x \leftrightarrow \log_a x$ established between the set of positive real numbers and the set of all real numbers. This means that every positive real number has a unique real number as its logarithm to the given base, and every real number (positive, negative, or zero) is the unique logarithm to this base of some positive real number. The following theorems, known collectively as the *Laws of Logarithms*, are the important logarithmic equivalents of the Laws of Exponents. For the statements of the theorems, in addition to our assumption that $a(\neq 1) > 0$, we shall assume that M and N are positive real numbers.

THEOREM 5.41. $\log_a MN = \log_a M + \log_a N$. (That is, a logarithm of the product of two numbers is equal to the sum of the logarithms of the numbers.)

PROOF. Since every positive real number can be expressed in exponential form with any base, $M = a^m$ and $N = a^n$, for real numbers m and n. The definition of a logarithm then implies that $m = \log_a M$ and $n = \log_a N$. By the laws of exponents, $MN = (a^m)(a^n) = a^{m+n}$, and so $m + n = \log_a MN$. But this means that $\log_a MN = \log_a M + \log_a N$, as desired.

THEOREM 5.42. $\log_a M/N = \log_a M - \log_a N$. (That is, a logarithm of the quotient of two numbers is equal to the difference of the logarithms of the numbers.)

PROOF. With the same notation as in the proof of Theorem 5.41, $M/N = a^m/a^n = a^{m-n}$, and so $\log_a M/N = m - n$. Hence $\log_a M/N = \log_a M - \log_a N$, as desired.

Corollary. $\log_a 1/N = - \log_a N$.

This result follows directly from the theorem if we note that $\log_a 1 = 0$.

THEOREM 5.43. $\log_a M^p = p \log_a M$, for any real number p. (That is, a logarithm of the pth power of a number is equal to the p-multiple of the logarithm of the number.)

PROOF. With the notation of the proof of Theorem 5.41, $M^p = (a^m)^p = a^{mp}$, and so $mp = \log_a M^p$. Hence $\log_a M^p = p \log_a M$, establishing the theorem.

EXAMPLE 1. Given that $\log_{10} 3 = 0.4771$ and $\log_{10} 2 = 0.3010$, find $\log_{10} 6$ and $\log_{10} 27$.

SOLUTION. By Theorem 5.41, $\log_{10} 6 = \log_{10} 3 + \log_{10} 2 = 0.4771 + 0.3010 = 0.7781$. Since $27 = 3^3$, an application of Theorem 5.43 gives $\log_{10} 27 = 3 \log_{10} 3 = 3(0.4771) = 1.4313$.

EXAMPLE 2. Use the data given in Example 1 to determine $\log_{10}\sqrt{3}$ and $\log_{10} \sqrt[5]{6}$.

SOLUTION. By Theorem 5.43, $\log_{10} \sqrt{3} = \log_{10} 3^{1/2} = \frac{1}{2} \log_{10} 3 = \frac{1}{2}(0.4771) = 0.2386$. By Theorems 5.41 and 5.43, $\log_{10} \sqrt[5]{6} = \log_{10} 6^{1/5} = \frac{1}{5} \log_{10} 6 = \frac{1}{5}(0.7781) = 0.1556$.

It happens quite often that it is necessary to change from one logarithmic base to another, and in such instances the following theorem is important.

THEOREM 5.44. For any two logarithmic bases a and b, $\log_b N = \log_a N/(\log_a b)$. (That is, to change a logarithm from base a to base b, divide the original logarithm by $\log_a b$.)

PROOF. The proof of this theorem follows directly from the following result noted in §5.3:

$$N = b^{\log_b N}.$$

For then, by Theorem 5.43,

$$\log_a N = \log_b N \cdot \log_a b,$$

and so

$$\log_b N = \log_a N/(\log_a b).$$

Corollary. $\log_b a = 1/(\log_a b)$.

Thus, if we let $N = a$ in the theorem and note that $\log_a a = 1$, the result follows immediately.

EXAMPLE 3. If $\log_{10} 2 = 0.3010$, determine $\log_5 2$.

SOLUTION. By Theorem 5.44, $\log_5 2 = \log_{10} 2/(\log_{10} 5)$. But $5 = \frac{10}{2}$, and so

$$\log_{10} 5 = \log_{10} 10 - \log_{10} 2 = 1 - \log_{10} 2 = 1 - 0.3010 = 0.6990.$$

Hence,

$$\log_5 2 = 0.3010/0.6990 = 0.4306.$$

The laws of logarithms allow one to break up a compact expression involving products and powers into a sum of simpler components. For example, $\log_a x^3 y^2/\sqrt{z} = 3 \log_a x + 2 \log_a y - (\frac{1}{2}) \log_a z$, and for some mathematical purposes this simpler sum is more useful. On the other hand, it is often desirable to express a sum of logarithmic terms in a final compact form, as in Example 4.

EXAMPLE 4. Express $(\frac{5}{2}) \log_2 x + 3 \log_2 y - 2 \log_2 xy = 4$ in an equivalent compact form.

SOLUTION. The laws of logarithms allow us to write the given equation in the form $\log_2 [x^{5/2} y^3/(xy)^2] = 4$ or, more simply, $\log_2 x^{1/2} y = 4$. This equation may now be written in equivalent exponential form as

$$x^{1/2}y = 2^4 \quad \text{or} \quad x^{1/2}y = 16.$$

PROBLEMS

1. Make explicit use of the theorems of this section to prove that $\log_a MNP = \log_a M + \log_a N + \log_a P$, for positive real numbers M, N, P.
2. With the symbolism and directions of Problem 1, prove that $\log_a (M/NP) = \log_a M - \log_a N - \log_a P$.
3. Given that $\log_a 2 = 0.693$, $\log_a 3 = 1.099$, $\log_a 5 = 1.609$; determine the logarithm to base a of each of the following numbers: (a) 6; (b) 20; (c) 36; (d) 150; (e) $\sqrt{30}$; (f) $(36)^{2/3}$; (g) $(225)^{3/5}$.
4. Use the information given in Problem 3 to determine the logarithm to base a of the following numbers: (a) $\frac{1}{12}$; (b) $\frac{1}{15}$; (c) $1/\sqrt{30}$; (d) $1/(18)^{5/6}$; (e) $(\frac{4}{9})^{2/3}$; (f) $(\frac{3}{25})^{1/4}$.
5. Use the data in Problem 3, if necessary, to determine each of the following: (a) $\log_a a^3$; (b) $\log_a a/2$; (c) $\log_a \sqrt{a}$; (d) $a^{\log_a \sqrt{a}}$.
6. Write each of the following expressions as a single logarithm:
   (a) $2 \log_a x + (\frac{1}{2}) \log_a xy^2 - 3 \log_a x^3$;
   (b) $\log_a (2 - x^2) - 3 \log_a (2 + x) + \log_a 2$;
   (c) $\log_a 3/\sqrt{x} - (\frac{2}{3}) \log_a x^{1/2} + \log_a \sqrt{x}$.
7. If $\log_b c = 0.234$, determine $\log_c b$. Is it ever true that $\log_b c = \log_c b$?
8. If $\log_b a = 2.3026$ and $\log_b 4 = 1.3863$, determine $\log_a b$ and $\log_a 4$.
9. Write the equation $\log_b y - \log_b c + kt = 0$ in an equivalent form involving an exponential function.

10. The formula $N = 10 \log_{10} P_2/P_1$ expresses the decibel gain for a telephonic element having input and output powers of P_1 and P_2, respectively. Express this formula without any use of logarithms.

11. Solve each of the following equations for a real number x: (a) $\log_6 1 = x$; (b) $\log_{10} x = -2$; (c) $\log_x 7 = -1$; (d) $\log_{16} x = -\frac{1}{2}$.

12. Solve the following equation for real x:
$$2 \log_a \tfrac{12}{5} + 3 \log_a 15 - \log_a 18 = \log_a x.$$

13. Express in equivalent logarithmic form, with base e, the equation
$$M = M_0 e^{-\alpha t}.$$

14. If $y/x^p = k$, for real numbers x and p, determine the relation between $\log y$ and $\log x$, and comment on the relation between $\log_a y$ and $\log_a x$.

15. Solve the following system of equations for real x and y, using logarithms to base 2:
$$x^2 y = 2^4,$$
$$x^5 y^3 = 2^{11}.$$

5.5　The Basis for Logarithmic Computation

We implied earlier that any positive number $a \neq 1$ can be used as an exponential or logarithmic base. However, while a number such as 2 occurs quite frequently in exponential functions, as in Example 4 of §5.2, there are two other special numbers which predominate as bases in logarithmic work. For computational work, base 10 is almost always used, and logarithms to this base are called *common* logarithms. For theoretical work, on the other hand, it is more customary to use as logarithmic base a certain irrational number e, an approximation to this number being $e = 2.71828\cdots$. Logarithms to base e are called *Naperian*, or *natural*, logarithms; the first name is in honor of John Napier (1550–1617) who invented logarithms, while the name "natural" refers to the many occurrences of this number in mathematical descriptions of natural phenomena. We shall use $\log x$ to refer to the common logarithm of a number x, while $\ln x$ will be used if natural logarithms are to be understood. When some other base b is used, we shall continue to designate such a logarithm as $\log_b x$.

The approximation to e shows that $2 < e < 3$, and it can be shown that the graph of the exponential function defined on R by $y = e^x$ crosses the y-axis at a point where the tangent line to the graph makes an angle of 45° with the x-axis. A portion of this graph is shown in Figure 30.

We shall introduce the manner in which logarithms are used for computation by means of an illustration. Let us suppose that we wish to simplify the expression $(27 \cdot 81 \cdot 9)/(243 \cdot 3)$. We notice that each number in the expression is a power of 3, and if we write these numbers as such powers and then use the laws of exponents, the computation is quite

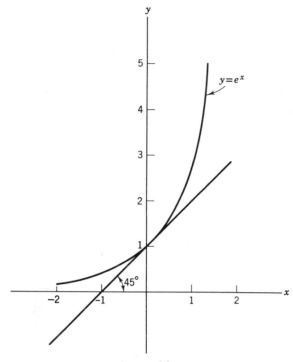

Figure 30

simple. Thus, $(27 \cdot 81 \cdot 9)/(243 \cdot 3) = (3^3 \cdot 3^4 \cdot 3^2)/(3^5 \cdot 3^1) = 3^{3+4+2}/3^{5+1} = 3^9/3^6 = 3^{9-6} = 3^3 = 27$. It should be observed that in this illustration, while the original problem was one of multiplication and division, the computation was accomplished with addition and subtraction, except for the first and last steps. This is the basic idea involved in the use of logarithms for computation, and if the student has appreciated what has been accomplished by this very simple example, he is well on his way to understanding this use.

It will have been observed by the alert student, of course, that the success of the above illustration depended on the fact that every number involved is a power of 3. However, it is evident that any other number would have been as easy to work with as 3, *and by means of common logarithms it is possible to express any positive number as a power of 10,* because we have already seen that $x = a^{\log_a x}$, for any positive real number x and any logarithmic base a, and in particular $x = 10^{\log x}$. The various laws of logarithms, as given in §5.4, are then merely convenient adaptations of the procedures used in a problem similar to the above illustration.

In order to carry out a computation by means of logarithms, two things are necessary: one must be able to find the logarithm of any positive real number; and one must be able to determine a real number from its logarithm. We shall consider both of these matters after the introduction of "scientific notation."

It is possible to write any positive real number as the product of a number between 1 and 10 and some integral power of 10. For example, we can write 245 as $2.45(10)^2$ and 0.00359 as $3.59(10^{-3})$. More generally, if $N = c(10)^x$, where x is an integer and $1 \leq c < 10$, the number N is said to be expressed in *scientific notation*. This notation is specially adapted for a determination of logarithms. Since $c = 10^{\log c}$, we have $N = c(10)^x = 10^{\log c} \cdot 10^x = 10^{\log c + x}$, and so $\log N = \log c + x$. Inasmuch as x can be read from inspection of the scientific notation for the number, the common logarithm of any number can be determined with a knowledge of the logarithms of all numbers between 1 and 10. The integer x is called the *characteristic* of $\log N$.

EXAMPLE 1

(a) $\log 245 = \log 2.45(10)^2 = \log 2.45 + 2.$
(b) $\log 0.00134 = \log 1.34(10)^{-3} = \log 1.34 - 3.$

The common logarithm of any "two-decimal" number between 1.00 and 9.99 can be read directly as a "four-decimal" number in Table 1 at the rear of the book. We shall accept these logarithms as given without any discussion of how they have been obtained, but it should be pointed out that the logarithms are rational *approximations* of the exact logarithms. In some cases, in this and in subsequent chapters, we shall use $\doteq$ to indicate an approximate equality rather than the usual $=$ of an equality. In Table 1 all decimal points have been omitted, but we should understand that they are located immediately *after* the first digit of any number whose logarithm is listed, and immediately *before* the first digit of its logarithm. Since $10^0 = 1$ and $10^1 = 10$, it is clear that the common logarithm of any number between 1 and 10 is a number between 0 and 1, and so this understanding about the location of decimal points in Table 1 is reasonable. For example, after inserting the decimal points as required, we find from Table 1 that

$$\log 2.45 = 0.3892 \text{ and } \log 1.34 = 0.1271.$$

It is now possible to complete Example 1:

$$\log 245 = 0.3892 + 2 = 2.3892,$$
$$\log 0.00134 = 0.1271 - 3 = -2.8729.$$

The determination of the logarithms in Example 1 illustrates two very important facts about logarithms: the common logarithm of any positive number less than 1 is negative; and the common logarithms of two numbers which differ only in the location of their decimal points differ only by an integer. For example, $\log 0.245 = \log 2.45(10)^{-1} = 0.3892 - 1$, and $\log 24500 = \log 2.45(10)^4 = 0.3892 + 4$. It should be realized that the second simplification property would not be available if a base different from 10 were used, and this explains the choice of base 10 for common logarithms.

The procedure for finding a number from its logarithm is simply to use Table 1 in reverse. The number is then sometimes called the "antilog" of the given logarithm. We illustrate with an example.

EXAMPLE 2.   If $\log N = 0.5465 - 2$, find N.

SOLUTION.   From Table 1 we note that

$$\log 3.52 = 0.5465.$$

Hence,

$$N = 3.52(10)^{-2} = 0.0352,$$

since,

$$\log c + x = \log c(10)^x.$$

It must be emphasized that a correct determination of an antilog requires that the logarithm be written in a form which exposes a *positive* decimal part, known as its *mantissa*. If a logarithm is not written this way initially, its form must be altered to satisfy this requirement, as illustrated in the following examples.

EXAMPLE 3.   Determine N if $\log N = -0.1267$.

SOLUTION. $\text{Log } N = -0.1267 = (1 - 0.1267) - 1 = 0.8733 - 1$. We now refer to Table 1 and note that

$$\log 7.47 = 0.8733.$$

Hence,

$$N = 7.47(10)^{-1} = 0.747.$$

EXAMPLE 4.   Determine N if $\log N = -2.6180$.

SOLUTION. $\text{Log } N = -2.6180 = (3 - 2.6180) - 3 = 0.3820 - 3$. Since antilog $0.3820 = 2.41$, it follows that $N = 2.41(10)^{-3} = 0.00241$.

PROBLEMS

1. Write down the characteristic of the common logarithm of each of the following numbers: (a) 356.2; (b) 0.00043; (c) 24000; (d) 0.0012.

2. State a convenient rule for a determination of the characteristic of the common logarithm of any positive real number.

3. Determine the common logarithm of each of the following numbers: (a) 352; (b) 0.0352; (c) 3.5200; (d) 352000; (e) 0.000352.

4. Determine the common logarithm of each of the following numbers: (a) 23.5; (b) 0.764; (c) 12.8; (d) 0.0043; (e) 34500.

5. Determine N if $\log N$ is: (a) $0.6031 + 2$; (b) $0.6580 - 2$; (c) 0.7168; (d) $0.8457 - 3$; (e) $0.7716 + 2$.

6. Determine N if $\log N$ is: (a) 2.8488; (b) 3.8169; (c) 1.9294; (d) 3.7404.

7. Determine N if $\log N$ is: (a) -2.2277; (b) -3.1355; (c) -1.1574; (d) -4.4522; (e) -0.4584.

8. Solve each of the following equations for real x: (a) $10^x = 3.87$; (b) $10^x = 0.542$; (c) $10^x = 34.5$; (d) $10^x = 0.002$.

9. Solve each of the following equations for real x: (a) $\log x = 2.5465$; (b) $\log x = 1.4713$; (c) $\log x = -2.2628$; (d) $\log x = -3.6819$.

10. Use Theorem 5.44 to compute each of the following: (a) $\log_3 12$; (b) $\log_7 35$; (c) $\log_9 56.7$; (d) $\log_2 17.5$.

11. Use the fact that $c = 10^{\log c}$, to determine each of the following: (a) $10^{1.6513}$; (b) $10^{-2.6038}$; (c) $10^{2.8102}$; (d) $10^{-1.2565}$.

12. If $N = \dfrac{(24.5)\,(15.7)\,(0.0025)}{(1.54)\,(0.113)}$, express each component number as a power of 10 and express the final answer as a single power of 10.

13. Repeat the directions of Problem 12 for $N = \dfrac{(0.1120)\,(4.65)\,(3450)}{(3.65)\,(76.8)}$.

14. Use Theorem 5.44 to express 25.3 as a power of: (a) 3; (b) 7; (c) 12.

5.6   Computation with Logarithms

Before discussing the matter of logarithmic computation, we wish to show how the use of Table 1 can be extended by means of interpolation. This process of interpolation can be used for finding either the logarithm of a number or a number from its logarithm. The basic assumption here is that if two numbers α and β are sufficiently close to each other, the graph of the logarithmic function between $x = \alpha$ and $x = \beta$ is approximately linear, and so we may use simple proportions. In interpolating from Table 1, we assume that "sufficiently close" means that α and β are adjacent entries in the table. We shall illustrate the procedure with an example.

EXAMPLE 1.   Use Table 1 to determine log 2.456.

SOLUTION.   We are not able to read log 2.456 directly from Table 1, but we can obtain the adjacent entries log 2.450 and 2.460. Thus,

$$\log 2.450 = \log 2.45 = 0.3892.$$
$$\log 2.460 = \log 2.46 = 0.3909.$$

and we assume that numbers and their logarithms between these entries are proportional. Since 2.456 is located $\frac{6}{10}$ of the way between 2.450 and 2.460, the approximate location of log 2.456 must be $\frac{6}{10}$ of the way between 0.3892 and 0.3909. Hence,

$$\log 2.456 = 0.3892 + (0.6)(0.0017) \doteq 0.3892 + 0.0010 = 0.3902.$$

The following example illustrates how interpolation can be used in the determination of a number from its logarithm.

EXAMPLE 2. If $\log N = 0.4658 - 2$, find N.

SOLUTION. We observe that 0.4658 does not occur in the body of Table 1, but 0.4654 and 0.4669 are present and 0.4658 lies between them.

$$\log 2.920 = \log 2.92 = 0.4654.$$
$$\log 2.930 = \log 2.93 = 0.4669.$$

The logarithm 0.4658 is located $\frac{4}{15}$ of the way between 0.4654 and 0.4669, and so the antilog of 0.4658 must be located approximately $\frac{4}{15}$ of the way between 2.920 and 2.930. Hence,

$$\text{antilog } 0.4658 \doteq 2.920 + \tfrac{4}{15}(0.010) \doteq 2.920 + 0.003 = 2.923,$$

whence,

$$N = 2.923(10)^{-2} = 0.02923.$$

The laws of logarithms were listed as theorems in §5.4, and we now use several examples to illustrate the use of these laws for computational purposes.

EXAMPLE 3. Use the laws of logarithms to compute the product $N = (12.3)(0.0651)$.

SOLUTION

$$\log 12.3 = \log 1.23(10)^1 = 0.0899 + 1$$
$$\log 0.0651 = \log 6.51(10)^{-2} = \underline{0.8136 - 2}$$
$$\log N = 0.9035 - 1, \text{ by Theorem 5.41,}$$

and since antilog $0.9035 = 8.008$, $N = 8.008(10)^{-1} = 0.8008$, or, approximately, $N = 0.801$.

EXAMPLE 4. Use the laws of logarithms to compute $N = 15.6/0.0212$.

SOLUTION

$$\log 15.6 = \log 1.56(10)^1 = 0.1931 + 1 = 1.1931 + 0$$
$$\log 0.0212 = \log 2.12(10)^{-2} = 0.3263 - 2 = \underline{0.3263 - 2}$$
$$\log N = 0.8668 + 2, \text{ by Theorem } 5.42$$

and since antilog $0.8668 = 7.358$, $N = 7.358(10)^2 = 735.8$, or, approximately, $N \doteq 736$.

EXAMPLE 5.   Use the laws of logarithms to compute $N = (0.128)^{2/3}$.

SOLUTION.   By Theorem 5.43,

$$\log N = \tfrac{2}{3} \log 0.128 = \tfrac{2}{3}(0.1072 - 1) = \tfrac{2}{3}(2.1072 - 3)$$
$$= 1.4048 - 2 = 0.4048 - 1.$$

Since antilog $0.4048 = 2.54$, $N = 2.54(10)^{-1} = 0.254$.

It may be seen, especially from Example 5, that one must take great care in manipulating negative logarithms. However, if a student realizes that a logarithm—whether positive or negative—is **merely a real number,** an application of a little common sense in these manipulations is likely to be more fruitful than an exhaustive set of rules. We wish to emphasize that the form in which we leave a logarithm is entirely dependent on what we are going to do with it. **Whenever an antilogarithm is to be found, however, it is necessary to keep the logarithm in such a form that the decimal part is positive.** It is to emphasize this fact that we usually separate the integral part (or characteristic) from the decimal part (or mantissa), and write the characteristic *after* the mantissa.

We complete this section with the solution of several somewhat more complicated computational problems. The student is urged to pay particular attention to the arrangement of the work in the displayed solutions.

EXAMPLE 6.   Compute $N = \dfrac{(23.4)\ (18.61)}{(0.0042)\ (396)}$.

SOLUTION

$\log 23.4 = 0.3692 + 1$	$\log 0.0042 = 0.6232 - 3$
$\log 18.61 = \underline{0.2697 + 1}$	$\log 396 = \underline{0.5977 + 2}$
$\ 0.6389 + 2$	$\ 1.2209 - 1 = 0.2209 + 0$
$\ \underline{0.2209 + 0}$	
$\log N = 0.4180 + 2$	

Hence, $N = 2.618(10)^2 = 261.8$, or, approximately, $N \doteq 262$.

EXAMPLE 7.   Determine x if $0.214^x = 84.2$.

SOLUTION. From the given equation, and Theorem 5.43, $x \log 0.214 = \log 84.2$, so that $x = \log 84.2/\log 0.214$.

$$\log 84.2 = 0.9253 + 1 = 1.9253$$
$$\log 0.214 = 0.3304 - 1 = -0.6696$$

Hence,

$$x = -\frac{1.9253}{0.6696}.$$

This quotient can be computed by long division, or it can be done by logarithms as indicated below.

$$\log 1.9253 \doteq \log 1.925 = 0.2845 + 0 = 1.2845 - 1$$
$$\log 0.6696 \doteq \log 0.670 = 0.8261 - 1 = \underline{0.8261 - 1}$$
$$\log |N| = 0.4584 + 0$$

It follows that $|N| = $ antilog $0.4584 = 2.873$, and so $N = -2.873$.

NOTE: In Example 7 we have illustrated a case where a negative logarithm is **not** left in the mantissa-characteristic form, but is reduced to a form more suitable for division. Example 7 also illustrates that, while a negative number does not have a logarithm, the presence of negative numbers in a computation does not disallow the use of logarithms in the computation, since the algebraic sign of the answer can always be determined by inspection.

EXAMPLE 8.   Compute $N = \sqrt[5]{\dfrac{(2.4)\sqrt{0.16}}{(3.46)^4}}$.

SOLUTION

$$\log 2.4 = 0.3802 = 0.3802 + 0$$
$$\tfrac{1}{2}\log 0.16 = \tfrac{1}{2}(0.2041 - 1) = \tfrac{1}{2}(1.2041 - 2) = \underline{0.6021 - 1}$$
$$0.9823 - 1$$
$$4 \log 3.46 = 4(0.5391) = 2.1564 = \underline{0.1564 + 2}$$
$$0.8259 - 3$$

$$\log N = \tfrac{1}{5}(0.8259 - 3) = \tfrac{1}{5}(2.8259 - 5) = 0.5652 - 1.$$

Hence, $N = 3.675(10)^{-1} = 0.3675$, or, approximately, $N \doteq 0.37$.

PROBLEMS

1. The "meaning" of the remark that log 100 = 2 is that 10^2 = 100. In a similar manner give the meaning of each of the following: (a) log 3.54 = 0.5490; (b) log 5.18 = 0.7143; (c) log 8.42 = 0.9253.

2. Apply the directions of Problem 1 to each of the following:
(a) log 707 = 0.8494 + 2; (b) log 55.2 = 0.7419 + 1; (c) log 3860 = 0.5866 + 3.

3. Apply the directions of Problem 1 to each of the following: (a) log 0.00123 = 0.0899 − 3; (b) log 0.0582 = 0.7649 − 2; (c) log 0.00023 = 0.3617 − 4.

4. Use logarithms to compute each of the following products: (a) (234.6) (0.00429); (b) (142.6) (34.9); (c) (0.00542) (0.059).

5. Use logarithms to compute each of the following quotients: (a) 435.8/0.543; (b) 436000/12.4; (c) 0.00542/0.954.

6. Use logarithms to determine each of the following: (a) $(34.7)^{1/2}$; (b) $(0.00543)^{2/3}$; (c) $(0.765)^{3/4}$.

7. Use logarithms to determine each of the following: (a) $(123600)^{1/2}$; (b) $(12.5)^{-1/2}$; (c) $(0.0054)^{-0.3}$.

8. Find rational approximations in decimal form for $10^{0.0001}$ and $e^{0.0001}$, where $e \doteq 2.718$.

Use logarithms to compute an approximation for each of the expressions given in Problems 9 through 13.

9. $\dfrac{(54.7)\,(0.00528)\,(54.73)}{(765.8)\,(0.00215)}$

10. $\dfrac{(54.32)^5\,(0.0183)}{\sqrt[5]{5.657}}$

11. $\sqrt[4]{\dfrac{(19.5)\,(437.9)}{(54.58)^3}}$

12. $\dfrac{\sqrt{43.6}\,(-0.463)^2}{(-62.6)\,(1.038)}$

13. $\dfrac{(43.7)\,(\log 12.6)}{\log 0.0142}$

14. An approximation to the period T of a simple pendulum of length L feet is given by $T = 2\pi \sqrt{L/32.2}$. Use logarithms to determine the period of a pendulum 4.12 feet in length.

15. If H units of horsepower are transmissible by cold-rolled shafting, $H = d^3N/50$ where N is the number of revolutions of the shaft per minute and d is the diameter of the shaft in inches. Determine the approximate diameter of a shaft which will deliver 27 units of horsepower with the shaft rotating at 240 rpm.

16. Use logarithms to compute the accumulated amount of $250 if this money is invested for twenty years at 5 per cent interest compounded semi-annually.

5.7   Exponential and Logarithmic Equations

In this final section of the chapter we introduce nothing really new, but rather review and assimilate earlier material which will be useful for solving equations involving exponential or logarithmic expressions. As always, the solution of such an equation is a determination of the substitutions for the variable, from some given universe, which will change the "conditional"

equation into a true equality. There are essentially three types of exponential equations. If α and β are suitable real numbers, these three types have
the form: (a) $\alpha^\beta = x$; (b) $\alpha^x = \beta$; (c) $x^\alpha = \beta$. We shall illustrate the method
of solving an equation of each type with an example. In these and subse-
quent examples the universe is assumed to be R.

EXAMPLE 1. Solve $(1.5)^{3.2} = x$ for x.

SOLUTION. By Theorem 5.43,

$$\log x = 3.2 \log 1.5 = 3.2(0.1761) = 0.5635.$$

Hence,

$$x = \text{antilog } 0.5635 = 3.66$$

or, to two-figure accuracy,

$$x = 3.7.$$

EXAMPLE 2. Solve $(3.5)^x = 0.214$ for x.

SOLUTION. By Theorem 5.43,

$$x \log 3.5 = \log 0.214,$$

and so

$$x = \frac{\log 0.214}{\log 3.5} = \frac{0.3304 - 1}{0.5441} = -\frac{0.6696}{0.5441} = -1.23.$$

[The final step of the solution could be accomplished by either long division
or logarithms.]

EXAMPLE 3. Solve $x^{2.05} = 1.46$ for x.

SOLUTION. By Theorem 5.43,

$$2.05 \log x = \log 1.46,$$

and so,

$$\log x = \frac{\log 1.46}{2.05} = \frac{0.1644}{2.05} = 0.0802.$$

Hence,

$$x = \text{antilog } 0.0802 = 1.203$$

or, to three-figure accuracy,

$$x = 1.20.$$

As a general rule for solving any exponential equation, the following is useful: Use Theorem 5.43 to reduce the given equation to a logarithmic equation, by equating the common logarithms of both members. The following example is a slight variant of the previous examples, but the same general rule is used.

EXAMPLE 4.   Solve $3^{x+1} = 2^x$ for x.

SOLUTION.   An application of the preceding rule gives

$$(x + 1) \log 3 = x \log 2.$$

Hence,

$$x \log 3 - x \log 2 = -\log 3$$
$$x(\log 3 - \log 2) = -\log 3$$
$$(0.4771 - 0.3010)x = -0.4771$$
$$0.1761x = -0.4771$$
$$x = -\frac{0.4771}{0.1761} = -2.71$$

If an exponential equation involves the number e, it is often convenient to remember that $\log e \doteq 0.4343$ and $\ln 10 \doteq 2.3026$.

EXAMPLE 5.   Solve $e^x = 1.47$ for x.

SOLUTION.   By Theorem 5.43,

$$x \log e = \log 1.47,$$

and so

$$x = \frac{\log 1.47}{\log e} = \frac{0.1673}{0.4343} = 0.385.$$

The following example illustrates how the same methods can be used to solve an inequality. In solving an inequality, it is basic that we make use of the graphically intuitive fact that $\log \alpha < \log \beta$ if and only if $\alpha < \beta$.

EXAMPLE 6.   Solve the inequality $(0.56)^x < \frac{5}{6}$ for x.

SOLUTION.   It follows from Theorem 5.43 and Theorem 5.42, along with the intuitive fact just recalled, that

$$x \log 0.56 < \log 5 - \log 6.$$

Hence,

$$(0.7482 - 1)x < 0.6990 - 0.7782$$
$$-0.2518x < -0.0792$$
$$0.2518x > 0.0792$$
$$x > \frac{0.0792}{0.2518} = 0.3145,$$

or $x > 0.315$, approximately.

It may happen that the original equation contains logarithms, and in such a case we proceed more directly to the solution.

EXAMPLE 7. Solve $\log (2x + 4) - \log (x - 2) = \log 6$ for x.

SOLUTION. By Theorem 5.43,

$$\log \frac{2x + 4}{x - 2} = \log 6,$$

and so

$$\frac{2x + 4}{x - 2} = 6.$$

Hence,

$$2x + 4 = 6x - 12, \ 4x = 16, \text{ and } x = 4.$$

This solution may be checked in the original equation by noting that $\log 12 - \log 2 = \log \frac{12}{2} = \log 6$.

EXAMPLE 8. Solve $\log (5x + 7) - \log 3x = 1.3424$ for x.

SOLUTION. By Theorem 5.43,

$$\log \frac{5x + 7}{3x} = 0.3424 + 1.$$

Hence,

$$\frac{5x + 7}{3x} = \text{antilog} (0.3424 + 1) = 2.20(10)^1 = 22,$$

and so

$$5x + 7 = 66x$$
$$61x = 7$$
$$x = \tfrac{7}{61} = 0.115.$$

We have noted earlier that the two logarithmic bases most widely used are 10 and e. It is then of importance to be able to change the logarithm of a number from one of these bases to the other. The pertinent theorem, of course, is Theorem 5.44 and its corollary. Since $\log e \doteq 0.4343$ and $\ln 10 \doteq 2.3026$, it is worthwhile to remember that:

$$\log \alpha = \frac{\ln \alpha}{\ln 10} \doteq \frac{\ln \alpha}{2.3026} \doteq 0.4343 \ln \alpha$$

$$\ln \alpha = \frac{\log \alpha}{\log e} \doteq \frac{\log \alpha}{0.4343} \doteq 2.3026 \log \alpha,$$

for any real number $\alpha > 0$.

In this connection, it should be observed that solving the equation $e^x = \alpha$ for x is equivalent to determining $\ln \alpha$, since $e^{\ln \alpha} = \alpha$. Hence $x = \ln \alpha \doteq 2.3026 \log \alpha$, a result which we could also obtain by the more general method of Example 5.

PROBLEMS

1. Solve for x:
   (a) $5^x = 3$;
   (b) $(0.02)^x = 3$;
   (c) $4^x = \frac{2}{3}$;
   (d) $(2.5)^x = 0.53$.

2. Solve for x:
   (a) $x^5 = 12$;
   (b) $x^{2/3} = 0.56$;
   (c) $x^{2/3} = 4.63$;
   (d) $x^{10} = 640.$

3. Solve for x:
   (a) $3^{1+x} = 2$;
   (b) $5^{2x+1} = 4$;
   (c) $4^{1-x} = 7^{2x+3}$;
   (d) $5^{x^2} = 65.3$.

4. Find $\ln x$ if $x = $ (a) 3.45; (b) 0.43; (c) 13.4; (d) 0.00156.

5. Express each x of Problem 4 in the form e^α, for some real α.

6. Use $\log e = 0.4343$ to express each of the following in the form 10^β, for some real β: (a) $e^{2.5}$; (b) $e^{0.45}$; (c) $e^{-2.56}$; (d) $e^{-1.52}$.

7. Solve for x:
   (a) $\log (2x - 5) - \log (3x - 2) = \frac{4}{3}$; (b) $\log (x^2 - 4) - \log (x + 2) = 4$.

8. Solve and check the following equation in x: $\log \left| \dfrac{3x + 1}{2x + 3} \right| = \log 2$.

9. Show that the following equation has no real solution:
   $$\log (5x - 1) - \log (2x - 1) = \log 2.$$

10. Find the two real solutions for x of $27^{x^2} = 382$.

11. Solve the following equation for n and approximate it by the next largest integer:
    $$\frac{(1.06)^n - 1}{0.06} = 18.$$

12. Use the directions in Problem 11 for the following equation:
    $$\frac{(1.08)^n - 1}{0.08} = 12.$$

13. Solve the following equations for x:
    (a) $\log \sqrt{x(2x - 1)} = 1$; (b) $\log (x^2 - 10x) = 2$.

14. Use an example to show that $\log x^2$ and $2 \log x$ are not necessarily equal.

15. If you just discovered that you have inherited the present value of $100 which had been invested 150 years ago at 4% interest compounded annually, use logarithms to determine the value of your inheritance.

16. Without referring to interest tables, determine how long $100 would need to be invested at 5 per cent interest compounded annually to accumulate to an amount in excess of $10,000.

17. Solve the following inequalities for integral $x < 5$:
    (a) $(0.53)^x < 4.57$; (b) $(3.74)^x > 157$; (c) $x^{-2.54} < 12$.

18. Find upper and lower bounds for x if $2 \leq \log x^2 \leq 4$.

19. Solve the following inequalities for x:
    (a) $2^{x-1} < (32)^{2x}$; (b) $0 < \log (2x - 1) < \log (x + 5)$.

20. Convert the formula $p = p_0 e^{-0.193h}$ to an equivalent exponential form involving 10 instead of e.

21. Can you find a real number α such that $(\log \alpha)^{-1} = \log \alpha^{-1}$?

CHAPTER 6

Basic Trigonometry

6.1 Right-Angle Trigonometry

The subject matter of trigonometry has been associated, historically, with a study of the sides, angles, and area of a triangle along with their inter-relationships. For example, it has been common knowledge among mathematicians for many thousands of years that the acute angles of a right triangle are uniquely determined by the ratio of any two sides of the triangle. It is, in fact, these ratios which define the so-called "trigonometric" functions. For example, if A is either angle ($\neq 90°$) of a right triangle, sine $A = o/h$, where h and o are measures in the same units of the hypotenuse and side opposite angle A, respectively. It should be noted that these trigonometric functions map *angles* onto real numbers, since A is an angle and the ratio of two measures of length is a real number. For the case of sine A, above, in the notation of functions, $A \rightarrow o/h$, where $o/h =$ sine A, and so the domains of these trigonometric functions are *sets of angles*.

In more modern times, the scope of trigonometry has changed, and the study of triangles has been relegated to a relatively minor spot in this expanded discipline. The modern study introduces "circular" functions, which are very much like the traditional trigonometric functions, but have domains of real numbers. The circular functions then take their place along side the polynomial, exponential, and logarithmic functions, within the family of "elementary" functions, all of which map real numbers onto real numbers. This is, to say the least, an aesthetic improvement over the former situations, where domains were sometimes sets of real numbers and at other times sets of angles, but it also allows a more uniform treatment of all these functions. In addition, it is a fact that many modern applications of the circular functions have nothing to do with angles or triangles.

122

In view of what we have said in the preceding paragraphs, it would seem reasonable to introduce the circular functions first in their complete generality, and later specialize their roles when we wish to concentrate on a study of angles. However, *for pedagogical reasons which we have found valid from experience*, we have decided not to do this, but we shall instead follow the historic sequence of events and first review the traditional trigonometric functions of angles. Many students of this book will have had an introduction to this kind of trigonometry. If we ignored this and first discussed the more sophisticated circular functions it would be very perplexing to many of these students. In this chapter we present a survey of much of traditional trigonometry; while in Chapter 7 we present the modern view of analytic trigonometry with circular functions.

We assume an intuitive familiarity with angles and triangles. Figure 31 shows a right triangle ABC, the letters A, B, C designating either the angles or the associated vertices, as the context indicates. The right angle is at C, while a, b, c are the measures of length (in some adopted unit) of the sides and hypotenuse opposite the angles A, B, C, respectively. The six trigonometric "functions of angle A" are then defined as follows:

$$\text{sine } A = \frac{a}{c} = \frac{\text{opposite side}}{\text{hypotenuse}} \qquad \text{cosecant } A = \frac{c}{a} = \frac{\text{hypotenuse}}{\text{opposite side}}$$

$$\text{cosine } A = \frac{b}{c} = \frac{\text{adjacent side}}{\text{hypotenuse}} \qquad \text{secant } A = \frac{c}{b} = \frac{\text{hypotenuse}}{\text{adjacent side}}$$

$$\text{tangent } A = \frac{a}{b} = \frac{\text{opposite side}}{\text{adjacent side}} \qquad \text{cotangent } A = \frac{b}{a} = \frac{\text{adjacent side}}{\text{opposite side}}$$

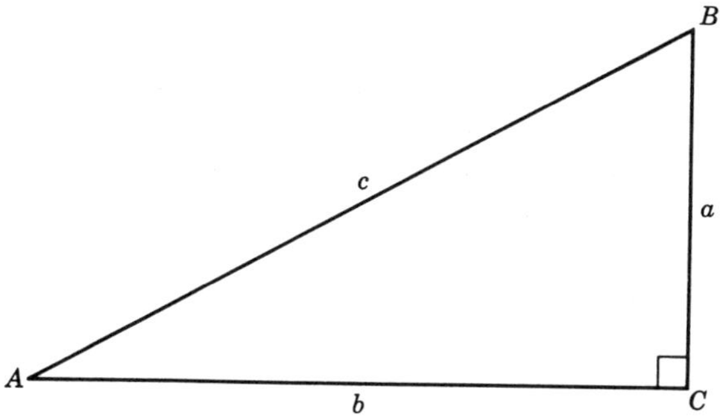

Figure 31

If we form any other triangle containing angle A, it follows from the geometry of similar triangles that we shall obtain the same functional values as before. Hence, these functional values are independent of everything *except* the angle A, and so we are justified in calling them "functions of *A*." In practice, the names of the six functions are usually abbreviated to sin, cos, tan, csc, sec, and cot.

A glance at the above definitions shows that csc $A = 1/\sin A$, sec $A = 1/\cos A$, and cot $A = 1/\tan A$, provided A is an angle ($\neq 90°$) of a right triangle. Hence, the cosecant, secant, and cotangent functions are reciprocal, on suitably restricted domains of angles, to the sine, cosine, and tangent functions, respectively. In view of this fact, very little attention is paid to the cosecant, secant, and cotangent functions in traditional trigonometry.

If we refer to angles *A* and *B* of Figure 31, and apply the above definitions to angle *B*, it is immediate that:

$$\sin B = \cos A \qquad\qquad \cos B = \sin A$$
$$\cos B = \sin A \qquad\qquad \sin B = \cos A$$
$$\tan B = \cot A \qquad\qquad \cot B = \tan A$$

Angles *A* and *B* are *complementary* to each other, in the sense that $A + B = 90°$. If we now regard the cosecant, cosine, and cotangent functions as "cofunctions" of the secant, sine, and tangent functions, respectively, we have discovered the following important relationship:

A trigonometric function of any positive angle ($< 90°$) is equal to the cofunction of its complementary angle.

For example, sin 37° = cos 53°; tan 70° = cot 20°; csc 15° = sec 75°; and so on.

If an angle is accurately constructed, along with the sides of a right triangle containing it, it is possible to compute approximations to the numerical values of the trigonometric functions of any *acute* ($< 90°$) angle. This merely involves an accurate measurement of the sides of the triangle and computation of the appropriate ratios. The values of these functions can be determined more accurately, however, by other methods, and in Table 2 we have given a four-place listing of these values. We note, incidentally, that the domain of each of the trigonometric functions, as defined in this section, is the set of all *positive acute* angles. For angles in excess of 45°, the labels at the *bottom* of the columns should be observed, along with the angle designations in the extreme *right* column. This table uses the economy of construction allowed by the relationship previously noted between trigonometric cofunctions. We shall see later how the table can be used to extend further the domains of these functions.

It will be observed that Table 2 lists the functional values of all positive acute angles measured to the nearest 0.1 degrees (or six minutes). If functions of angles which have been measured with more precision are needed, we can extend the usefulness of the table somewhat by interpolation. This interpolation process is simply a matter of proportions, as was demonstrated with logarithms in Chapter 5, and we illustrate with an example.

EXAMPLE 1.   Use Table 2 to determine sin 26°34'.

SOLUTION.   Since $34' = 0.566 \cdots °$, we round off the angle measurement to 26.57°. From Table 2,

$$\begin{aligned} \sin 26.6° = \sin 26.60° &= 0.4478 \\ \sin 26.5° = \sin 26.50° &= \underline{0.4462} \\ & \;\, 0.0016 \end{aligned}$$

We note that 57 is $\frac{7}{10}$ of the way from 50 to 60 and so, by proportional parts,

$$\sin 26.57° = 0.4462 + \tfrac{7}{10}(0.0016) = 0.4462 + 0.0011 = 0.4473.$$

In using the interpolation process it should be observed, of course, that while the sine, secant, and tangent functional values increase with increasing acute angles, the values of the reciprocal functions (cosecant, cosine, cotangent) decrease.

If Table 2 is to be used to determine an angle from a given functional value, it is necessary to use the table in reverse—a process similar to determining a number from its logarithm. We illustrate with an example.

EXAMPLE 2.   Determine angle A if sec $A = 1.9556$.

SOLUTION.   From Table 2 we note that the nearest listing *below*

1.9556 is: sec 59.2° = sec 59.20° = 1.9530

but also: sec A = 1.9556   = 1.9556

          0.0026

          0.0057

and: sec 59.3° = sec 59.30° = 1.9587

Since sec A exceeds sec 59.2° by 0.0026, and the excess of sec 59.3° over sec 59.2° is 0.0057, it follows by proportional parts that

$$A = 59.20° + \tfrac{26}{57}(0.10)° = 59.20° + 0.05° = 59.25°.$$

NOTE: If an angle were to be determined from the value of a *decreasing* function (cosine, cotangent, or cosecant), we would work from the nearest table entry *above* the given value.

In its historic setting, the use of trigonometry was confined principally to the "solution" of triangles. This involved a determination of an unknown part (angle or side) of a triangle from certain given parts. The technique used, in the case of a right-angled triangle, is based on the following simple rule, the validity of which is evident:

Use a trigonometric function to connect the unknown part with two known parts, and solve for the unknown.

EXAMPLE 3.   Find the height of a tree, if the length of its shadow is 28 feet, when the angle of elevation of the sun is 37°.

SOLUTION.   The problem is depicted in Figure 32, with BC representing the tree and AC its shadow. If the height of the tree is h feet, we use the tangent function to connect h, 28, and 37°. Thus, tan 37° = 0.7536 = $h/28$, whence h = 28(0.7536) = 21.1. The approximate height of the tree is then 21 feet.

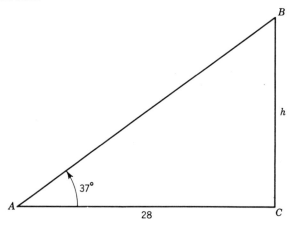

Figure 32

PROBLEMS

1. Use a protractor to construct the indicated angle; draw a triangle of convenient size which contains the angle; and compute approximations for each of the following functional values from actual measurements of the sides of the triangle: (a) sin 35°24′; (b) sec 64°44′; (c) cot 39°15′; (d) tan 84°36′.
2. Use Table 2 and interpolation, if necessary, to determine the angle A from each of the following conditions: (a) sin A = 0.4221; (b) sec A = 1.5462; (c) tan A = 2.3456; (d) cot A = 1.8372; (e) csc A = 1.7563.
3. Express each of the following as a functional value of a positive angle less than 45°: (a) cos 64°14′; (b) sec 86°30′; (c) csc 74°53′; (d) cot 83°55′; (e) tan 88°55′.
4. Use a different function, but the same angle, to express each of the following: (a) sin 66°; (b) cos 54°50′; (c) tan 37°45′; (d) cot 40°.
5. Use a different function and a different angle to express the values given in Problem 4.

6. Determine the unknown parts of the right triangle ABC, with right angle at C, given that: (a) $A = 44°50'$, $a = 15$; (b) $B = 53.6°$, $c = 25$; (c) $A = 48.5°$, $c = 41.6$.

7. The angle of elevation of the top of a cliff as seen from a small boat on a lake below is observed to be $36°40'$. If the cliff is known to be 50 feet high, how far is the boat from the base of the cliff?

8. Solve each of the following equations for an *acute* angle A:
   (a) $\sin(5A + 13°) = \cos 2A$; (b) $\tan A/2 = \cot A$; (c) $\sin(A + 60°) = \cos(3A + 12°)$.

9. A pilot of a sea plane notes that his elevation is 6,000 feet as he approaches a small island. According to his best estimate, the angle of depression of the farthest tip of the island is $40°$, while the angle of depression of the closest point is $60°$. Determine the approximate dimension of the island in the direction of flight.

10. Find the acute angle between a diagonal and an adjacent edge of a cube.

11. If a 30-inch pendulum is moved from its vertical position by $15°$, by how much has the pendulum bob been raised?

12. A 20-foot ladder, with its base fixed at one spot in an alley, will reach 12 feet up the side of a building on one side and 15 feet up another building on the other side of the alley. How wide is the alley?

13. A microwave tower stands on top of a 200-foot building. From a spot on the ground 450 feet from the base of the building, the angle between the lines of sight of the top and bottom of the tower is $15°$. Determine the approximate height of the tower.

14. From a certain spot on a plain, the angle of elevation of the top of a small mountain is $45°$. If the angle of elevation is $60°$ from a spot at the same elevation but 2,000 feet closer to the base of the mountain, determine the height of the mountain.

15. Is it possible to construct a right triangle which contains an angle $A < 30°$ such that $\sin(30° + A) = \cos(30° - A)$?

6.2   General Trigonometric Functions

It is clear that the definitions of the trigonometric functions, as given in §6.1, are meaningful only if the angles involved are positive and acute. Only this kind of an angle can be interior to a right triangle. In other words, the domains of the trigonometric functions, as we have defined them so far, are sets of positive acute angles. In this section, we shall extend these domains to define related functions *with the same names*, but with domains including angles which are not acute as well as angles which are not positive. This extension will be accomplished in such a way, however, that the values of the new functions for positive acute angles will agree with the values of the primary functions as we have already defined them.

An angle is formed by two line segments which intersect at a point called the "vertex" of the angle. It is sometimes convenient to think of an angle as an amount of "rotation," to make it analogous to a line segment as an amount of "linear distance" between two points. From this point of view, one side of an angle is considered its "initial" side, while the other—or "rotating" side—is its "terminal" side. Let us now consider an angle constructed so that its vertex is at the origin of a rectangular Cartesian coordinate system, and with its initial side lying along the positive x-axis. Such an angle is said to be *in standard position*. A typical angle in standard position is shown in Figure 33, the terminal side of the angle lying along *OT*. If the angle has been considered generated by a counterclockwise rotation about its vertex *O*, the angle is *positive*, while a clockwise rotation will generate a *negative* angle. It is noteworthy that it is impossible to tell merely from the position of the terminal side whether an angle is positive or negative, or even what its numerical magnitude may be. For example, the angles 150°, −210°, 510°, ... have an identical terminal side when they are placed in standard position, but they are quite different angles when regarded as amounts of rotation. We shall see shortly, however, that such angles do have many common properties.

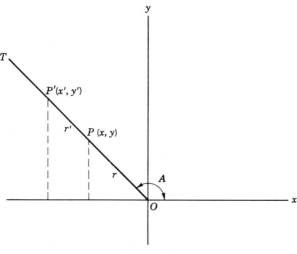

Figure 33

With reference to Figure 33, let $P(x, y)$ be an arbitrary point on the terminal side of an angle A in standard position. The abscissa of P is x; its ordinate is y; while its distance from the origin is r. The extended trigonometric functions, *with the same names as before*, are now defined as follows:

$$\sin A = \frac{y}{r}, \qquad\qquad \csc A = \frac{r}{y},$$

$$\cos A = \frac{x}{r}, \qquad\qquad \sec A = \frac{r}{x},$$

$$\tan A = \frac{y}{x}, \qquad\qquad \cot A = \frac{x}{y}.$$

There are three important points to observe with respect to these definitions:

1. The functions are indeed functions of the *angle A*, in spite of the presence of r and the coordinates of P in the definitions. For if another point $P'(x', y')$ is taken on the same terminal side, the distance of P' from O being r', it follows from elementary geometry that $x/r = x'/r', y/r = y'/r'$, and $y/x = y'/x'$.

2. The definitions involve only the *terminal side* of A, rather than its actual size or the amount of rotation which it designates. We say that two angles are *coterminal* if they have the same terminal sides when they are placed in standard position. Hence we are noting that *the trigonometric functional values of coterminal angles are the same.* For example, the angles $120°$, $-240°$, $480°$, etc., are coterminal, and so their trigonometric functional values are identical.

3. The definitions specialize to the definitions of §6.1 if A is an acute angle. In Figure 34 we have depicted an acute angle A, with $Q(x, y)$ a point on its terminal side, r units from the origin. Then OMQ is a right triangle, in which x = measure of length of side adjacent to A, y = measure of length of side opposite A, r = measure of length of the hypotenuse. The definitions of these two sections are then in complete agreement.

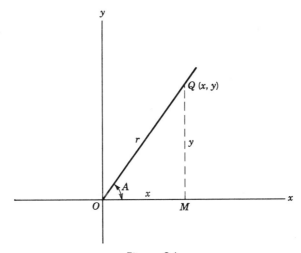

Figure 34

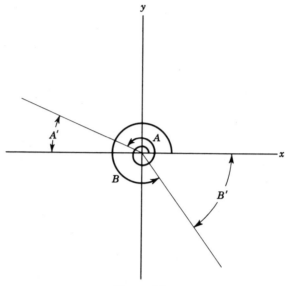

Figure 35

The acute angle, considered positive, formed by the terminal side of a given angle A and the x-axis is called the *reference* angle of A. For example, in Figure 35, A' is the reference angle of A and B' is the reference angle of B. It is clear that there are infinitely many different angles—both positive and negative—which have equal reference angles. We shall now show that all of these angles have very similar trigonometric functional values.

To this end, with reference to Figure 36, let OP, OQ, OR, OS be four rays—one in each quadrant—which form the terminal sides of four angles *whose reference angles are equal*. Moreover, it is no loss of generality if we assume that the points P, Q, R, S are located on the same circle of radius r. It is an immediate consequence of elementary geometry that the coordinates of these four points are the same, except for some algebraic signs. Since the generalized trigonometric functions of these angles have been defined in terms of these coordinates and r, it follows that the numerical or absolute values of any given trigonometric function are the same for all four angles. The algebraic sign of any functional value can be determined from the quadrant in which the terminal side of the angle lies, because this quadrant determines the signs of x and y. These signs are recorded in the mnemonic diagram below, but it is not necessary to commit it to memory, since its entries should be evident from the definitions of the various functions.

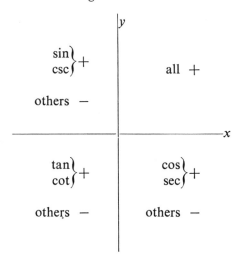

We are now able to state the following practical rule for determining a trigonometric functional value of any angle:

The Reduction Principle

Let T be *any* trigonometric function, A an angle, and A' the reference angle of A. Then $T(A) = \pm T(A')$, where the sign is chosen by inspection of the quadrant in which the terminal side of A lies.

Since the reference angle A' is a positive acute angle, and the functional

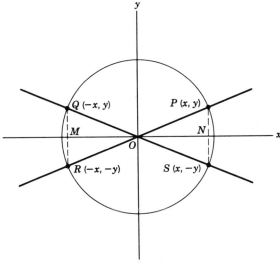

Figure 36

values for any such angle are listed in Table 2, this principle allows us essentially to extend the Table to include all angles—for which a consistent definition is possible.

EXAMPLE 1.   Determine the designated functional values: (a) sin 480°; (b) cos (−340°); (c) cot (−200°); (d) tan 580°.

SOLUTION.   The angles involved, along with their related reference angles, are illustrated in Figure 37. The desired values may then be obtained from the Reduction Principle and Table 2.
(a) sin 480° = sin 60° = 0.8660; (b) cos (−340°) = cos 20° = 0.9397; (c) cot (−200°) = −cot 20° = −2.747; (d) tan 580° = tan 40° = 0.8391.

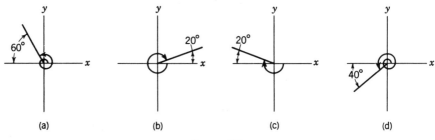

Figure 37

EXAMPLE 2.   If cos A = −0.8480, determine A such that 90° < A < 180°.

SOLUTION.   From Table 2, the reference angle of A is 32°. Hence A = 148°.

PROBLEMS

1. With reference to Figure 36, give the geometric proof that triangles OPN, ONS, OQM, and OMR are congruent.
2. Find the reference angle of each of the following angles: (a) 212°; (b) −550°; (c) 634°; (d) −660°; (e) −245°; (f) 800°.
3. Determine the sign of sin A if the terminal side of A, in standard position, lies in the: (a) second quadrant; (b) fourth quadrant.
4. Determine the sign of cos A if the terminal side of −A, in standard position, lies in the: (a) first quadrant; (b) third quadrant.
5. Write down three other angles of numerically smallest size whose trigonometric functional absolute values are the same as: (a) 12°; (b) 63°; (c) −47°; (d) 125°; (e) −236°; (f) 48°.
6. Use Table 2 to determine each of the following functional values: (a) sin 234°; (b) cos 136°; (c) tan 534°; (d) cot 438°.

7. Use Table 2 to determine each of the following functional values: (a) cos 143°18′; (b) sin ($-532°45′$); (c) tan ($-142°48′$).

8. Use Table 2 to determine each of the following functional values: (a) cos 532°18′; (b) sec 236°20′; (c) tan ($-330°50′$).

9. If sin $A = 0.5482$, determine A such that $0° < A < 360°$, if the terminal side of A lies in the: (a) second quadrant; (b) first quadrant.

10. Do Problem 9 subject to the condition that $-360° < A < 0°$.

11. Solve each of the following equations for angle A, subject to the given condition: (a) sin $A = -0.6452$, $180° < A < 270°$; (b) cos $A = 0.2648$, $270° < A < 360°$; (c) tan $A = 2.546$, $-180° < A < -90°$; (d) sec $A = -1.6543$, $-270° < A < -180°$.

12. Solve each of the following equations for angle A, subject to the given condition: (a) tan $A = 1.4982$, $-360° < A < -270°$; (b) sin $A = 0.2395$, $90° < A < 180°$; (c) cot $A = -1.543$, $-180° < A < 0°$; (d) cos $A = 0.1264$, $270° < A < 360°$.

13. We may define the *coreference* angle of a given angle as the positive acute angle formed by the terminal side of the given angle in standard position and the y-axis. Establish the following Reduction Principle for coreference angles: If T is any trigonometric function, A is any angle and A'' its coreference angle, $|T(A)| = |\text{co-}T(A'')|$, where co-$T$ is the cofunction of T.

14. Use the Reduction Principle of Problem 13 to express each of the following as a functional value of a positive angle less than 45°: (a) sin 64°; (b) cos 137°; (c) sec ($-100°$); (d) sin 250°50′.

15. Use the result of Problem 13 to express each of the following as a trigonometric functional value of a positive angle less than 45°: (a) sin 285°40′; (b) cos ($-254°45′$); (c) tan 300°45′; (d) cot 100°.

16. If $0° < A < 90°$, use the Reduction Principle of the text to express each of the following as a function of A: (a) sin ($180° - A$); (b) cos ($180° - A$); (c) tan ($180° + A$); (d) sin ($-A$); (e) cos ($-A$); (f) cot ($180° + A$).

17. If $0° < A < 90°$, use the Reduction Principle of Problem 13 to express each of the following as a function of A: (a) sin ($90° + A$); (b) cos ($90° + A$); (c) sec ($270° - A$); (d) cot ($270° + A$); (e) sin ($270° - A$); (f) csc ($270° + A$).

18. If the given point is on the terminal side of angle A in standard position, determine sin A, cos A, and tan A: (a) (2, -3); (b) (-2, -2); (c) (-3, 1); (d) (1, 4); (e) (3, -2).

19. For which angles A do we have no definition for: (a) tan A; (b) sec A; (c) cot A?

20. What are the domains of the extended trigonometric functions as we have defined them in this section?

6.3 Some Special Angles

The definitions we have given the trigonometric functions are quite general in the sense that the angles involved are not bounded in size or restricted in algebraic sign. In the more modern terminology of contemporary mathematics, this means that the domains of these functions are maximal subsets of angles. However, it is not true that $T(A)$ is a well-defined real number for every trigonometric function T and every angle A. This is because the abscissa or ordinate of a point can be 0, and a fraction with denominator 0 is without meaning. The angles, whose terminal sides have points like this, are the so-called "quadrantal" angles, i.e., the angles which are integral multiples of 90°. One coordinate of any point on the terminal side of such an angle is 0, which prohibits its use as the denominator of a fraction. The various situations which can appear are illustrated in Figure 38. A direct

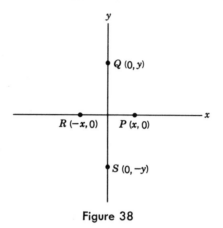

Figure 38

application of the definitions yields the table below which gives the functional values for some of the more common quadrantal angles. An entry $\cdot\,\cdot$ indicates that the function has not been defined for this particular angle or that this angle is not in the domain of the function.

A	0°	90°	180°	270°
sin A	0	1	0	-1
cos A	1	0	-1	0
tan A	0	$\cdot\,\cdot$	0	$\cdot\,\cdot$
csc A	$\cdot\,\cdot$	1	$\cdot\,\cdot$	-1
sec A	1	$\cdot\,\cdot$	-1	$\cdot\,\cdot$
cot A	$\cdot\,\cdot$	0	$\cdot\,\cdot$	0

We note that sin A and cos A are well-defined numbers, even when A is a quadrantal angle, and so the domain of either of these functions is the set of all angles. The domains of the other functions, however, do not include all quadrantal angles. For example, the domain of the tangent function is the set of all angles which are not *odd* multiples of 90°.

In addition to the quadrantal angles, certain other angles have played important roles in the early development of trigonometry. They have also been very prominent in the study of Euclidean geometry. We are referring to the angles 30°, 45°, and 60°. Since they are positive acute angles, we may consider each of them as an angle of a right triangle, and so the equivalent definitions of the functions given in §6.1 may be used.

In Figure 39, we have constructed a right triangle with acute angles of 30° and 60°. If we make the smallest side 1 unit in length, it is a well-known fact from elementary geometry that the hypotenuse is 2 units in length, while it follows from the Pythagorean Theorem that the other side must measure $\sqrt{3}$ units. The values of the trigonometric functions of 30° and 60° may then be read directly from the triangle.

In Figure 40, we have depicted an isosceles right triangle with its equal sides 1 unit in length. The acute angles are then 45°, and the Pythagorean Theorem requires that the length of the hypotenuse is $\sqrt{2}$ units. The trigonometric functional values for 45° may then be determined from the triangle. In the table below, we have listed all functional values for the angles 30°, 45°, and 60°.

A	30°	45°	60°
sin A	$\dfrac{1}{2}$	$\dfrac{1}{\sqrt{2}}$	$\dfrac{\sqrt{3}}{2}$
cos A	$\dfrac{\sqrt{3}}{2}$	$\dfrac{1}{\sqrt{2}}$	$\dfrac{1}{2}$
tan A	$\dfrac{1}{\sqrt{3}}$	1	$\sqrt{3}$
csc A	2	$\sqrt{2}$	$\dfrac{2}{\sqrt{3}}$
sec A	$\dfrac{2}{\sqrt{3}}$	$\sqrt{2}$	2
cot A	$\sqrt{3}$	1	$\dfrac{1}{\sqrt{3}}$

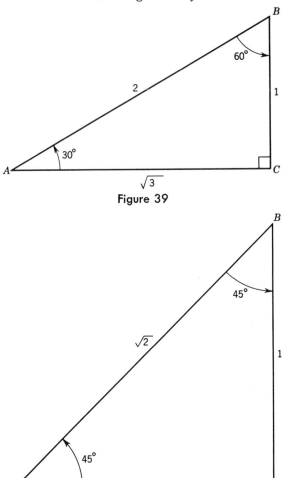

Figure 39

Figure 40

EXAMPLE.   Determine: (a) cos 150°; (b) tan (−225°).

SOLUTION

(a) By the Reduction Principle, cos 150° $=$ −cos 30° $=$ −$\sqrt{3}/2$.
(b) By the Reduction Principle, tan (−225°) $=$ −tan 45° $=$ −1.

PROBLEMS

1. Describe the domains of the cosecant, secant, and cotangent functions.
2. Without the use of Table 2, evaluate each of the following:

(a) sin 225°;   (b) cos (−135°);   (c) sec 120°;
(d) cot (−120°);   (e) cos 315°;   (f) csc 240°.

3. Evaluate each of the following pairs of expressions:
 (a) sin (180° − 60°), sin 180° − sin 60°;
 (b) tan (60° − 30°), tan 60° − tan 30°;
 (c) sin 120°, 2 sin 60°;
 (d) cos 30°, $(\frac{1}{2})$ cos 60°.

4. Each of the following angles is considered to be constructed in standard position. Determine the coordinates of the point of intersection of the terminal side of each angle with the unit circle: (a) 60°; (b) 120°; (c) −150°; (d) 225°; (e) 135°; (f) −60°.

5. Use the directions of Problem 4 for each of the following angles: (a) 180°; (b) 90°; (c) −270°; (d) 450°; (e) −810°; (f) 540°.

6. Evaluate 2 cos 60° + sin 30° − 3 tan 120°.

7. Evaluate in decimal form cos 0° − tan 45° + 2 sin 120°.

8. Evaluate cos 120° + tan (−120°) + 2 cot 135°.

9. Evaluate tan 225°/[2 sin 60° + cos 120° − tan 135°].

For Problems 10 through 18, solve each of the given equations for *A*, subject to the condition that $0° \le A \le 360°$.

10. sin $A = -\frac{1}{2}$.   11. cos $A = 1/\sqrt{2}$.   12. tan $A = 1$.
13. cot $A = -1$.   14. sec $A = -2/\sqrt{3}$.   15. tan $A = \sqrt{3}$.
16. sin $A = $ cos A.   17. tan $A = $ cot A.   18. cos $A = $ sin $(-2A)$.

For Problems 19 through 22, determine *A* such that $-180° \le A \le 180°$, and subject to the given condition.

19. sin $A = -1$, terminal side of *A* in third quadrant.
20. tan $A = -1/\sqrt{3}$, terminal side of *A* in second quadrant.
21. sin $A = -\frac{1}{2}$, terminal side of *A* in third quadrant.
22. sec $A = -2$, terminal side of *A* in third quadrant.

23. Verify each of the following assertions: (a) sin 60° = 2 sin 30° cos 30°; (b) tan 120° = 2 tan 60°/[1 − (tan 60°)²]; (c) sin (120° − 30°) = sin 120° cos 30° − cos 120° sin 30°; (d) cos (30° + 60°) = cos 30° cos 60° − sin 30° sin 60°; (e) cos 120° = (cos 60°)² − (sin 60°)².

24. If the angle of elevation of the sun is estimated to be 60°, determine the approximate length of the shadow of a 20-foot vertical pole.

25. Determine log sin 45° and log |sec 120°|.

26. If log cos $A = 0$, determine all possible *A* such that $-180° \le A \le 180°$.

27. Find a solution for *A* of the equation log |sin *A*| $= 0$ which is not a solution of log sin $A = 0$.

28. The angle of elevation of a projectile is observed to be 30° when it is directly over a tracking station known to be three miles distant. Determine the height of the projectile if the terrain is assumed to be flat.

6.4 Elementary Properties

We now take another critical look at the trigonometric functions of a general angle. In Figure 41, we have shown such an angle A in standard position, with $P(x, y)$ a point on its terminal side. If $r(> 0)$ is the distance

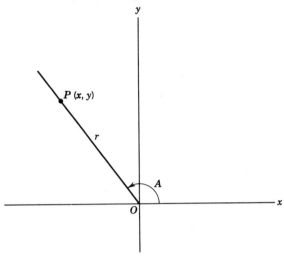

Figure 41

of P from the origin 0, it follows that $|x| \leq r$ and $|y| \leq r$, with one of the equalities holding if A is a quadrantal angle. Since $|\sin A| = |y|/r$ and $|\cos A| = |x|/r$, we have discovered the following facts:

$$|\sin A| \leq 1, \text{ i.e., } -1 \leq \sin A \leq 1,$$
$$|\cos A| \leq 1, \text{ i.e., } -1 \leq \cos A \leq 1.$$

It is the Basic Postulate of Analytic Geometry, to which we have referred before, that there is a one-to-one correspondence between the real numbers and the points on the "real line." Hence, if we let $r = 1$, it is intuitive that there is a point on the circumference of the unit circle which has for its ordinate any real number y subject only to $-1 \leq y \leq 1$. If this point is on the terminal side of an angle, we have implied that an angle A always exists such that $\sin A = y/1 = y$, for any $y \in [-1, 1]$. A similar argument applies for the cosine function, and so we may state the following important fact:

The range of both the sine and cosine functions is the closed interval $[-1, 1]$.

In view of the reciprocal relationship of sine with cosecant and cosine with secant, we may also make the following observation:

The range of both the cosecant and secant functions is the set $\{y | y \in R, |y| \geq 1\}$.

If we examine the tangent and cotangent functions in a similar way, we obtain a quite different result. For, with an appropriate choice of x and y, either y/x or x/y can be made equal to any desired number. Hence, *the range of both the tangent and cotangent functions is the set R of all real numbers.*

If $\sin A = y/r \leq 1$, there always exists a point P on the terminal side of A, with ordinate y and r units from the origin. For a point r units from the origin always exists on any line segment through the origin and, since the value of sine A is given, the ordinate of this point must be y. A similar remark may be made for the other functions. Hence, if A is sufficiently restricted, the values of all the trigonometric functions of A are uniquely determined by the value of any one of them. These functions are then by no means independent of one another.

EXAMPLE 1.   Determine $\cos A$ and $\tan A$ if $\sin A = \frac{1}{3}$ and $90° < A < 180°$.

SOLUTION.   The terminal side of A must lie in the second quadrant, and there must exist a point on this terminal side which is 3 units from the origin and has ordinate 1. A glance at Figure 42 indicates that the abscissa of this point must be $-2\sqrt{2}$, and so $\cos A = -2\sqrt{2}/3$ and $\tan A = -\sqrt{2}/4$.

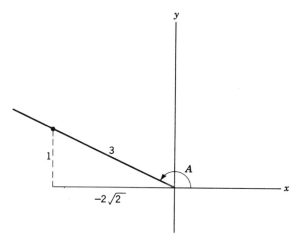

Figure 42

EXAMPLE 2.   If $\cos A = -1/\sqrt{2}$ and $0° < A < 360°$, determine $\sin A$ and $\tan A$.

SOLUTION.   In this case, A can be either of two angles, one with the terminal side in the second quadrant and one with the terminal side in the third quadrant. Since $\cos A = x/r$, for *any* point $P(x, y)$ on this terminal side and r units from the origin, we may choose $r = \sqrt{2}$ and thereby select the point $P_1(-1, 1)$ for the first case and $P_2(-1, -1)$ for the second case. A glance at Figure 43 now shows the two possible values of $\sin A$ and $\tan A$:

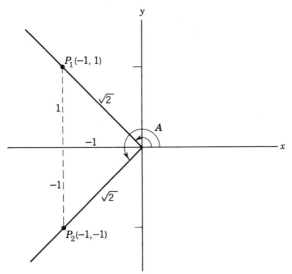

Figure 43

$$\sin A = \frac{1}{\sqrt{2}}, \tan A = \frac{1}{(-1)} = -1,$$

$$\sin A = \frac{(-1)}{\sqrt{2}} = \frac{-1}{\sqrt{2}}, \tan A = \frac{(-1)}{(-1)} = 1.$$

It may be observed that the two possibilities for A, in this example, are 135° and 225°.

A number of so-called "identities" arise in any study of trigonometry, each of them expressing a relationship between two or more of the trigonometric functions. An *identity* is actually a special sort of equation which may be defined as follows:

An equation in x is an *identity on a set E* if the indicated equality is valid for every replacement of x by an element of E.

Many equations (such as $x + x = 2x$) are valid for every real number x, and such equations are regularly referred to simply as "identities." It is also customary to use this simple designation for an identity on E if E consists of all replacements of the variable for which both members of the equation have meaning. An identity of this sort is $1/(x - 1) + 1/(x + 1) = 2x/(x^2 - 1)$, this being actually an identity on E where $E = \{x | x \in R, x \neq 1, -1\}$.

There are many identities (on sets of angles) involving trigonometric functions, and we have already taken note of the following:

$$(1) \qquad \qquad \csc A = \frac{1}{\sin A},$$

$$(2) \qquad \qquad \sec A = \frac{1}{\cos A},$$

$$(3) \qquad \qquad \cot A = \frac{1}{\tan A}.$$

In Figure 41, let $P(x, y)$ be an arbitrary point on the terminal side of an angle A in standard position. Then, since $y/x = (y/r)/(x/r)$ and $x/y = (x/r)/(y/r)$, the following two identities are immediate:

$$(4) \qquad \qquad \tan A = \frac{\sin A}{\cos A},$$

$$(5) \qquad \qquad \cot A = \frac{\cos A}{\sin A}.$$

An application of the Pythagorean Theorem to Figure 41 yields $y^2 + x^2 = r^2$, which is equivalent to $y^2/r^2 + x^2/r^2 = 1$ or $(y/r)^2 + (x/r)^2 = 1$. In terms of trigonometric functions, this last equation gives us $(\sin A)^2 + (\cos A)^2 = 1$. It is customary to write powers such as $(\sin A)^2$ and $(\cos A)^2$ as $\sin^2 A$ and $\cos^2 A$, respectively, and so the identity just derived may be expressed in the form:

$$(6) \qquad \qquad \sin^2 A + \cos^2 A = 1.$$

If we write $x^2 + y^2 = r^2$ in the form $1 + (y/x)^2 = (r/x)^2$, we obtain:

$$(7) \qquad \qquad 1 + \tan^2 A = \sec^2 A$$

Finally, if we write $y^2 + x^2 = r^2$ in the form $1 + (x/y)^2 = (r/y)^2$, we derive:

$$(8) \qquad \qquad 1 + \cot^2 A = \csc^2 A$$

It is worthy of note that whereas identity (6) is valid for *every* angle A, the others are valid only when zero denominators are excluded. That is, (6) is an identity on the set of all angles, while the others are identities on certain proper subsets of this set.

There are many other identities of the kind we have been deriving, but we shall postpone any further discussion along this line until Chapter 7. The eight identities we have listed above are often called the *Fundamental Identities*, and they should be entirely familiar to every student of trigonometry.

EXAMPLE 3.   Establish the validity of the following identity:

$$\frac{2 + 3 \cos A}{\sin A} = 2 \csc A + 3 \cot A.$$

SOLUTION

$$\frac{2 + 3 \cos A}{\sin A} = 2\left(\frac{1}{\sin A}\right) + 3\left(\frac{\cos A}{\sin A}\right) = 2 \csc A + 3 \cot A.$$

The validity of the identity in Example 3 was established by showing that the left member of the conjectured identity is in fact equal to the right member. Sometimes it is more convenient to show that both members are equal to the same third expression and so are equal to each other.

EXAMPLE 4.   Prove that $\tan^2 A / \sin^2 A = 1 + \tan^2 A$ is an identity.

SOLUTION

$$\frac{\tan^2 A}{\sin^2 A} = \left[\frac{\sin^2 A}{\cos^2 A}\right]\left[\frac{1}{\sin^2 A}\right] = \frac{1}{\cos^2 A} = \sec^2 A.$$

Moreover, $1 + \tan^2 A = \sec^2 A$, by (7), and so the given identity is verified.

PROBLEMS

1. Determine $\sin A$ and $\sec A$ if $\tan A = \frac{2}{3}$ and $180° < A < 270°$.
2. Determine $\tan A$ and $\csc A$ if $\cos A = \frac{2}{3}$ and $270° < A < 360°$.
3. Determine $\cot A$ and $\sec A$ if $\sin A = -\frac{3}{4}$, and the terminal side of A lies in the third quadrant.
4. Determine $\tan A$, $\sec A$, and $\csc A$ if we know that the point $(-1, 4)$ lies on the terminal side of A.
5. The point $(3, -7)$ lies on the terminal side of A. Determine $\sin A$, $\cos A$, and $\cot A$.
6. Prove that $|\tan A| \geq |\sin A|$, and $|\tan A| < |\sec A|$, for any angle A, such that the given functional values have meaning.
7. Examine the Fundamental Identities (1) through (4) and describe the angles A for which each is without meaning.
8. Use the direction of Problem 7 for the Fundamental Identities (5) through (8).

9. If $\sin A = \frac{3}{5}$, determine the two possible values of $(\csc A + \tan A)/\cos A$.

10. Evaluate $(\tan A - 2 \sec A)/\cos A$, if $\sin A = \frac{1}{3}$ and $90° < A < 180°$.

11. Evaluate $\sin A \cos B + \cos A \sin B$, if $\tan A = \frac{2}{3}$, $\csc B = \frac{3}{2}$, $180° < A < 270°$, $90° < B < 180°$.

Establish the validity of the identities given in Problems 12 through 19.

12. $\dfrac{\cot A - \tan A}{\cot A + \tan A} = 1 - 2 \sin^2 A.$ **13.** $\dfrac{1}{1 - \sin A} = \sec^2 A + \sec A \tan A.$

14. $\tan A \sin A + \cos A = \sec A.$ **15.** $\dfrac{1 + \sin A}{\cos A} = \sec A + \tan A.$

16. $\dfrac{2 + 5 \cos A}{\sin A} = 2 \csc A + 5 \cot A.$ **17.** $\dfrac{\cot A + \csc A}{1 + \cos A} = \csc A.$

18. $1 + \cot^2 A = \dfrac{\sec^2 A}{\sec^2 A - 1}.$ **19.** $\dfrac{1}{1 - \sin A} + \dfrac{1}{1 + \sin A} = 2 \sec^2 A.$

20. Express each of the following in simplest form: (a) $\dfrac{\cos (180° + A) \sin A}{1 - \sin^2 (180° - A)}$;

     (b) $\dfrac{\sin^3 A - \cos^3 A}{\sin A - \cos A}$; (c) $\dfrac{\sin A}{\sec A + 1} + \dfrac{\sin A}{\sec A - 1}.$

6.5   General Triangle Trigonometry

The general principle stated in §6.1 is quite adequate for the solving of any right triangle. However, if the triangle is not right angled, other methods are needed. We first derive a preliminary result, and then proceed to these methods.

Let $P(x_1, y_1)$ and $Q(x_2, y_2)$ be any two points in a plane, as shown in Figure 44. Then, with the construction of the indicated horizontal and vertical lines, PQ is the hypotenuse of a right angled triangle, and the

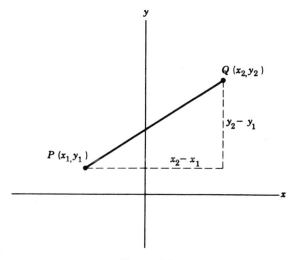

Figure 44

Pythagorean Theorem may be applied. If $|PQ|$ designates the length of PQ, if follows that

$$|PQ|^2 = (x_2 - x_1)^2 + (y_2 - y_1)^2$$

and

$$|PQ| = \sqrt{(x_2 - x_1)^2 + (y_2 - y_1)^2}.$$

In this formula, we note that $x_2 - x_1$ and $y_2 - y_1$ are both squared, and so it makes no difference in a numerical problem which of two points is considered (x_1, y_1) and which (x_2, y_2).

EXAMPLE 1. Find the distance between the points $(-1, 2)$ and $(3, -3)$.

SOLUTION. If d is the desired distance, the preceding formula gives us:

$$d^2 = (3 + 1)^2 + (-3 - 2)^2 = 16 + 25 = 41.$$

Hence

$$d = \sqrt{41}.$$

In Figure 45 we have shown a general triangle ABC, wherein A, B, C designate either the vertices or the associated interior angles (as is convenient). The lengths of the sides opposite angles A, B, C are a, b, c, respectively. In addition, rectangular coordinate axes have been drawn so that the origin is at C, and the positive x-axis lies along CB. The definitions of the sine and cosine functions for a general angle now show that the

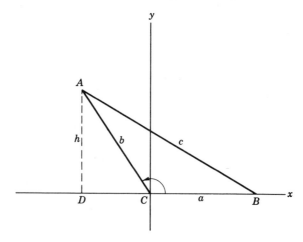

Figure 45

coordinate pair of A is $(b \cos C, b \sin C)$. Since the coordinate pair of B is $(a, 0)$, we can use the distance formula just derived to determine c. Thus $c^2 = (b \cos C - a)^2 + (b \sin C - 0)^2 = b^2 \cos^2 C - 2ab \cos C + a^2 + b^2 \sin^2 C = b^2(\sin^2 C + \cos^2 C) + a^2 - 2ab \cos C = a^2 + b^2 - 2ab \cos C$. This is the *Law of Cosines*, which may be expressed in any of three ways:

$$a^2 = b^2 + c^2 - 2bc \cos A,$$
$$b^2 = c^2 + a^2 - 2ca \cos B,$$
$$c^2 = a^2 + b^2 - 2ab \cos C.$$

The Law of Cosines is useful for solving triangles in which two sides and the included angle are given or in which all three sides are given.

EXAMPLE 2.　In triangle ABC, determine a if $b = 10$, $c = 20$, and $A = 50°$.

SOLUTION.　In this case, we use the Law of Cosines in the form:

$$a^2 = b^2 + c^2 - 2bc \cos A.$$

Hence,

$$a^2 = 100 + 400 - 400(\cos 50°) = 500 - 400 \cos 50°$$
$$= 500 - 400(0.6428) = 500 - 257.12 = 242.88 \doteq 243,$$

whence $a \doteq 16$.

EXAMPLE 3.　In triangle ABC, determine B if $a = 5$, $b = 10$, and $c = 12$.

SOLUTION.　The appropriate form of the Law of Cosines for this problem is $b^2 = c^2 + a^2 - 2ca \cos B$, and we transform this further into:

$$\cos B = \frac{c^2 + a^2 - b^2}{2ca}.$$

Hence,

$$\cos B = \frac{144 + 25 - 100}{120} = \frac{69}{120} = \frac{23}{40} = 0.5750,$$

and we find from Table 2 that:

$$B = 54.9° = 54°54'.$$

Another important trigonometric relationship which we now discuss is called the *Law of Sines*. In Figure 46, we have shown a general triangle, with the usual associated symbolism, placed so that angle C is in standard position with respect to a rectangular coordinate system. If h is the ordinate of the vertex at A, the definition of the sine function shows that $h = b \sin C$.

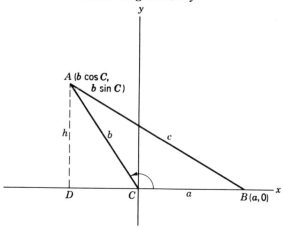

Figure 46

But *ADB* is a right triangle, so that the definition of sine, as given in §6.1, yields $\sin B = h/c$ and $h = c \sin B$. A combination of these two expressions for h shows us that $b \sin C = c \sin B$, i.e.,

$$\frac{\sin B}{b} = \frac{\sin C}{c}.$$

A simple variation of this proof gives

$$\frac{\sin B}{b} = \frac{\sin A}{a}$$

which, when combined with the earlier result, gives us the *Law of Sines*:

$$\frac{\sin A}{a} = \frac{\sin B}{b} = \frac{\sin C}{c}.$$

Expressed verbally, the Law of Sines states that *the lengths of the sides of any triangle are proportional to the sines of the opposite angles*.

The Law of Sines is useful in solving triangles in cases for which the Law of Cosines is not applicable. But there is one difficulty. If we wish to determine an angle from its sine, there may be two solutions, one being an acute angle and the other obtuse. For example, if $\sin A = 0.5$, with A an interior angle of a triangle so that $0° < A < 180°$, we know that $A = 30°$ *or* $A = 150°$. However, this ambiguity causes no real trouble if a little common sense is applied.

The Law of Sines is useful whenever a "pair of opposites" is given, for example, A and a. If, in addition, another angle is given, the triangle has a unique solution. On the other hand, if the additional part is a side, say c, then there are three possibilities which may arise in a determination of C from the equation $\sin C = (c \sin A)/a$:

(1) If $(c \sin A)/a > 1$, no solution for C is possible.

(2) If $(c \sin A)/a = 1$, there is one solution for $C(C = 90°)$, and the triangle is right angled.

(3) If $(c \sin A)/a < 1$, there are two solutions for C, one an acute and the other an obtuse angle. Whether both are acceptable as angles for a triangle under the conditions of the problem can be determined from the fundamental geometric relation in any triangle that $A + B + C = 180°$.

These various possibilities are illustrated in the several parts of Figure 47, with a, A and c as the given parts. The left figure of (3) typifies the truly ambiguous case, with two triangle solutions, while the final figure illustrates a case with a single solution. We note then that a unique solution may exist under the conditions of (3), as well as under the conditions of (2) when the triangle is right-angled.

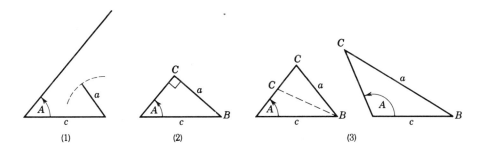

Figure 47

EXAMPLE 4. If $a = 15$, $A = 55°$, $b = 10$, for a triangle ABC, use the Law of Sines to determine B.

SOLUTION. $\sin B = (b \sin A)/a = 10(0.8192)/15 = 0.5461$. Hence $B = 33°6'$ or $B = 146°54'$. However, we note that $55° + 146°54' > 180°$, and so the only acceptable solution is $B = 33°6'$. If c and C are also desired, c can be obtained with another application of the Law of Sines, while C is determined by the relationship $A + B + C = 180°$.

PROBLEMS

1. Use an acute angled triangle to prove one form of the Law of Cosines.

2. Use an acute angled triangle to prove the Law of Sines.

3. Determine the distance between the following points: (a) $(-2, 3)$, $(1, 1)$; (b) $(3, -4)$, $(2, 2)$; (c) $(1, 1)$, $(-3, 5)$.
4. Interpret the Law of Sines for a right-angled triangle.
5. Find the remaining parts of triangle ABC if: (a) $a = 15$, $b = 30$, $C = 40°$; (b) $b = 3.8$, $c = 6.4$, $A = 28°48'$; (c) $a = 16.5$, $c = 39.6$, $B = 69°36'$
6. If a triangle exists, determine all unknown parts of triangle ABC, subject to the given conditions: (a) $a = 15$, $c = 30$, $A = 67°15'$; (b) $b = 12$, $c = 8$, $B = 54°36'$; (c) $a = 38$, $b = 43$, $A = 58°$.
7. Two planes leave an airport together in directions which differ by 35°. If their respective speeds are 175 and 225 miles per hour, determine approximately their distance apart after 30 minutes of flight.
8. A force of 500 pounds is to be resolved into two components whose directions differ by 40°. If one of the components is 350 pounds, determine the magnitude of the other component.
9. A ship sailing a straight course observes a lighthouse 22° to the left of its course. After sailing an additional 8 miles, the lighthouse is seen to bear 32° to the left of the ship's course. Determine how close the ship will come to the lighthouse.
10. The weight of an object is the force of gravity acting vertically downward. If a 3,500 pound automobile is resting on a 15° slope, find the components of its weight acting parallel and perpendicular to the hill.
11. Prove the following rule in any triangle ABC:

$$\frac{a - b}{a + b} = \frac{\sin A - \sin B}{\sin A + \sin B}.$$

(*Hint:* Let $a/\sin A = b/\sin B = k$, and substitute in the left member of the conjectured identity.)

12. Two military posts A and B are 300 feet apart. An observer in each post notices a shell burst in enemy territory at point C. If $\angle CAB = 60°$, and $\angle CBA = 72°$, determine the approximate distance of each post from C.
13. Three circles of radii 3, 4, and 5 inches are drawn on a plane to touch each other at an external point. Find the angles between their lines of centers.
14. Two observers in cities eight miles apart observe the same object in the sky at the same time in the same general direction. If the angles of elevation of the object for the respective observers are 30° and 50°, find the approximate height of the object.
15. Prove that $a^2 = 2b^2(1 - \cos A)$ for an isosceles triangle ABC, in which $c = b$.
16. Prove that angle A in a triangle ABC is acute only if $b^2 + c^2 > a^2$.
17. Establish the validity of the expression $\frac{1}{2} ab \sin C$ for the area of a triangle ABC.
18. Use the appropriate form of the Law of Cosines to prove that:

$$1 + \cos A = \frac{(b + c + a)(b + c - a)}{2bc}.$$

19. A man hears the noon whistles of two factories three and five seconds after 12 noon. If the angle between the lines of sight to the factories is 39°, and sound travels 1,100 feet per second, determine the approximate distance between the factories, assuming that both whistles blew accurately.

6.6   Radian Measure of Angles

Up to this point in the text, we have assumed that angles have been measured in degrees. This is the familiar system in which a "circle," or one rotation of a line segment about an endpoint, is divided into 360 equal parts, each equal to one "degree." There is another system, however, which is of great use in theoretical work with angles, and this "radian" measure provides us with a simple transition from "triangle" trigonometry to the analytic trigonometry of Chapter 7.

Definition.   The measure of an angle is one *radian* if its sides intercept an arc equal in length to the radius of any circle drawn with center at the vertex of the angle.

In other words, for radian measure of an angle, we use as our unit the radius of any circle drawn with center at the vertex and determine *in this unit* the length of the circular arc intercepted by the sides of the angle.

The above definition may be intuitively quite clear, but there is a theoretical complication which has not arisen in our previous work, because we must use a linear unit (a radius) to measure the length of an arc which is not linear. A linear unit can be used to measure the length of any polygon, regardless of the number of its sides, because these sides are line segments. But it is impossible to make any finite part of a line segment fit any part of a nonlinear curve, except for the degenerate case when both consist of one point. We are able to surmount this difficulty, however, with the help of the rather deep property of "completeness" of the real number system, a property which we discussed briefly in §1.6.

In Figure 48, we have shown an angle $A < 90°$, with $\overset{\frown}{BC}$ a circular arc of radius r. We wish to assign to $\overset{\frown}{BC}$ a real number as its length. Points $P_1, P_2, \ldots, P_n$ are chosen on the arc, in this order, between B and C, the figure showing the case when $n = 3$. These points are then joined with line segments to form an "inscripture" S of the arc $\overset{\frown}{BC}$. Any inscripture S, being made up of line segments, has a length $|S|$, where,

$$|S| = |BP_1| + |P_1P_2| + \cdots + |P_nC|;$$

for the case of Figure 48,

$$|S| = |BP_1| + |P_1P_2| + |P_2P_3| + |P_3C|.$$

If tangent lines are drawn to the circle at the points B and C, with D their point of intersection, it follows from elementary geometry that:

$$|S| < |BD| + |CD|.$$

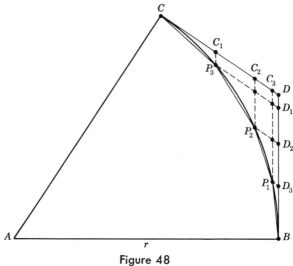

Figure 48

All that is needed in this verification is a consideration of parallelograms, whose opposite sides are known to be equal. The general case may be deduced from the special case of three inscripture points as shown in the figure. Since $|S| < |BD| + |CD|$ is true for *any* inscripture of $\widehat{BC}$, it follows that $|BD| + |CD|$ is an upper bound of the set of lengths of all these inscriptures. In case the angle A is not acute, it can be subdivided into four or less acute angles, and the lengths of the inscriptures of arcs containing each of these acute angles has an upper bound, as in the illustration. Hence every inscripture of an arc on a circle is bounded above, for any central angle $A \leq 360°$, and the existence of a least upper bound of the set of lengths for all inscriptures of the arc is guaranteed by the "completeness" property of the real numbers. The following definition of length is then seen to be appropriate.

Definition.   The *length* of an arc on a circle is the least upper bound of the set of lengths of all inscriptures of the arc.

With the notion of length of arc on a circle now being meaningful, the earlier definition of radian measure of an angle is more satisfactory. To repeat the earlier definition: the *radian measure* of an angle is the length of arc intercepted by any circle, drawn with center at the vertex of the angle, using the circle radius as the unit. It is to be understood, of course, that if an angle is in excess of 360°, its intercepted arc is in excess of a complete circumference of the circle. As an illustration of radian measure, the angle in Figure 49 is 2 radians because the intercepted arc BC has length $2r$, where r is the radius of the circle.

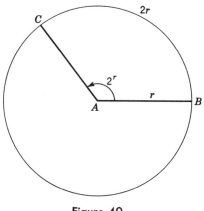

Figure 49

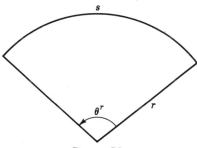

Figure 50

It is apparent from the definition of a radian that, if a central angle of θ radians intercepts on a circle of radius r an arc of length s,

$$s = r\theta.$$

This relationship is illustrated in Figure 50, where it must be emphasized that the formula is valid *only* if θ is the *radian* measure of the angle.

EXAMPLE 1. An arc of length 3 units is intercepted on a circle of radius 7 by the sides of an angle. Determine the size of the angle in radians.

SOLUTION. Since $s = r\theta$, $3 = 7\theta$ and so $\theta = \frac{3}{7}$. Hence the size of the angle is $\frac{3}{7}$ of a radian.

It is important to know the relationship existing between the radian and degree measures of an angle. To obtain this, consider a semicircle of radius r. The length of the semicircular arc is πr units, while the central angle subtended is $180°$. Since $s = r\theta$, for a circular arc of length s units, it follows that $\pi r = r\theta$, whence $\theta = \pi$. Hence $180° = \pi$ radians or, in the usual symbolism,

$$\pi^r = 180°.$$

In particular,

$$1^r = (180/\pi)° \doteq 57.3°$$

and

$$1° = (\pi/180)^r \doteq 0.01745^r.$$

It is also often important to know that $90° = \pi/2^r$, $60° = \pi/3^r$, $45° = \pi/4^r$, and $30° = \pi/6^r$. In Table 2 we have supplied an automatic conversion to radians for all acute angles, measured to a precision of $0.1°$. For an angle in excess of $90°$, we need—in addition to the table—the fact mentioned above that $90° = \pi/2^r$.

EXAMPLE 2.   Express $22°$ in radians and 3.2^r in degrees.

SOLUTION

$$22° = [22(\pi/180)]^r = [11\pi/90]^r \doteq 0.3839^r.$$
$$3.2^r = [3.2(180/\pi)]° \doteq 183°.$$

EXAMPLE 3.   Find the length of arc intercepted on a circle of radius 6 inches by a central angle of $22°$.

SOLUTION.   By the result of Example 2, $22° \doteq 0.3839^r$. We now use the formula $s = r\theta$, and obtain $s = 6(0.3839) = 2.3034 \doteq 2.3$ inches.

If a particle moves with a constant velocity v along an arc of a circle, $v = s/t$, where the particle traverses s units of distance in t units of time. Let us now suppose that the arc of length s units subtends a central angle of θ radians, so that $s = r\theta$, where r is the radius of the circle. Hence $v = r(\theta/t)$, and it is natural to refer to θ/t as the *angular velocity* ω in radians per unit of time, of the particle, and so we have the following result:

$$v = r\omega.$$

That is, the linear velocity of a particle moving uniformly around a circle of radius r is r times the angular velocity in radians of the central angle swept out by the particle.

EXAMPLE 4.   A wheel of radius 6 inches is rotating at the rate of 100 rpm. Determine the speed of a point on its circumference.

SOLUTION. An angular velocity of 100 rpm is equivalent to $100(2\pi)$ or 200π radians per minute. Since $v = r\omega$, $v = 6(200\pi) = 1{,}200\pi \doteq 3{,}770$ inches per minute.

PROBLEMS

1. With reference to Figure 48, supply the geometric argument needed to prove that $|S| < |BD| + |CD|$.
2. Express each of the following angles in degrees: (a) 2.5^r; (b) 1.6^r; (c) 5^r; (d) -3.2^r; (e) -6^r.
3. Express each of the following angles in degrees: (a) $\pi/7^r$; (b) $2\pi/3^r$; (c) $4\pi/3^r$; (d) $-5\pi/6^r$; (e) $6\pi/7^r$.
4. Express each of the following angles in radians involving π: (a) $30°$; (b) $-225°$; (c) $135°$; (d) $-270°$; (e) $240°$; (f) $-315°$.
5. Express each of the following angles in radians, correct to two decimal places: (a) $34°$; (b) $162°$; (c) $26°36'$; (d) $35°24'$; (e) $-72°$; (f) $-132°42'$.
6. If an arc on a circle of radius 12 inches is 3.2 inches in length, determine the central angle subtended by the arc in: (a) radians; (b) degrees.
7. What is the length of arc intercepted on a circle of circumference 24 inches by a central angle of $32°36'$?
8. Determine each of the following, by first converting the angle to degrees: (a) $\sin 2.6^r$; (b) $\cos 1^r$; (c) $\tan 4.2^r$; (d) $\sec \frac{2}{3}^r$.
9. Use Table 2 directly to determine: (a) $\sin 0.2436^r$; (b) $\cos 1.4352^r$; (c) $\tan 2.654^r$; (d) $\sin 6.32^r$; (e) $\cos (-10.4)^r$; (f) $\tan 1^r$.
10. A circle has a 5-inch radius. Determine the length of arc intercepted by a central angle of: (a) $\pi/6^r$; (b) $2\pi/3^r$; (c) $5\pi/6^r$.
11. A circle has a radius of 10 inches. Determine the length of arc intercepted by a central angle of: (a) $30°$; (b) $43°$; (c) $73°36'$.
12. A diameter of the sun subtends at a point on the earth an angle of approximately 0.0093 radians. If we assume the approximate distance of the sun to be 93,000,000 miles, determine the length of a diameter of the sun.
13. If we assume that the earth is a sphere of diameter 8,000 miles, determine the approximate distance between two points on the equator located at $72°$ West Longitude and $95°$ East Longitude, respectively.
14. A wheel with radius 10 inches is rotating at the rate of 25 rpm. Determine: (a) the angular velocity in radians per second of a spoke of the wheel; (b) the velocity in inches per second of a point on the rim of the wheel.
15. Without using Table 2, evaluate each of the following: (a) $\sin \pi/2^r + 2 \cos \pi/6^r$; (b) $2 \tan \pi/3^r - 3 \sec 3\pi/4^r$; (c) $2 \tan 5\pi/6^r + \cos \pi^r$; (d) $\cos 4\pi/3^r - \sin (-\pi/3)^r$.
16. Derive the expression $r^2\theta/2$ for the area of a sector of a circle of radius r and central angle θ radians. (*Hint:* Observe that the area of a circular sector is proportional to its central angle.)

CHAPTER 7

Analytic Trigonometry

7.1   The Circular Functions

Whatever the exact definition we adopt for a function, its essential feature is that it determines and is determined by a mapping of the elements of one set onto those of another. In the proper language, a function always maps one set—its domain—onto another set—its range. For example, the functions f, defined on R by $f(x) = x^2$, maps every real number onto its square; the function g, defined on the subset of all positive real numbers by $g(x) = \ln x$, maps each positive real number onto its natural logarithm. While pure mathematics deals with complete abstractions, most of elementary mathematics is concerned with the properties of certain subsets of real numbers and their mappings. Angles, important as they are in geometry, do not have any really basic importance in general mathematics—no more important, say, than the sides of a triangle—and so it seems a little less than appropriate to assign them the prominent place that we did in Chapter 6. In that chapter, we recall that each of the trigonometric functions has for its domain a certain set of angles. A consequence of this is that special methods must be used in the study and applications of these functions, methods which are quite alien to a study of the other elementary functions of mathematics—the polynomial, exponential, and logarithmic functions. It is much more satisfying to the mathematician—and it turns out to be much more useful—to redefine the trigonometric functions so that their domains, as well as their ranges, are subsets of *real numbers*. In so doing, we remove many of the artificial features of the original functions, and we may then subject them to precisely the same kind of treatment as the other elementary functions which we have mentioned. The collection of elementary functions then becomes more unified and—as we indicated above—also more useful. We now proceed to the definitions of these new

154

functions, which are called *circular* because of their close association with circles.

An angle may be measured in degrees, radians, or any other angular unit, but it is trite to remark that the angle remains the same and in no way depends on the unit used to measure it! Thus the measure of angle A may be x degrees and θ radians, where $\theta = \pi x/180$, so we can write:

$$A = x° = \theta^r.$$

The *circular* functions have the same names (sine, cosine, tangent, cosecant, secant, cotangent) as the trigonometric functions, and *the value of any one of them at a real number θ is defined to be the same as the associated trigonometric function of θ radians*. Thus, if θ is any real number, it is a matter of **Definition** that:

$$\sin \theta = \sin \theta^r, \qquad \csc \theta = \csc \theta^r,$$
$$\cos \theta = \cos \theta^r, \qquad \sec \theta = \sec \theta^r,$$
$$\tan \theta = \tan \theta^r, \qquad \cot \theta = \cot \theta^r,$$

provided that the right hand members of these equations have been defined. If a right hand member has not been defined for a certain θ^r, the associated circular function for θ is also undefined. We note that the domains of these circular functions are sets of real numbers, so we have removed the objection discussed above in connection with trigonometric functions.

In fact, while we have defined the circular functions in terms of closely related trigonometric functions, it is quite easy to eliminate completely any mention of angles. To this end, in Figure 51 we have shown a unit circle (radius 1) with its center at the origin of a Cartesian coordinate system. Let us now imagine an endless flexible tape wrapped around the circle in a counterclockwise direction, with the 0 of the tape at the point $(1, 0)$ on the circle. At the same time we may imagine another similar tape wrapped around the circle in a clockwise direction. If we consider the numbers on the first tape to be positive (and 0), while the numbers on the second are negative (and 0), every real number is on one of the tapes. We now set up a correspondence whereby each real number t (on either tape) corresponds to the point beneath it on the unit circle. The point associated with t is called the *trigonometric point $P(t)$*. The correspondence $t \leftrightarrow P(t)$ is not one-to-one, for t is a measure of arc length, as discussed in §6.6, and many circular arcs will terminate at the same trigonometric point. For example, $(1, 0)$ will be the trigonometric point corresponding to $0, \pm 2\pi, \pm 4\pi, \ldots$, while $(0, 1)$ is the trigonometric point corresponding to $\pi/2, 5\pi/2, -3\pi/2, \ldots$. In fact, every point on the unit circle will be the trigonometric point of infinitely many real numbers, each being the measure of length of an arc which terminates at the point. In Figure 51, we have labeled some of these trigonometric points $P(t)$, where $0 \leq t \leq 2\pi$.

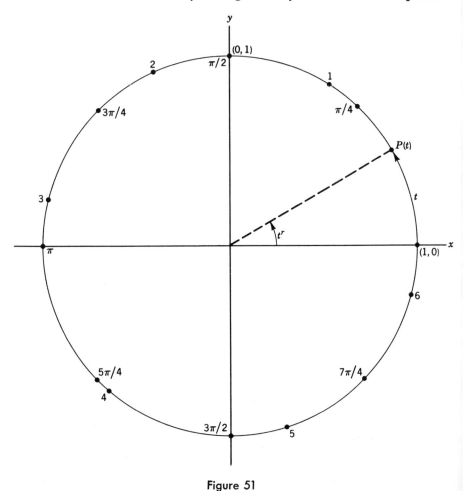

Figure 51

We now make the following equivalent definitions of the circular functions, with $P(t) = (x, y)$ the trigonometric point of the real number t:

$$\sin t = y, \qquad \csc t = \frac{1}{y},$$

$$\cos t = x, \qquad \sec t = \frac{1}{x},$$

$$\tan t = \frac{y}{x}, \qquad \cot t = \frac{x}{y}.$$

These definitions are quite independent of any discussion of angles, but they may be seen to be equivalent to the definitions we gave earlier in this section. For if t is a real number associated with the trigonometric point $P(t)$, t measures the length of a circular arc from $(1, 0)$ to $P(t)$, and *so gives the radian measure of the central angle subtended by the arc.* That is, the central angle subtended by an arc of length t on the unit circle is t radians. Hence,

$$\sin t = y = y/1 = \sin t^r,$$
$$\cos t = x = x/1 = \cos t^r,$$
$$\tan t = y/x = \tan t^r, \text{ etc.,}$$

as before, It is to be understood, of course, that if more than one complete circumference is contained in t, the same number of multiples of 2π is also contained in the radian measure of the subtended central angle. In this connection, it is necessary to recall that the circumference of the unit circle is 2π units in length.

EXAMPLE.   Find the trigonometric point designated as (a) $P(2\pi/3)$; (b) $P(-9\pi/4)$.

SOLUTION
(a) Since $\pi^r = 180°$, $2\pi/3^r = 120°$. Hence, if $P(2\pi/3) = (x, y)$, $x = \cos 120° = -\cos 60° = -\frac{1}{2}$, and $y = \sin 120° = \sin 60° = \sqrt{3}/2$. The desired point is then $(-\frac{1}{2}, \sqrt{3}/2)$.

(b) Since $(-9\pi/4)^r = [-(\frac{9}{4})180]° = -405°, P(-9\pi/4) = (x, y)$, where $x = \cos(-405°)$ and $y = \sin(-405°)$. But $\cos(-405°) = \cos(-45°) = \sqrt{2}/2$, and $\sin(-405°) = \sin(-45°) = -\sqrt{2}/2$, so that $P(-9\pi/4) = (\sqrt{2}/2, -\sqrt{2}/2)$.

Both parts of this Example are illustrated in Figure 52.

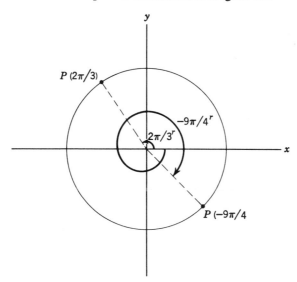

Figure 52

The trigonometric point associated with any given real number t can be found approximately from Table 2, by using the fact that t is also the radian measure of the associated central angle. The actual computation of circular functional values without the use of Table 2 is not simple, for there is no elementary formula which connects the length of a circular arc with the length of its subtended chord. However, in more advanced courses, it is possible to use infinite series to express these functional values. For example, it is well known that

$$\sin \theta = \theta - \frac{\theta^3}{3!} + \frac{\theta^5}{5!} - \cdots$$

$$\cos \theta = 1 - \frac{\theta^2}{2!} + \frac{\theta^4}{4!} - \cdots$$

for any real number θ. These series "converge" and represent the given functional value, in the sense that as more and more terms are included, the closer is the approximation to $\sin \theta$ or $\cos \theta$, respectively.

PROBLEMS

1. Determine the exact trigonometric point associated with each of the following numbers: (a) $4\pi/3$; (b) $3\pi/4$; (c) $5\pi/6$; (d) $7\pi/6$.
2. Determine the exact trigonometric point associated with each of the following numbers: (a) $-\pi/6$; (b) $-5\pi/4$; (c) $-7\pi/6$; (d) $-7\pi/4$.
3. Use Table 2 to find approximately the trigonometric point associated with each of the following numbers: (a) 2; (b) -3; (c) 6; (d) -6; (e) 1.
4. Use Table 2 to find the approximate trigonometric point associated with each of the following numbers: (a) 2.5; (b) -5.2; (c) 8.4; (d) 12.5.
5. Noting that the radius of the circle in Figure 51 is two inches (i.e., two inches was chosen as the unit), use a straight ruler to determine the approximate value of each of the following: (a) $\sin 2$; (b) $\cos 2$; (c) $\sin 3$; (d) $\cos 3$; (e) $\sin 5$; (f) $\cos 5$.
6. Use the result of Problem 5 to compute approximations for: (a) $\tan 2$; (b) $\tan 3$ (c) $\cot 5$.
7. Use Figure 51 to compute approximations for $\sin 1$, $\cos 1$, and $\tan 1$. (See Problem 5.)
8. Find a real number t such that $\pi < t < 3\pi/2$ and: (a) $\sin t = -\frac{1}{3}$; (b) $\cos t = -\frac{1}{2}$; (c) $\tan t = \sqrt{3}$.
9. List the quadrant in which each of the following trigonometric points lies: (a) $P(30)$; (b) $P(-23)$; (c) $P(45)$; (d) $P(-50)$.
10. Determine the smallest nonnegative real number θ such that (a) $\sin \theta = 0$; (b) $\cos \theta = 1$; (c) $\sin \theta = -1$; (d) $\tan \theta = -1$; (e) $\sec \theta = -2$.
11. Describe the real number domains of the sine, cosine, and tangent functions.
12. Describe the real number domains of the cosecant, secant, and cotangent functions.

13. Use Table 2 to determine approximations for each of the following: (a) sin 2.5; (b) cos 3.6; (c) tan 5.3; (d) sin 8.4; (e) cos 7.3.

14. Use Table 2 to determine approximations for each of the following: (a) cos 8.3; (b) sin (−5.4); (c) tan 12.6; (d) sin 0.45; (e) cos 15.4.

15. A point is considered to move around a circle of radius six inches, at the rate of 12 rps. Determine the speed of the projective point on a diameter, t secs after the point crosses the diameter. (The projective point on a diameter is the point on the diameter which is nearest the given point.)

16. Determine the exact value of each of the following:
    (a) $\sin 2\pi/3 + 3 \cos \pi/4 + 2 \cos \pi$;
    (b) $\dfrac{\sin \pi/6 + \cos 3\pi/2 - 3 \sin 2\pi/3}{1 + \sin \pi/2 + \cos 2\pi}$;
    (c) $\sin \pi/3 \cos \pi/6 + \cos \pi/3 \sin \pi/6$.

17. One end of a six-foot connecting rod is fastened to a piston while the other end rotates around the rim of a wheel two feet in diameter. The wheel is rotating in a counterclockwise direction at the rate of 60 rpm. If the piston is farthest from the wheel at time $t = 0$, determine the distance from the center of the wheel to the point where the connecting rod meets the piston at time $t = T$.

18. Determine sin θ if: (a) $\tan \theta = \frac{2}{3}$ and $\pi < \theta < 3\pi/2$; (b) $\cos \theta = \frac{1}{2}$ and $3\pi/2 < \theta < 2\pi$; (c) $\cos \theta = \frac{3}{4}$ and $\tan \theta$ is negative.

19. If $\sin \theta = \sin x°$, where $|x|$ is as small as possible, express x in terms of π when θ is: (a) 1; (b) 2; (c) 2.5; (d) −1.5; (e) 4.

20. Use the directions of Problem 19 when θ is: (a) −3.5; (b) −2; (c) 6; (d) 10; (e) −5.5.

21. Determine the exact circular functions of $\pi/5$. [*Hint:* Find the point on a radius of the unit circle which divides it into the "Golden Section," i.e., the point t such that $1/t = t/(1 - t)$.]

7.2 Graphs of the Circular Functions

It is possible to construct a graph of a circular function, as for other functions, by making a graph of the "ordered pair" elements of the function. If T is any circular function, we then graph the pairs $(\theta, T(\theta))$, for all θ in the domain of T. We shall consider each circular function from this graphical point of view.

We first make the general observation that *all* circular functions are "periodic," according to the following definition.

Definition. A function f is *periodic* if there exists a real number $c > 0$, such that $f(x + c) = f(x)$, for every x in the domain of f. The *period* of f is the smallest c that satisfies this condition.

If we consider the unit circle, it is apparent that as θ increases indefinitely (in either a positive or negative direction), the trigonometric points $P(\theta)$

repeat after each "cycle" of $\theta = 2\pi$. Since the circular functions of θ are defined in terms of the coordinates of $P(\theta)$, it follows that $T(\theta + 2\pi) = T(\theta)$, for each θ in the domain of the circular function T. The circular functions are then all periodic with periods *not exceeding* 2π.

First let us consider the sine function in detail, recalling that $\sin \theta = y$, where $(x, y) = P(\theta)$. As θ varies from 0 to $\pi/2$, $\sin \theta$ increases from 0 to 1; as θ varies from $\pi/2$ to π, $\sin \theta$ decreases from 1 to 0; as θ varies from π to $3\pi/2$, $\sin \theta$ decreases from 0 to -1; and as θ varies from $3\pi/2$ to 2π, $\sin \theta$ increases from -1 to 0. It is apparent that from this value of $\theta(=2\pi)$, and not before, the sequence of sine values repeats, and so the sine function has a period of 2π. The graphical importance of the periodic nature of a function is that once one "cycle" of the function (i.e., the values associated with one period of the domain) has been graphed, the rest of the graph consists of duplications of this portion. The fact that $P(\theta)$ is on the unit circle implies that $\sin \theta = y \le 1$ and $\sin \theta = y \ge -1$. Hence the sine function is *bounded* and $-1 \le \sin \theta \le 1$ for every real number θ. The complete graph of the sine function is then confined between the horizontal lines one unit above and below the θ-axis as shown in Figure 53.

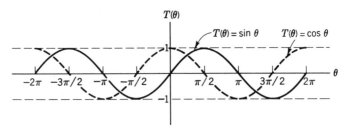

Figure 53

The analysis of the cosine function is very similar to that of the sine, with the x of $P(\theta)$ replacing the y of the preceding discussion. The cosine function is bounded by ± 1 and is periodic of period 2π, the argument being the same as for the sine function. Let us consider that $P(\theta)$ [$=(x, y)$] makes one circuit of the unit circle in a counterclockwise direction, starting at $(1, 0)$ where $\theta = 0$. Then $\cos \theta (=x)$ decreases from 1 to 0 as θ varies from 0 to $\pi/2$, decreases from 0 to -1 as θ varies from $\pi/2$ to π, increases from -1 to 0 as θ varies from π to $3\pi/2$, and increases from 0 to 1 as θ varies from $3\pi/2$ to 2π, at which point the cycle repeats. The graph is then very similar to that of the sine function and is in fact identical with the sine graph considered translated $\pi/2$ units to the left. The graph of a portion of the cosine function is also shown in Figure 53.

If we make use of the reciprocal relationship between the sine and cosecant and between the cosine and secant functions it is easy to obtain the graphs of the cosecant and secant functions from Figure 53. It is merely necessary to note that the reciprocal of a number of very small absolute value is very large, and becomes infinite ($+$ or $-$) as the number approaches 0. The graph of the cosecant (secant) function then has an "asymptote" at each point where the graph of the sine (cosine) function crosses the θ-axis, the function being undefined at such a point but unbounded in any interval containing it. The reciprocal relationship requires that $|\csc \theta| \geq 1$ and $|\sec| \theta \geq 1$, and the graphs of the sine and cosecant (cosine and secant) functions touch only at the points where the values of both are 1 or -1. These graphs are shown in Figure 54.

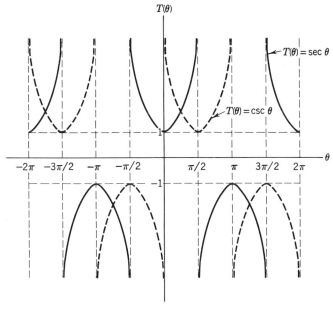

Figure 54

When we consider the tangent function, we must recall that $\tan \theta = y/x$, where $P(\theta) = (x, y)$. Furthermore, it is apparent that as x and y are allowed to vary arbitrarily between -1 and 1, the value of y/x will assume any desired positive or negative value for appropriate choices of x and y. The range of the tangent function is then the whole set R of real numbers. This function has an asymptote at each point θ where the abscissa x of $P(\theta)$ is 0. As $P(\theta)$ is considered to traverse the unit circle in a counterclockwise direction from $(1, 0)$, $\tan \theta$ increases without bound from 0 as θ varies from 0 to $\pi/2$, increases from unbounded negative values to 0 as θ varies from $\pi/2$ to π, and at this point the sequence of values begins to repeat. This means that the period of the tangent function is π. The cotangent function is reciprocal to the tangent function, and so either graph can easily be constructed from the other. The cotangent function, of course, becomes infinite and so is undefined at points where the tangent function has 0 values; and at points where the tangent function becomes infinite the cotangent function assumes 0 values. The graphs of these two functions are shown in Figure 55.

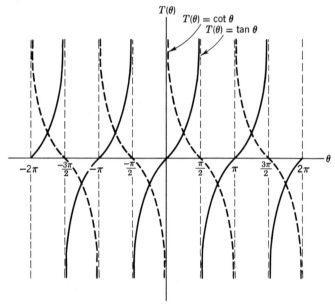

Figure 55

The graph of the sine function in Figure 53 plays an important role in physics and engineering, and in such a context it is often referred to as the "sine curve." It is of much more frequent occurrence than the others, and usually is involved in a graphical description of a periodic motion.

PROBLEMS

1. Use an appropriate graph to determine an approximation for each of the following: (a) sin 7; (b) cos (-2.5); (c) tan 1; (d) sin $6\pi/7$.
2. Use an appropriate graph to determine an approximation for each of the following: (a) sec 2; (b) csc 8; (c) tan (-1); (d) sec (-5); (e) cot 4.5.
3. Use an appropriate graph to deduce the truth of each of the following assertions: (a) sin $(-\theta) = -\sin \theta$; (b) cos $(-\theta) = \cos \theta$; (c) tan $(-\theta) = -\tan \theta$.
4. Use an appropriate graph to deduce the truth of each of the following assertions: (a) sin $(\pi + \theta) = -\sin \theta$; (b) cos $(\pi/2 - \theta) = \sin \theta$; (c) tan $(\pi - \theta) = -\tan \theta$.
5. A function is said to be *increasing* or *decreasing* on an interval, according as the functional values increase or decrease with steadily increasing elements from

the interval. State whether the designated function is increasing, decreasing, or neither, on the given interval: (a) sine on $[0, \pi/2]$; (b) cosine on $[\pi/2, 3\pi/2]$; (c) tangent on $[\pi/4, 3\pi/4]$; (d) secant on $[0, \pi/4]$; (e) cotangent on $[\pi/4, 3\pi/4]$.

6. If $x_1 < x_2$, use a graph to illustrate that it is not necessarily the case that $\sin x_1 < \sin x_2$. Consider the cosine and tangent functions similarly.

7. A graph is *symmetric with respect to the x-axis* if the point $(x, -y)$ is on the graph whenever (x, y) is present. Decide which, if any, of the circular functions have this kind of symmetry.

8. A graph is *symmetric with respect to the y-axis* if the point $(-x, y)$ is on the graph whenever (x, y) is present. Decide which, if any, of the circular functions have this kind of symmetry.

9. A graph is *symmetric with respect to the origin* if the point $(-x, -y)$ is on the graph whenever (x, y) is present. Decide which, if any, of the circular functions have this kind of symmetry.

10. Construct a unit circle with center at the origin O of a Cartesian coordinate system, labeling as M the point $(1, 0)$. With $P(\theta)$ an arbitrary trigonometric point, draw the radius OP and extend it to cut the vertical line through M at A. Then prove each of the following assertions: (a) length of AM is $|\tan \theta|$; (b) $\tan \theta \geq \sin \theta$, for $0 < \theta < \pi/2$.

11. With reference to the diagram drawn in Problem 10, indicate why it is intuitively evident that $\theta < \tan \theta$, for $0 < \theta < \pi/2$.

12. Use Table 2 to decide the largest interval of real numbers θ in which θ is indistinguishable to 2 significant figures from: (a) $\sin \theta$; (b) $\tan \theta$.

7.3 Inverse Circular Functions

In §7.2 we have made use of three real variables, x, y, and θ, for the sake of clarity in our definitions of the circular functions. However, we now propose to abandon the third variable θ, except when we specifically wish to use it. Thus, for example, we shall speak of the sine function defined on R by $y = \sin x$, with x playing the role previously played by θ. Intuitively, we are now thinking of x as a variable which measures arc length on the unit circle, while $\cos x$ and $\sin x$ are the coordinates of the trigonometric point $P(x)$. In this way we obtain a symbolic unification of all the elementary functions, with x and y corresponding elements of the domain and range, respectively.

A glance at the graphs in the preceding section shows immediately that these functions are not one-to-one, for each functional value is repeated periodically. For example, $\sin \pi/2 = \sin 5\pi/2$ with $\pi/2 \neq 5\pi/2$, $\cos 0 = \cos 2\pi$ with $0 \neq 2\pi$, $\tan \pi/4 = \tan 5\pi/4$ with $\pi/4 \neq 5\pi/4$, etc. We have seen earlier, in §4.5, that a function must define a one-to-one mapping if an inverse exists for the function, and so the circular functions do not have inverses. However, *it is possible to restrict the domains of these functions so that inverse functions do exist for these restricted circular functions.* There is some variation in which intervals of the domain are selected for the restricted functions, but it is important that the restricted functions have the same ranges as the original functions.

First, let us consider the portion of the graph of the sine function, as shown in Figure 56. We must select a subdomain of the domain R of the sine function such that every real number in the interval $[-1, 1]$ occurs as $\sin x$ for exactly one x in the subdomain. A suitable choice for this subdomain is $[-\pi/2, \pi/2]$, as may be observed from Figure 56. Another suitable choice for subdomain would be $[-\pi, -\pi/2] \cup [\pi/2, \pi]$, while $[0, \pi]$ would not be suitable. (Why?) The subdomain $[-\pi/2, \pi/2]$ is the one which is usually chosen, and it is somewhat customary to refer to this restricted sine function as the Sine, or Cap-sine, function, it being distinguished from the ordinary sine function by the capital letter S. The solid curve in Figure 56 is then the complete graph of the Sine function, and this function, by

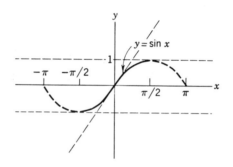

Figure 56

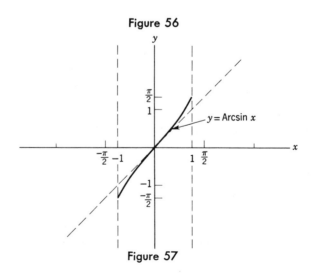

Figure 57

construction, defines a one-to-one mapping, and so has an inverse. This function, which is inverse to the Sine function, is known as the "Arcsine" function, and is more completely defined as follows, where we conveniently write Arcsin x (or sometimes $\text{Sin}^{-1} x$) for Arcsine x:

Definition. The *Arcsine* function is a function defined on $[-1, 1]$ so that Arcsin $x = y$, where $x = \sin y$ and $-\pi/2 \leq y \leq \pi/2$.

The graph of the Arcsine function is shown in Figure 57, and it may be observed that the graphs of the two functions shown in Figures 56 and 57 are the geometric reflection of each other in the diagonal line through quadrants I and III. This is, of course, a characteristic property of all inverse functions. The values of the Arcsine function—which lie in the interval $[-\pi/2, \pi/2]$—are sometimes known as the "principal values" of the sine function, but this terminology is no longer in common use.

In a similar manner, it is possible to suitably restrict the domains of the other circular functions to obtain the corresponding "Cap" functions, which define one-to-one mappings. These other "Cap" functions then have inverses, which make up the set of inverse circular functions. For reasons which are evident from their graphs, the domain of the Cosine function is chosen as $[0, \pi]$, while the domain of the Tangent function is taken as $[-\pi/2, \pi/2]$. The definitions of their inverse function are then evidently given by the following definitions, where we write Arccos x instead of Arccosine x, and Arctan x instead of Arctangent x:

Definitions

The *Arccosine* function is the function defined on $[-1, 1]$ so that Arccos $x = y$, where $x = \cos y$ and $0 \leq y \leq \pi$.

The *Arctangent* function is the function defined on R so that Arctan $x = y$, where $x = \tan y$ and $-\pi/2 \leq y \leq \pi/2$.

The graphs of the Cosine and Tangent functions, along with their inverses the Arccosine and Arctangent functions, are shown in Figures 58 and 59. It should be observed that the range of the Arcsine and Arctangent functions are both $[-\pi/2, \pi/2]$, while the range of Arccosine is $[0, \pi]$.

It is possible to define the other "Cap" functions, Cosecant, Secant, and Cotangent, along with their inverses, but there is no general agreement as to what domains to use for these "Cap" functions, or equivalently, what the best ranges are for the inverse functions. Certain choices possess some advantages, but all advantages are not possessed by any one choice. Inasmuch as an expression involving one of these inverse functions can usually be replaced by an equivalent expression containing one of the inverse functions previously discussed, we shall include no further discussion of

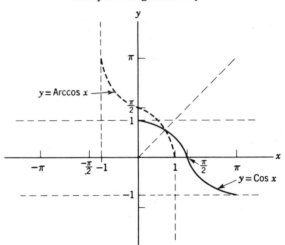

Figure 58

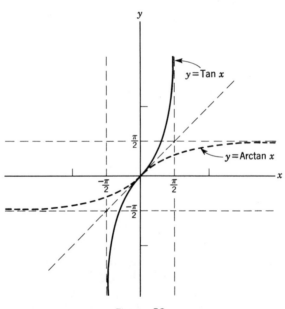

Figure 59

the Arccosecant, Arcsecant, or Arccotangent functions. The student is strongly urged, if he ever encounters these particular inverse functions, to be sure of the ranges that are to be understood for them.

We wish to emphasize a final point in connection with the inverse circular functions. While the domains of the "Cap" circular functions and the ranges of their inverses *can* be sets of angles (for, notationally, we have not distinguished the trigonometric from the circular functions), usually they are not. This is particularly true in any problem involving mensuration. For example, in Figure 60 we have shown a portion of the graph of the function defined on R by $y = 1/(x^2 + 1)$. From a study of calculus, it is found that the measure of area of the indicated shaded region is Arctan b − Arctan a. This answer would be quite ridiculous if the Arctan values were to be considered angles!

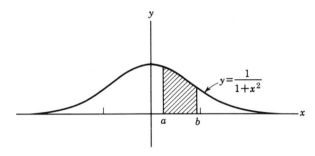

Figure 60

EXAMPLE 1.   Determine: (a) Arcsin $\sqrt{2}/2$; (b) Arccos $(-\frac{1}{2})$; (c) Arctan (-0.4171).

SOLUTION

(a) We know from earlier study that $\sin \pi/4 = \sqrt{2}/2$. Since $-\pi/2 < \pi/4 < \pi/2$, it follows that Arcsin $\sqrt{2}/2 = \pi/4$.

(b) It is known that $\cos 2\pi/3 = -\frac{1}{2}$. Hence, since $0 < 2\pi/3 < \pi$, we see that Arccos $(-\frac{1}{2}) = 2\pi/3$.

(c) From Table 2, we find that $\tan 0.4171 = 0.4431$, and so $\tan (-0.4171) = -0.4431$. Hence, since $-\pi/2 < -0.4431 < \pi/2$, it follows that Arctan $(-0.4431) = -0.4171$.

EXAMPLE 2.   Determine $\cos$ [Arcsin $(-\frac{2}{3})$].

SOLUTION.   We first note that Arcsin $(-\frac{2}{3})$ is a number x such that $\sin x = -\frac{2}{3}$, and $-\pi/2 < x < \pi/2$. Since the trigonometric point $P(x)$ is in the fourth quadrant, $\cos x = \sqrt{1 - \sin^2 x} = \sqrt{1 - \frac{4}{9}} = \sqrt{\frac{5}{9}} = \sqrt{5}/3$.

EXAMPLE 3.   Prove that Arcsin x + Arccos $x = \pi/2$, for any real x such that $-1 \leq x \leq 1$.

PROOF. It is known that Arcsin x is a number y such that $\sin y = x$, and $-\pi/2 \leq y \leq \pi/2$. If we let $z = \pi/2 - y$, it follows that $0 \leq z \leq \pi$, and $\cos z = \cos(\pi/2 - y) = \sin y = x$. Hence, $z = \text{Arccos } x$, and Arcsin x + Arccos $x = y + z = \pi/2$, as desired.

PROBLEMS

1. Which of the following are without meaning according to the definitions of this section: Sin 2; Cos 2; Sin $\pi/6$; Tan $2\pi/3$; Sin $(-\pi/3)$; Cos (-1.3); Tan (-1)?
2. Determine the unique value of each of the following: (a) Arcsin $\frac{1}{2}$; (b) Arccos $(-\frac{1}{2})$; (c) Arctan (-1); (d) Arcsin 0.
3. Determine the unique value of each of the following: (a) Arcsin $(-\sqrt{3}/2)$; (b) Arcsin $(-\sqrt{2}/2)$; (c) Arccos (-1); (d) Arctan 1.
4. Use Table 2 to determine the unique value of each of the following: (a) Arcsin (-0.1246); (b) Arctan 1.6843; (c) Arccos (-0.4369).
5. Use an example to illustrate that Arcsin (sin x) is not necessarily equal to x. On the other hand, why is sin (Arcsin x) always equal to x?
6. Determine each of the following: (a) cos (Arcsin $\sqrt{3}/2$); (b) Sin [Arccos $(-\frac{1}{2})$]; (c) Sec (Arcsin $\frac{1}{2}$); (d) cot (Arcsin $\sqrt{3}/2$).
7. Determine each of the following: (a) sin (Arccos $\frac{2}{3}$); (b) cos [Arctan $(-\frac{1}{3})$]; (c) Arctan [cot (-1)]; (d) csc [Arccos $(-\frac{3}{4})$].
8. Prove that 3 Arcsin $\sqrt{3}/2$ = Arccos 0 + $\pi/2$.
9. Prove that Arcsin $\frac{1}{2}$ + Arcsin (-1) + Arcsin $\sqrt{3}/2$ = 0.
10. Simplify Arccos $(-\frac{1}{2})$ + Tan $\pi/6$ − Tan $\pi/4$.
11. Prove that sin (Arccos x) = cos (Arcsin x).
12. Prove that Arcsin $(-x)$ = − Arcsin x.
13. Use Table 2 to obtain an approximate solution of each of the following equations for t: (a) Arcsin $\frac{3}{5}$ + Arccos $\frac{4}{5}$ = Arcsin t; (b) Arctan $(-\frac{1}{3})$ − Arctan $\frac{2}{3}$ = Arctan t.
14. Express a solution of each of the following equations for x: (a) y = Arcsin $2x$; (b) $y = \pi/2 - 2$ Arccos x; (c) $4y = \pi/6 - 2$ Arccos $(2x + 1)$.
15. Solve for real x: Arccos x + Arcsin $(1 - x)$ = 0.
16. Determine an algebraic form for cos [Arctan x], where x is any real number.

7.4 Special Graphing Methods

The subject matters of algebra, trigonometry, and geometry overlap to such an extent that at times it is impossible to know with which of these disciplines we are most intimately involved. A treatment of trigonometry from the viewpoint of circular functions is, of course, a part of the general analysis of functions, while the graphical aspects of function analysis certainly overlaps much of analytic geometry—except in viewpoint. In analysis, the graph of a function is merely a pictorial representation of a *mapping* of its domain onto its range; whereas in geometry the same graph is considered a *set of points* which usually make up a geometric "curve." In analysis we emphasize $x \rightarrow y = f(x)$ for the function f, while in geometry the emphasis is on the points (x, y) which comprise its graph. The functions of most common occurrence have for their domains the maximal subsets of real numbers for which the defining rules of the functions have meaning. The domain is often the set R or a closed interval in R. *In this section, we shall always assume that the domain of every function is "maximal" in the above sense.* If the defining rule of such a function is given by an equation—which in geometry is referred to as "the equation of the curve"—it is important to be able to graph the function or the curve. If unlimited time and space are available, it is possible to graph an arbitrarily large number of points, but more frequently it is of importance to be able to give a rough "sketch" of a graph, without the tedium of plotting more than a very few actual points. In this section, it is our aim to give a few hints which will be useful for these sketches, although our discussion will be far from complete.

The description of the circular and inverse circular functions concluded our definitions of what are known as the basic elementary functions of mathematics. However, while these functions are basic, the functions usually encountered in practice are not these but rather slight variations from or combinations of these basic functions. For example, the basic sine function may occur very seldom, whereas functions of the type $y = A \sin (ax + b)$ occur frequently. The basic exponential function may be rarely seen, but many functions defined by an equation of the form $y = Ae^{bx}$ are found in the descriptions of physical phenomena. In addition, a function defined as the sum of two more elementary functions—such as $y = 3 \sin 2x + 4x^2$—may occur in many applied problems. The hints which we give here for obtaining a quick sketch of these functions are classified into three categories: (1) effect of a multiplicative factor; (2) effect of an additive term; (3) sum of two functions. In the general discussion it will always be understood that the graph of an elementary function f is familiar. For convenience in writing, we shall refer to "the function $y = f(x)$" as an abbreviation for "the function defined by $y = f(x)$," with domain understood to be maximal, as explained above.

1. *Effect of a Multiplicative Factor.* There two cases to consider: $y = kf(x)$ and $y = f(kx)$, for a real number k. In the first case, it is apparent that the effect of k is to multiply each y—the ordinate—by k, for any given x. In the second case, if we note that kx plays the role in the transformed equation previously played by x, each "new" x must be $1/k$ times the original x. Hence, each abscissa of the "new" curve must be $1/k$ times as

large as it was originally. These considerations give us the following rules:

 (a) The graph of $y = kf(x)$ can be constructed from the graph of $y = f(x)$ by *multiplying* all the ordinates of the latter graph by k.

 (b) The graph of $y = f(kx)$ can be constructed from the graph of $y = f(x)$ by *dividing* all the abscissas of the latter graph by k.

EXAMPLE 1. Sketch graphs of $y = 2 \sin x$ and $y = e^{2x}$.

SOLUTION. By (a) above, the graph of $y = 2 \sin x$ may be obtained from the graph of $y = \sin x$ by multiplying all the ordinates of the latter graph by 2. The result is shown in Figure 61. By (b) above, the graph of $y = e^{2x}$ may be obtained from the graph of $y = e^x$ by dividing all the abscissas of the latter graph by 2. This result is shown in Figure 62.

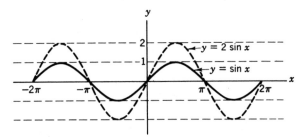

Figure 61

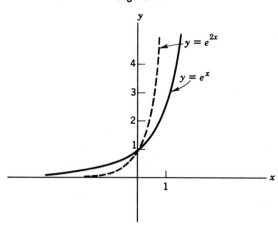

Figure 62

2. *Effect of an Additive Term.* There are two cases to consider: $y = f(x) + k$ and $y = f(x + k)$, for a real number k. In the first case, it is immediate that each y—an ordinate—has simply been increased by k,

for any given x. In the second case, we note that $x + k$ plays the role in the transformed equation previously played by x, and so the "new" x—an abscissa—must have been decreased by k. These considerations give us the following rules:

    (a) The graph of $y = f(x) + k$ can be constructed from the graph of $y = f(x)$ by *increasing* all ordinates of the latter graph by k, i.e., by translating the graph of $y = f(x)$ in a vertical direction k units.

    (b) The graph of $y = f(x + k)$ can be constructed from the graph of $y = f(x)$ by *decreasing* all abscissas of the latter graph by k, i.e., by translating the graph of $y = f(x)$ a distance of $-k$ units in a horizontal direction.

EXAMPLE 2.   Sketch graphs of $y = \ln x + 2$ and $y = \sin (x - \pi/2)$.

    SOLUTION.   By (a) above, the graph of $y = \ln x + 2$ may be obtained from the graph of $y = \ln x$ by increasing each ordinate of the latter graph by 2. The resulting graph is shown in Figure 63. By (b) above, the graph of $y = \sin (x - \pi/2)$ can be obtained from the graph of $y = \sin x$ by translating the latter graph $\pi/2$ units to the right. [Note that *decreasing* by $-\pi/2$ is equivalent to *increasing* by $\pi/2$.] The resulting graph is shown in Figure 64.

    3. *Sum of Two Functions.*   If we wish to graph the function f defined by $f = f_1 + f_2$, it is often convenient to do so by the method of "composition of ordinates." By this method, we graph the two basic functions f_1 and f_2 with the same coordinate axes and then add algebraically their respective ordinates. We illustrate this with an example.

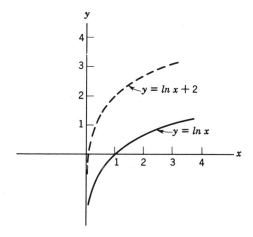

Figure 63

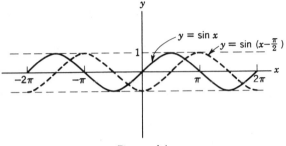

Figure 64

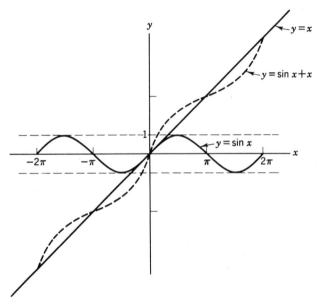

Figure 65

EXAMPLE 3.   Sketch the graph of $y = \sin x + x$.

SOLUTION.   We first graph the functions defined by $y = \sin x$ and $y = x$, respectively, these being the basic sine and linear functions. On adding the ordinates of the graphs of the basic functions, we obtain the desired graph as shown in Figure 65.

Of course, it may happen that a given defining function equation is more complicated than the result of applying any one of the above operations to a basic function. However, it will usually be possible to break the complex operation into a sequence of simple operations of the types discussed above. For example, the graph of $y = 2 \sin (3x + \pi/4)$ is the result of three operations performed *in sequence* on the graph of $y = \sin x$:

multiply ordinates by 2; decrease abscissas by $\pi/4$; divide abscissas by 3.

If the underlying *basic* graph is not desired in the final display, it is usually easier to translate a coordinate axis than to translate a curve. For we observe that *a translation of a curve k units to the left,* say, is equivalent to *a translation of the y-axis k units to the right.* A similar remark applies to vertical translations.

As a final illustration of the graphical methods of this section, let us consider the graph of the function $y = A \sin(ax + b)$. We first write this equation in the form $y = A \sin[a(x + b/a)]$ and note that the desired graph may be obtained from the graph of $y = \sin x$ by performing the following operations in sequence: (1) multiply ordinates by A; (2) divide abscissas by a; (3) translate the y-axis (curve) b/a units to the right (left). If we recall that the period of the basic sine curve is 2π, it is immediate that the *period* of $y = A \sin(ax + b)$ is $2\pi/a$, since all abscissas have been divided by a. The term b/a is referred to as the *phase shift* and is negative if the graph of $y = \sin ax$ must be shifted to the left to coincide with the graph of $y = \sin(ax + b)$, and is positive if this shift is to the right. If M and m are, respectively, the largest and smallest ordinates of a periodic function, the number $(M - m)/2$ is sometimes called the *amplitude* of the function. The numbers M and m are the "bounds" of the periodic function, as discussed in Chapter 4. The amplitude of the function $y = A \sin(ax + b)$ is then seen to be A, while the amplitude of the basic sine function is 1.

PROBLEMS

For these problems, and in accordance with the understanding throughout this section, the domain of each function is to be considered maximal. For the graphs, of course, it will be appropriate to consider a subinterval of this maximal domain, in each case.

In Problems 1 through 8, sketch the function defined by the given equation.

1. (a) $y = \sin 3x$; (b) $y = 2 \cos x$; (c) $y = \tan x/2$; (d) $y = \tan 2x$; (e) $y = \text{Arcsin } 2x$; (f) $y = \text{Arccos } 2x$.
2. (a) $y = e^{3x}$; (b) $y = 3e^x$; (c) $y = \ln 2x$; (d) $y = 4 \ln x$.
3. (a) $y = 3x^2$; (b) $y = x^2/4$; (c) $y = x^2 + 5$; (d) $y = (2x)^2$; (e) $y = \text{Arcsin } x - 3$; (f) $y = \text{Arctan } x + 2$.
4. (a) $y = \cos x + 2x$; (b) $y = 2x + e^x$; (c) $y = 3x + \ln x$; (d) $y = 3x + \text{Arcsin } x$; (e) $y = \text{Arctan } x + 2x^2$.
5. (a) $y = \sin x - 2x$; (b) $y = e^x - \sin x$; (c) $y = 2x^2 - 3x$; (d) $y = \sin x - \text{Arcsin } x$.
6. (a) $y = - \sin x$; (b) $y = - \cos x$; (c) $y = - x^2$; (d) $y = - \ln x$; (e) $y = - \text{Arccos } x$.
7. (a) $y = 2 \sin 2x$; (b) $y = 3e^{x/2} + 3$; (c) $y = 2 \cos 4x$.
8. (a) $y = 2x^2 + 3x + 1$; (b) $y = e^{2x} + 4x + 1$; (c) $y = x + 2 + \cos 2x$.
9. Determine the amplitude, period, and phase shift for the function defined as

follows: (a) $y = 3 \sin (2x - 3)$; (b) $y = (\frac{1}{4}) \cos (x + 2)$; (c) $y = 3 \sin (x/2 + \frac{3}{4})$; (d) $y = 2 \sin (\pi x + 2)$.

10. Determine the amplitude of the periodic function defined by: (a) $y = 2 \sin 3x + 4$; (b) $y = 8 + 5 \cos 2x$; (c) $y = |3 \sin (\pi x + 2)|$.

11. Decide which of the following functions defined below are periodic, and state the period for each such case: (a) $y = x \cos x$; (b) $y = 2 \sin x + \cos x$; (c) $y = x^2 - \sin x$; (d) $y = e^{\sin 2x}$; (e) $y = 2$.

12. If f and g are periodic functions with periods c_1 and c_2, respectively, decide which of the functions defined below are periodic, and give the period for each such case: (a) $F(x) = f(x) \cdot g(x)$; (b) $F(x) = g(x^3)$; (c) $F(x) = [f(x)]^2$; (d) $F(x) = f[g(x)]$; (e) $F(x) = g[f(x)]$; (f) $F(x) = f(\sin x)$.

13. A periodic function is defined by the equation $y = e^{\cos x}$. Determine the amplitude and period of the function, and sketch two cycles of its graph.

14. Determine the amplitude and period of the periodic function defined by $y = 2 \sin^2 3\pi x$.

15. The graph of $y = \sin 3x + 5$ may be obtained from the graph of $y = \sin x$ by: (a) multiplying the abscissas of the latter curve by α, followed by a translation of the resulting curve β units in the positive horizontal direction; (b) translating the latter curve β' units in the positive horizontal direction, followed by a multiplication of the abscissas of the resulting curve by α'. Compare the numbers α and β in (a) with α' and β' in (b).

7.5 The Addition Formulas

After a brief interlude devoted to the graphing of functions, we return to the subject matter of analytic trigonometry. The eight basic identities of §6.4 give rise to similar identities for circular functions, and we first restate the originals in the more general environment of this chapter. In each case, θ is a real number in the domain of the function involved.

$$(1) \qquad \csc \theta = \frac{1}{\sin \theta},$$

$$(2) \qquad \sec \theta = \frac{1}{\cos \theta},$$

$$(3) \qquad \cot \theta = \frac{1}{\tan \theta},$$

$$(4) \qquad \tan \theta = \frac{\sin \theta}{\cos \theta},$$

$$(5) \qquad \cot \theta = \frac{\cos \theta}{\sin \theta},$$

$$(6) \qquad \sin^2 \theta + \cos^2 \theta = 1,$$

$$(7) \qquad 1 + \tan^2 \theta = \sec^2 \theta,$$

$$(8) \qquad 1 + \cot^2 \theta = \csc^2 \theta.$$

It is often of interest and importance to know, for a given function f, how $f(x + y)$ is related to $f(x)$ and $f(y)$, for arbitrary numbers x, y in the domain of f. Any formula which connects these quantities in some way may be called an "addition formula." In the case of a linear function f, defined so that $f(x) = mx$, for a real number m, the answer is simple: because $f(x + y) = m(x + y) = mx + my = f(x) + f(y)$. For an exponential function g, defined by $g(x) = a^x$, it is immediate that $g(x + y) = a^{x+y} = a^x \cdot a^y = g(x) \cdot g(y)$, for arbitrary x, y in the domain of g. There is no simple formula of this type for a logarithmic function, since $\log_a (x + y)$ is not related in a simple way to $\log_a x$ and $\log_a y$. In this section, we shall consider the question of the existence of addition formulas for the circular functions.

To this end, let $P(\theta_1)$, $P(\theta_2)$, and $P(\theta_1 - \theta_2)$ be the three trigonometric points associated on the unit circle of Figure 66 with the real numbers θ_1, θ_2, and $\theta_1 - \theta_2$. Irrespective of which real numbers θ_1 and θ_2 are selected, the distance along the circle from $P(\theta_2)$ to $P(\theta_1)$ is equal to the distance along the circle from $P(0)$ or $(1, 0)$ to $P(\theta_1 - \theta_2)$, where we assume distance is measured in a counterclockwise direction and $\theta_1 > \theta_2$. (If $\theta_1 < \theta_2$ we have merely to interchange the numbers to have our assumed inequality, so there is no loss in generality.) Moreover, it follows from elementary geometry that the chords subtended by these arcs are also of equal lengths. It follows from the definitions of the sine and cosine functions, that the coordinates of $P(\theta_1)$, $P(\theta_2)$, and $P(\theta_1 - \theta_2)$ are $(\cos \theta_1, \sin \theta_1)$, $(\cos \theta_2, \sin \theta_2)$, and $(\cos \overline{\theta_1 - \theta_2}, \sin \overline{\theta_1 - \theta_2})$, respectively. Hence, by the distance formula of §6.5,

$$(\cos \overline{\theta_1 - \theta_2} - 1)^2 + (\sin \overline{\theta_1 - \theta_2} - 0)^2 = (\cos \theta_2 - \cos \theta_1)^2 + (\sin \theta_2 - \sin \theta_1)^2,$$

and so

$$\cos^2 (\theta_1 - \theta_2) - 2 \cos (\theta_1 - \theta_2) + 1 + \sin^2 (\theta_1 - \theta_2) =$$
$$\cos^2 \theta_2 - 2 \cos \theta_1 \cos \theta_2 + \cos^2 \theta_1 + \sin^2 \theta_2 - 2 \sin \theta_1 \sin \theta_2 + \sin^2 \theta_1.$$

An application of Identity (6) to this equality now gives:

$$2 - 2 \cos (\theta_1 - \theta_2) = 2 - 2 \cos \theta_1 \cos \theta_2 - 2 \sin \theta_1 \sin \theta_2,$$

so that,

$$\cos (\theta_1 - \theta_2) = \cos \theta_1 \cos \theta_2 + \sin \theta_1 \sin \theta_2.$$

We rewrite this as our first *addition formula*, listing it serially with the previous identities.

(9) $$\cos (\theta_1 - \theta_2) = \cos \theta_1 \cos \theta_2 + \sin \theta_1 \sin \theta_2.$$

We emphasize that the validity of the proof of (9) in no way depends on either the size or algebraic sign of θ_1 or θ_2.

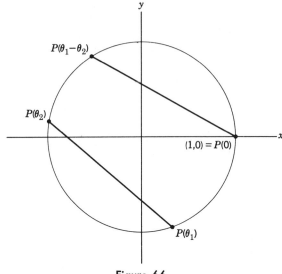

Figure 66

EXAMPLE 1.   Determine $\cos \pi/12$ from known functional values.

SOLUTION

$$\cos \frac{\pi}{12} = \cos \left(\frac{\pi}{4} - \frac{\pi}{6} \right) = \cos \frac{\pi}{4} \cos \frac{\pi}{6} + \sin \frac{\pi}{4} \sin \frac{\pi}{6}$$

$$= \left(\frac{\sqrt{2}}{2} \right) \left(\frac{\sqrt{3}}{2} \right) + \left(\frac{\sqrt{2}}{2} \right) \left(\frac{1}{2} \right) = \left(\frac{\sqrt{6} + \sqrt{2}}{4} \right).$$

It is a geometrically evident fact, that the trigonometric points $P(\theta)$ and $P(-\theta)$ have coordinates which differ at the most in algebraic sign. In fact, these points are always symmetrically located with respect to the x-axis, so that their abscissas (x) agree, while their ordinates (y) are either 0 or of opposite signs. It follows from the definitions of the circular functions that the following identities are valid:

(10) $\sin(-\theta) = -\sin \theta,$

(11) $\cos(-\theta) = \cos \theta,$

(12) $\tan(-\theta) = -\tan \theta.$

These formulas can also be derived from the above addition formula (9), as we indicate in the problems.

We saw earlier that any trigonometric function of an acute angle is equal to the cofunction of its complement. In terms of circular functions, this implies that $\sin(\pi/2 - \theta) = \cos\theta$ and $\cos(\pi/2 - \theta) = \sin\theta$, for $0 \le \theta \le \pi/2$. Moreover, the addition formula (9) is valid for arbitrary real numbers θ_1 and θ_2. Hence, if $\theta_1 = \pi/2$ and $\theta_2 = \theta$, we obtain directly:

$$\cos\left(\frac{\pi}{2} - \theta\right) = \cos\frac{\pi}{2}\cos\theta + \sin\frac{\pi}{2}\sin\theta = \sin\theta.$$

In addition, by this result,

$$\sin\left(\frac{\pi}{2} - \theta\right) = \cos\left[\frac{\pi}{2} - \left(\frac{\pi}{2} - \theta\right)\right] = \cos\theta.$$

By the definition of the tangent function,

$$\tan\left(\frac{\pi}{2} - \theta\right) = \frac{\sin(\pi/2 - \theta)}{\cos(\pi/2 - \theta)} = \frac{\cos\theta}{\sin\theta} = \cot\theta.$$

A similar result can be established for each of the other circular functions, which proves the following generalization of the result stated above for acute angles:

(13)   If T is any circular function, $T(\pi/2 - \theta) = \text{co-}T(\theta)$, for any real number θ in the domain of the cofunction co-T of T.

Since (9) is valid whether θ_1 and θ_2 are positive or negative, we now are able to obtain the following results with the help of (13).

(14) $\cos(\theta_1 + \theta_2) = \cos[\theta_1 - (-\theta_2)] = \cos\theta_1\cos(-\theta_2) + \sin\theta_1\sin(-\theta_2)$
$\qquad = \cos\theta_1\cos\theta_2 - \sin\theta_1\sin\theta_2.$

(15) $\sin(\theta_1 + \theta_2) = \cos\left[\frac{\pi}{2} - (\theta_1 + \theta_2)\right] = \cos\left[\left(\frac{\pi}{2} - \theta_1\right) - \theta_2\right]$

$\qquad\qquad = \cos\left(\frac{\pi}{2} - \theta_1\right)\cos\theta_2 + \sin\left(\frac{\pi}{2} - \theta_1\right)\sin\theta_2$

$\qquad\qquad = \sin\theta_1\cos\theta_2 + \cos\theta_1\sin\theta_2.$

(16) $\sin(\theta_1 - \theta_2) = \sin[\theta_1 + (-\theta_2)] = \sin\theta_1\cos(-\theta_2) + \cos\theta_1\sin(-\theta_2)$
$\qquad\qquad = \sin\theta_1\cos\theta_2 - \cos\theta_1\sin\theta_2.$

There are two more addition formulas which can be obtained from the preceding, by methods of elementary algebra, and which we now list.

(17) $$\tan(\theta_1 + \theta_2) = \frac{\tan\theta_1 + \tan\theta_2}{1 - \tan\theta_1\tan\theta_2}.$$

(18) $$\tan(\theta_1 - \theta_2) = \frac{\tan\theta_1 - \tan\theta_2}{1 + \tan\theta_1\tan\theta_2}.$$

There are many other formulas of this type which could be included in our list, but this will suffice. A working knowledge of trigonometry requires that the student be completely familiar with the above eighteen formulas.

EXAMPLE 2.　Determine $\sec 5\pi/12$ without the use of Table 2.

SOLUTION

$$\cos \frac{5\pi}{12} = \cos \left(\frac{\pi}{4} + \frac{\pi}{6}\right) = \cos \frac{\pi}{4} \cos \frac{\pi}{6} - \sin \frac{\pi}{4} \sin \frac{\pi}{6}$$

$$= \left(\frac{\sqrt{2}}{2}\right)\left(\frac{\sqrt{3}}{2}\right) - \left(\frac{\sqrt{2}}{2}\right)\left(\frac{1}{2}\right) = \frac{(\sqrt{6} - \sqrt{2})}{4}.$$

Hence,　$\sec \dfrac{5\pi}{12} = \dfrac{4}{(\sqrt{6} - \sqrt{2})} = \dfrac{4(\sqrt{6} + \sqrt{2})}{(6 - 2)} = \sqrt{6} + \sqrt{2}.$

PROBLEMS

1. Use (9) to prove that $\cos (-\theta) = \cos \theta$.
2. Use (9) and $\sin \theta = \cos (\pi/2 - \theta)$ to prove that $\sin (-\theta) = -\sin \theta$.
3. Derive the formulas for $\tan (\theta_1 + \theta_2)$ and $\tan (\theta_1 - \theta_2)$ from the earlier addition formulas.
4. Establish the following identities:
   (a) $\sin (\theta_1 - \theta_2) \sin (\theta_1 + \theta_2) = \sin^2 \theta_1 - \sin^2 \theta_2$;
   (b) $\cos (\theta_1 - \theta_2) \cos (\theta_1 + \theta_2) = \cos^2 \theta_1 - \sin^2 \theta_2$.
5. Establish the following identities:
   (a) $\tan (\theta + \pi/4) - \tan (\theta - 3\pi/4) = 0$;
   (b) $\dfrac{1 + \tan \theta}{1 - \tan \theta} = \tan (\pi/4 + \theta)$.
6. Prove that:
   (a) $\cos (\theta + \pi/6) - \cos (\theta - \pi/6) = -\sin \theta$;
   (b) $\sin (\theta + \pi/3) - \cos (\theta + \pi/6) = \sin \theta$.
   Use an appropriate addition formula to establish each of the identities in Problems 7 through 9.
7. (a) $\sin (\pi + \theta) = -\sin \theta$;　　　　(b) $\cos (\pi - \theta) = -\cos \theta$;
   (c) $\tan (\theta - \pi) = \tan \theta$;　　　　(d) $\tan (\theta + \pi) = \tan \theta$.
8. (a) $\sin (\pi/2 + \theta) = \cos \theta$;　　　　(b) $\cos (\pi/2 + \theta) = -\sin \theta$;
   (c) $\tan (\pi/2 + \theta) = -\cot \theta$.
9. (a) $\sec (\pi/2 + \theta) = -\csc \theta$;　　　　(b) $\csc (\pi/2 + \theta) = -\sec \theta$;
   (c) $\cot (\theta - 3\pi/2) = -\tan \theta$.
10. Obtain the circular functions of 0 from the addition formulas.
11. Use (15) and (16) to prove that:
    $$\sin \theta_1 \cos \theta_2 = [\sin (\theta_1 - \theta_2) + \sin (\theta_1 + \theta_2)]/2.$$
12. Use (9) and (14) to prove that:
    (a) $\sin \theta_1 \sin \theta_2 = -[\cos (\theta_1 + \theta_2) - \cos (\theta_1 - \theta_2)]/2$;
    (b) $\cos \theta_1 \cos \theta_2 = [\cos (\theta_1 + \theta_2) + \cos (\theta_1 - \theta_2)]/2$.
13. Put $\theta_1 + \theta_2 = \alpha$ and $\theta_1 - \theta_2 = \beta$ in the results of Problems 11 or 12 to establish the following identities:

(a) $\sin \alpha + \sin \beta = 2 \sin \dfrac{(\alpha + \beta)}{2} \cos \dfrac{(\alpha - \beta)}{2}$;

(b) $\sin \alpha - \sin \beta = 2 \cos \dfrac{(\alpha + \beta)}{2} \sin \dfrac{(\alpha - \beta)}{2}$.

14. Use the directions of Problem 13 to establish the following identities:

(a) $\cos \alpha + \cos \beta = 2 \cos \dfrac{(\alpha + \beta)}{2} \cos \dfrac{(\alpha - \beta)}{2}$;

(b) $\cos \alpha - \cos \beta = - 2 \sin \dfrac{(\alpha + \beta)}{2} \sin \dfrac{(\alpha - \beta)}{2}$.

15. Express as a circular function of θ: (a) $\sin (\pi/3 + \theta)$; (b) $\cos (\pi/6 - \theta)$; (c) $\tan (\theta - \pi/3)$; (d) $\sec (\theta - 3\pi/4)$; (e) $\csc (2\pi/3 + \theta)$.

16. Use an addition formula and known functional values of θ with $0 \leq \theta \leq \pi/2$, to evaluate each of the following: (a) $\cos 2\pi/3$; (b) $\csc \pi/12$; (c) $\tan \pi/12$; (d) $\sec 7\pi/12$; (e) $\cos 5\pi/12$; (f) $\cot \pi/12$.

17. If $P(\theta_1)$ and $P(\theta_2)$ are trigonometric points in the first and third quadrants, respectively, determine $\sin (\theta_1 + \theta_2)$ and $\cos (\theta_1 + \theta_2)$ where: (a) $\sin \theta_1 = \frac{1}{3}$ and $\cos \theta_2 = -\frac{2}{3}$; (b) $\cos \theta_1 = \frac{2}{3}$ and $\sin \theta_2 = -\frac{1}{2}$.

18. If $P(\theta_1)$ and $P(\theta_2)$ are trigonometric points in the second and third quadrants, respectively, determine $\sin (\theta_1 - \theta_2)$ and $\cos (\theta_1 - \theta_2)$ where: (a) $\cos \theta_1 = -\frac{4}{5}$ and $\csc \theta_2 = -2$; (b) $\sec \theta_1 = -\frac{3}{2}$ and $\tan \theta_2 = 1$.

19. Use the results of Problems 13 and 14 to express each of the following as a product: (a) $\sin \pi/3 + \sin 2\pi/3$; (b) $\cos \pi/6 - \cos \pi/3$; (c) $\sin 3\pi/4 - \sin \pi/3$; (d) $\cos 2\pi/3 + \cos \pi/3$.

20. Use the results of Problems 11 and 12 to express each of the following products as a sum: (a) $2 \sin \pi/3 \cos \pi/4$; (b) $2 \cos 2\pi/3 \cos \pi/6$; (c) $\cos \pi/6 \sin \pi/8$; (d) $\sin 5\pi/6 \sin 2\pi/3$.

21. Prove that $\operatorname{Arcsin} s + \operatorname{Arcsin} t \neq \operatorname{Arcsin} (s + t)$.

Establish the identities in Problems 22–25.

22. $2 \operatorname{Arctan} \frac{1}{3} + \operatorname{Arctan} \frac{1}{7} = \pi/4$.

23. $\operatorname{Arctan} \frac{1}{2} + \operatorname{Arctan} \frac{1}{3} = \pi/4$.

24. $\operatorname{Arctan} 2 + \operatorname{Arctan} 3 = 3\pi/4$.

25. $\tan (\operatorname{Arctan} a - \operatorname{Arctan} b) = (a - b)/(1 + ab)$.

26. Derive an expression for $\tan (\operatorname{Arctan} a + \operatorname{Arctan} b)$, and compare with the result of Problem 25.

27. Put each of the following equations in an equivalent form $y = A \sin (ax + b)$, with $A > 0$: (a) $y = -2 \sin (x + \pi)$; (b) $y = -3 \sin (2x - 3)$; (c) $y = 3 \cos (3x - \pi/2)$; (d) $y = - 4 \cos 2x$.

28. Put the following equations in an equivalent form $y = A \cos (ax + b)$, with $A > 0$: (a) $y = -2 \cos (3\pi + 2x)$; (b) $y = 5 \sin (x - \pi/2)$; (c) $y = -2 \cos (x + 1)$; (d) $y = - \cos \pi x$.

29. Prove that it is always possible to express $A \sin ax + B \cos ax$ in the form $C \sin (ax + b)$, with $C > 0$.

30. Prove that it is always possible to express $A \sin ax + B \cos ax$ in the form $C \cos (ax + b)$, with $C > 0$.

7.6   Other Formulas

We can obtain a number of useful formulas by specializing some of those in §7.5. If we let $\theta_1 = \theta_2 = \theta$ in the addition formulas for $\sin(\theta_1 + \theta_2)$, $\cos(\theta_1 + \theta_2)$, and $\tan(\theta_1 + \theta_2)$, we obtain the following results:

$$\sin 2\theta = \sin \theta \cos \theta + \cos \theta \sin \theta,$$

or

(19) $$\sin 2\theta = 2 \sin \theta \cos \theta.$$

$$\cos 2\theta = \cos \theta \cos \theta - \sin \theta \sin \theta,$$

or

(20) $$\cos 2\theta = \cos^2 \theta - \sin^2 \theta.$$

$$\tan 2\theta = \frac{(\tan \theta + \tan \theta)}{(1 - \tan^2 \theta)},$$

or

(21) $$\tan 2\theta = \frac{2 \tan \theta}{1 - \tan^2 \theta}.$$

These three formulas, which we have listed serially with those of §7.5, are familiarly known as the "double angle" formulas of trigonometry, in view of the early association of trigonometry with angles. They relate the functions of twice a number (or angle) with functions of the number (or angle). For example, we noted earlier that $\sin \pi/3 \neq 2 \sin \pi/6$ (or $\sin 60°$ $\neq 2 \sin 30°$), and Formula (19) shows us that the correct relationship existing between $\sin \pi/3$ and $\sin \pi/6$ is $\sin \pi/3 = 2 \sin \pi/6 \cos \pi/6$. It is to be understood, of course, that every identity involving circular functions generates a similar formula involving trigonometric functions of angles. This remark applies to the formulas already derived, as well as those to be derived subsequently.

EXAMPLE 1.   Use the appropriate formula of this section to determine: (a) $\sin 2\pi/3$; (b) **sin** $122°36'$.

SOLUTION

(a) $\sin 2\pi/3 = 2 \sin \pi/3 \cos \pi/3 = 2(\sqrt{3}/2)(\frac{1}{2}) = \sqrt{3}/2$.
(b) **sin** $122°36' = $ **sin** $122.6° = 2 \sin 61.3° \cos 61.3°$
$\qquad\qquad = 2(0.8771)(0.4802) \doteq 0.8424$.

It is easy to transform (20) to obtain several useful formulas, known as the "half angle" formulas. In this we make use of Identity (6) of §7.5. Thus $\cos 2\theta = \cos^2\theta - \sin^2\theta = 1 - \sin^2\theta - \sin^2\theta = 1 - 2\sin^2\theta$, so that $2\sin^2\theta = 1 - \cos 2\theta$ and $\sin^2\theta = (1 - \cos 2\theta)/2$. If we replace θ by $\theta/2$, with no loss of generality, this result has the form:

$$(22) \qquad \sin^2\frac{\theta}{2} = \frac{1 - \cos\theta}{2}.$$

Similarly,

$$\cos 2\theta = \cos^2\theta - (1 - \cos^2\theta) = 2\cos^2\theta - 1,$$

so that,

$$\cos^2\theta = \frac{1 + \cos 2\theta}{2}.$$

A replacement of θ by $\theta/2$ gives us:

$$(23) \qquad \cos^2\frac{\theta}{2} = \frac{1 + \cos\theta}{2}.$$

We note that Formulas (22) and (23) do not give us the algebraic sign of $\sin\theta/2$ or $\cos\theta/2$, and in both cases the correct sign must be determined from the quadrant in which $P(\theta/2)$ is located. It is immediately apparent that

$$\tan^2\frac{\theta}{2} = \frac{\sin^2\dfrac{\theta}{2}}{\cos^2\dfrac{\theta}{2}} = \frac{1 - \cos\theta}{1 + \cos\theta},$$

but it is possible to obtain a more satisfactory formula for $\tan\theta/2$, which includes the correct sign. Thus,

$$\tan\frac{\theta}{2} = \frac{\sin\dfrac{\theta}{2}}{\cos\dfrac{\theta}{2}} = \frac{2\sin\dfrac{\theta}{2}\cos\dfrac{\theta}{2}}{2\cos^2\dfrac{\theta}{2}} = \frac{\sin\theta}{1 + \cos\theta},$$

and we rewrite this result as our final formula:

$$(24) \qquad \tan\frac{\theta}{2} = \frac{\sin\theta}{1 + \cos\theta}.$$

Formulas (22), (23), and (24) express functions of half a number (or angle) in terms of functions of the number (or angle).

EXAMPLE 2. Determine the exact value of: (a) $\cos\pi/8$; (b) $\tan\pi/12$; (c) $\sin 4\pi/3$, given that $\cos 8\pi/3 = \cos 2\pi/3 = -\frac{1}{2}$.

SOLUTION

(a) From (23), $\cos^2 \dfrac{\pi}{8} = \dfrac{1 + \cos \pi/4}{2} = \dfrac{1 + \sqrt{2}/2}{2} = \dfrac{2 + \sqrt{2}}{4}.$

Since $P(\pi/8)$ is in the first quadrant, $\cos \pi/8$ is positive, and so

$$\cos \frac{\pi}{8} = \frac{\sqrt{2 + \sqrt{2}}}{2}.$$

(b) From (24), $\tan \dfrac{\pi}{12} = \dfrac{\sin \pi/6}{1 + \cos \pi/6} = \dfrac{1/2}{1 + \sqrt{3}/2} = \dfrac{1}{(2 + \sqrt{3})} = 2 - \sqrt{3}.$

(c) From (22), $\sin^2 \dfrac{4\pi}{3} = \dfrac{1 - \cos 8\pi/3}{2} = \dfrac{1 + 1/2}{2} = \dfrac{3}{4}.$ Since $P(4\pi/3)$ is in the third quadrant, it follows that $\sin 4\pi/3 = -\sqrt{3}/2.$ (This result could have been obtained much more easily, of course, by an application of the Reduction Principle.)

EXAMPLE 3.   Simplify the expression $\sin 2\theta/\sin \theta - \cos 2\theta/\cos \theta.$

SOLUTION

$$\frac{\sin 2\theta}{\sin \theta} - \frac{\cos 2\theta}{\cos \theta} = \frac{2 \sin \theta \cos \theta}{\sin \theta} - \frac{2 \cos^2 \theta - 1}{\cos \theta}$$
$$= 2 \cos \theta - 2 \cos \theta + \sec \theta = \sec \theta.$$

EXAMPLE 4.   Verify the following identity:

$$\left(\sin \frac{\theta}{2} + \cos \frac{\theta}{2} \right)^2 = \frac{\csc \theta + 1}{\csc \theta}.$$

SOLUTION

$$\left(\sin \frac{\theta}{2} + \cos \frac{\theta}{2} \right)^2 = \sin^2 \frac{\theta}{2} + 2 \sin \frac{\theta}{2} \cos \frac{\theta}{2} + \cos^2 \frac{\theta}{2}$$
$$= 1 + 2 \sin \frac{\theta}{2} \cos \frac{\theta}{2} = 1 + \sin \theta.$$

Also,

$$\frac{\csc \theta + 1}{\csc \theta} = \frac{1/(\sin \theta) + 1}{1/(\sin \theta)} = \frac{(1 + \sin \theta)/(\sin \theta)}{1/(\sin \theta)} = 1 + \sin \theta.$$

Since both members of the conjectured identity are equal to $1 + \sin \theta$, the identity has been verified.

We close this section with a reminder that an identity in θ is not necessarily a true equality for *every* real number replacement of θ, but only for those which reduce both members to a well-defined real number. The number replacements which are excluded in any given case will depend on what functions are involved in the expressions.

PROBLEMS

1. Find exact values of all circular functions of $\pi/8$.
2. Use formulas in this section to obtain the circular functions of $\pi/3$ from the circular functions of $\pi/6$.
3. Assume the circular functions of π and use formulas of this section to obtain the known functions of $\pi/2$.
4. Without using the Reduction Principle, consult Table 2 to obtain: (a) sin 140°; (b) cos 136.6°; (c) tan 152°42′; (d) sec 100°30′.
5. Without using the Reduction Principle, consult Table 2 to obtain: (a) sin 2.6; (b) cos 3.0; (c) tan 1.96.
6. Derive a formula for $\cot \theta/2$ similar in form to (24).
7. Simplify each of the following expressions:

(a) $\cos 2\theta \cos \theta + \sin 2\theta \sin \theta$; (b) $\dfrac{\sec \theta - 1}{\sec \theta}$;

(c) $\dfrac{\tan \theta}{1 + \tan^2 \theta}$; (d) $\dfrac{\sin 2\theta + \sin \theta}{1 + \cos 2\theta + \cos \theta}$;

(e) $\dfrac{\sec^2 \theta}{2 - \sec^2 \theta}$; (f) $\dfrac{\sin^2 \theta}{1 - \cos \theta} - 1$.

8. Express each of the following in terms of $\sin \theta$, where $0 < \theta < \pi/2$: (a) $\tan \theta$; (b) $\sec \theta$; (c) $\cos 2\theta$; (d) $\csc \theta/2$; (e) $\cot \theta$; (f) $\cos (\pi + \theta/2)$.
9. Prove that $|\sin t + \cos t| = \sqrt{1 + \sin 2t}$.
10. Prove that $\tan (a + b)$ can be written in the form $\dfrac{\sin 2a + \sin 2b}{\cos 2a + \cos 2b}$.
11. Find an expression for $\tan 2\theta + \sec 2\theta$, which involves only $\sin \theta$ and $\cos \theta$.

In Problems 12 through 24, either establish the conjectured identity or exhibit a number substitution for the variable which shows that the given equation is not an identity.

12. $\sin 2\theta = \dfrac{2 \tan \theta}{1 + \tan^2 \theta}$.

13. $\tan 2\theta = \dfrac{1 + \cos 2\theta}{\sin 2\theta}$.

14. $\sin^2 \theta \cos^2 \theta = (1 - \cos 4\theta)/8$.

15. $\cos 3t = 3 \sin t - 4 \sin^3 t$.

16. $\cot \theta/2 = \csc \theta + \cot \theta$.

17. $\sin^4 \theta = (3 - 4 \cos 2\theta + \cos 4\theta)/8$.

18. $\ln \tan t = \ln (\csc 2t - \cot 2t)$.

19. $\ln (\tan^2 t + 2 \cot 2t \tan t) = 0$.

20. $\dfrac{1 + \sin \theta - \cos \theta}{1 + \sin \theta + \cos \theta} = \tan \dfrac{\theta}{2}$.

21. $\dfrac{\sin 3\theta}{\sin \theta} - \dfrac{\cos 3\theta}{\cos \theta} = 2$.

22. $\sin \left(\dfrac{\pi}{4} - \theta \right) \sin \left(\dfrac{\pi}{4} + \theta \right) = \dfrac{\cos 2\theta}{2}$.

23. $\csc 2t + \cot 2t = \cot t$.

24. $\dfrac{\sin 2t + \sin 3t}{\cos 2t - \cos 3t} = \cot \dfrac{t}{2}$.

25. Derive (23) by using the addition formula for $\cos (\theta - \theta/2)$.

26. Determine the subinterval of $[0, 2\pi]$ on which $\cos t + \sin 2t < 0$.

27. Prove that $A \sin x + B \cos x = \sqrt{A^2 + B^2} \sin (x + \alpha)$, where:

$$\sin \alpha = \frac{B}{\sqrt{A^2 + B^2}} \quad \text{and} \quad \cos \alpha = \frac{A}{\sqrt{A^2 + B^2}}.$$

Use the result of Problem 27 in working Problems 28 through 30.

28. Reduce $3 \sin t + 4 \cos t$ to the form $C \sin (x + \alpha)$, with $C > 0$.

29. Reduce $\sin 2\theta + 4 \cos 2\theta$ to the form $C \cos (2\theta + \beta)$, with $C > 0$.

30. Reduce $4 \cos 2t - 3 \sin 2t$ to the form $C \cos (2t + \beta)$, with $C > 0$.

7.7 Equations and Approximations

An equation differs from an identity in that the solution set of an equation, which is *not* an identity, is much more restricted. We shall see in Chapter 9, for example, that there can be at most n distinct complex number solutions of a polynomial equation of degree n. In this section, we shall consider a few elementary methods of solving certain types of equations which involve circular and inverse circular functions. Equations of this kind belong to the general category of nonalgebraic or "transcendental" equations. The solving of transcendental equations is, in general, extremely difficult, and we must usually be content with approximate answers. But even approximate solution methods, with any degree of generality, are beyond the scope of this book.

Of course, the method adopted for solving an equation depends not only on the equation itself, but also on the universe of the variable whose solutions interest us. This universe is also sometimes referred to as the "range" of the variable. For example, the equation $2x + 1 = 0$ has no integral solution, but it does have the rational number solution $-\frac{1}{2}$. If we wish to solve an equation involving circular functions, we must know whether we are in quest of real number solutions—as is usually the case in analytic trigonometry—or angles. This is an inevitable consequence of the common ambiguous usage of these functions! The magnitude of a solution may also be of concern to us. For example, the equation $\tan x = 1$ has for its complete real number solution set:

$$\{\pi/4, -3\pi/4, 5\pi/4, -7\pi/4, \ldots\}$$

or

$$\{(-1)^{n+1} (2n - 1)\pi/4, n \text{ a positive integer}\}.$$

If x is to be an angle, the complete solution set is:

$$\{(-1)^{n+1} (2n - 1)\pi/4^r\}$$

or

$$\{(-1)^{n+1} (2n - 1)45°\},$$

each with n an arbitrary positive integer. On the other hand, if we are interested only in a real number solution x such that $0 < x < \pi/2$, or an angle solution which is positive and acute, the unique solution is $\pi/4$ or 45°, respectively. In practice, the conditions of a problem usually designate the type as well as any limitations which are to be imposed on the magnitude or sign of its solutions.

The techniques which we present in the examples to follow are essentially the techniques of algebraic equations. They rest heavily on the field property (with the field usually R) that the product of two elements is 0 if and only if at least one of the factors is 0.

EXAMPLE 1.   Solve the equation $\sin x(2 \cos x + 1) = 0$ for x, such that $\pi/2 < x < \pi$.

SOLUTION.   The solution set of the given equation is the union of the solution sets of the two equations:

$$\sin x = 0,$$
$$\cos x + \tfrac{1}{2} = 0.$$

The first of these equations has no solution in the desired range, but the second has the unique solution $2\pi/3$. This is then the only solution to the given equation.

EXAMPLE 2.   Solve the equation $\sin^2 x - \sin x - 2 = 0$ for x, where x is an angle such that $0° \leq x \leq 360°$.

SOLUTION.   The given equation can be written $(\sin x - 2)$ $(\sin x + 1) = 0$, and its solution set is the union of the solution sets of the two equations:

$$\sin x - 2 = 0$$
$$\sin x + 1 = 0$$

The first equation requires that $\sin x = 2$, an equation with no solution. The second requires that $\sin x = -1$, and the only solution of this equation in the range stipulated is 270°. This is then the unique solution to the equation.

It is often necessary to make use of trigonometric identities to put an equation in an appropriate form for solving.

EXAMPLE 3.   Solve $\sin 2\theta + \cos \theta = 0$, for θ such that $0 \leq \theta < 2\pi$.

SOLUTION.   Since $\sin 2\theta = 2 \sin \theta \cos \theta$, the given equation becomes $2 \sin \theta \cos \theta + \cos \theta = 0$, which may be written $\cos \theta (2 \sin \theta + 1) = 0$. Hence, $\cos \theta = 0$ or $\sin \theta = -\frac{1}{2}$. The solution set, in the given universe, is then $\{\pi/2, 3\pi/2, 7\pi/6, 11\pi/6\}$.

EXAMPLE 4.   Solve $\sin^2 \theta - \cos \theta - 1 = 0$ for θ, such that $|\theta| \leq \pi$.

SOLUTION.   Since $\sin^2 \theta = 1 - \cos^2 \theta$, the given equation may be written:

$$1 - \cos^2 \theta - \cos \theta - 1 = 0,$$
$$\cos^2 \theta + \cos \theta = 0,$$
$$\cos \theta (\cos \theta + 1) = 0.$$

Hence, $\cos \theta = 0$ or $\cos \theta = -1$. The solution set, in the given universe, then $\{\pi/2, \pi, -\pi/2, -\pi\}$.

EXAMPLE 5.   Solve the equation $\text{Arctan}\,(1 + x) + \text{Arctan}\,(1 - x) = \pi/2$ for all real x.

SOLUTION.   Since $\cot (\theta_1 + \theta_2) = 1/\tan (\theta_1 + \theta_2)$, an application of Identity (17) of §7.5 transforms the given equation into:

$$\frac{1 - (1 + x)(1 - x)}{(1 + x) + (1 - x)} = \cot \pi/2$$

or, more simply,

$$\frac{x^2}{2} = \cot \frac{\pi}{2},$$

whence

$$x^2 = 2 \cot \frac{\pi}{2} = 0.$$

We note that the domain of the Arctangent function requires that:

$$\frac{-\pi}{2} < 1 + x < \frac{\pi}{2}$$

and also

$$\frac{-\pi}{2} < 1 - x < \frac{\pi}{2},$$

but regardless of this condition the only solution of the equation is $x = 0$.

For a sufficiently small positive real number, the difference between $\sin \theta$, $\tan \theta$, and θ is very small. If $0 < \theta < \pi/2$, it is intuitively evident that

$\sin \theta < \theta < \tan \theta$. Reference to this type of geometric observation was given in Problems 10 and 11 of §7.2. We are able to transform this inequality to give us useful bounds on $\sin \theta$, $\cos \theta$, and $\tan \theta$, and to these results we now proceed.

If we divide all members of the above inequality by $\sin \theta$, we obtain:

$$1 < \frac{\theta}{\sin \theta} < \sec \theta,$$

and then,

$$\cos \theta < \frac{\sin \theta}{\theta} < 1.$$

But,

$$\cos \theta = \sqrt{1 - \sin^2 \theta} > \sqrt{1 - \theta^2},$$

therefore

$$\sqrt{1 - \theta^2} < \frac{\sin \theta}{\theta} < 1,$$

and so we have obtained

(1) $$\theta \sqrt{1 - \theta^2} < \sin \theta < \theta.$$

Since,

$$\cos \theta = 1 - 2 \sin^2 \frac{\theta}{2}, \cos \theta > 1 - 2 \left(\frac{\theta^2}{4}\right) = 1 - \frac{\theta^2}{2}.$$

Hence

(2) $$1 - \frac{\theta^2}{2} < \cos \theta < 1$$

Finally, if we divide all members of the original inequality by $\tan \theta$, we obtain

$$\cos \theta < \frac{\theta}{\tan \theta} < 1,$$

so that

$$\sqrt{1 - \theta^2} < \frac{\theta}{\tan \theta} < 1.$$

It follows that

$$1 < \frac{\tan \theta}{\theta} < \frac{1}{\sqrt{1 - \theta^2}},$$

and so

(3) $$\theta < \tan \theta < \frac{\theta}{\sqrt{1 - \theta^2}}.$$

Inequalities (1), (2), and (3) can be used to estimate $\sin \theta$, $\cos \theta$, and $\tan \theta$, for a small real number $\theta > 0$. The analytic expressions which we gave at the end of §7.1 may also be truncated to approximate $\sin \theta$ and $\cos \theta$, but it may be necessary to include many terms to reach a desired accuracy in our computed results.

EXAMPLE 6.   Determine approximations for $\sin \pi/100$, $\cos \pi/100$, and $\tan \pi/100$.

SOLUTION.   From (1), $\frac{\pi}{100} \sqrt{1 - \pi^2/10000} < \sin \pi/100 < 0.03142$, i.e., $0.03140 < \sin \pi/100 < 0.03142$. Thus, correct to four decimal places, $\sin \pi/100 = 0.0314$ and is not to be distinguished from $\pi/100$.

From (2), $1 - \pi^2/20000 < \cos \pi/100 < 1$, i.e., $1 - 0.00049 < \cos \pi/100 < 1$.

Hence, $0.99951 < \cos \pi/100 < 1$ and, correct to three decimal places,

$$\cos \pi/100 = 0.999.$$

From (3), $\pi/100 < \tan \pi/100 < \dfrac{\pi/100}{\sqrt{1 - \pi^2/10000}}$, which is equivalent to

$$0.031416 < \tan \frac{\pi}{100} < \frac{0.031416}{0.9995} = 0.03143 \cdots.$$

Thus, correct to four decimal places, $\tan \pi/100 = 0.0314$ and is, like $\sin \pi/100$, indistinguishable from $\pi/100$.

We close this section and chapter with a word of warning. In any analytic expression involving θ and circular functions of θ, it is imperative that θ be considered a real number and *not* an angle. For example, in more advanced courses, it is established that $\sin \theta/\theta$ is arbitrarily close to 1 if θ is sufficiently close to 0. But if A is an angle, it is meaningless even to consider the "value" of $\sin A/A$! A similar remark would apply to the infinite series representations of $\sin \theta$ and $\cos \theta$ given at the close of §7.1. At the same time, of course, we have already pointed out that we may regard θ as the *radian measure* of an angle, if we so desire.

PROBLEMS

For Problems 1 through 14, solve the given equation for x, where x is a real number or an angle in the designated universe.

1. $\cot x \,(1 + \cos x) = 0, 0 \leq x \leq 2\pi$.   2. $\cos^2 x = 3, 0 \leq x \leq \pi$.
3. $2 \tan x \cos x = \tan x, 0° \leq x \leq 360°$.   4. $\cos 2x = \frac{1}{2}, 180° \leq x \leq 360°$.
5. $6 \tan^2 x + \sec x + 5 = 0, 0 < x < \pi$.   6. $\sec^2 x = 4, -180° \leq x < 0°$.
7. $\sin 2x = \cos 2x, 0 < x < 2\pi$.   8. $\sin x = \cos 2x, -\pi < x < \pi$.
9. $3 \cos^2 x + \cos x - 2 = 0, |x| < \pi$.   10. $\sin x + \cos x = 1, |x| < \pi$.
11. $3 \sec^2 x + \cot^2 x - 7 = 0, 0 < x < \pi$.   12. $\cos 2x = \sin 4x, |x| < \pi$.
13. $\cos x - \sin x = \sqrt{2}, 0° < x < 360°$.   14. $\cos 2x + \cos x + 1 = 0, |x| < \pi$.
15. Determine simultaneous solutions of the equations $r = 1 - \cos \theta$, $r = \cos \theta$, where $r > 0$ and $0 \leq \theta < 2\pi$.
16. Use the directions of Problem 15 for the equations $r = 4 \cos \theta$ and $r = 3 \sec \theta$.
17. If $r = 1 - 2 \cos \theta$, determine θ such that $0 \leq \theta < 2\pi$ and (a) $r = 0$; (b) r is maximal.
18. Use the directions of Problem 17 for the equation $r = 1 - \sqrt{2} \sin \theta$.
19. Use the inequalities of this section to determine the best approximations for $\sin \pi/60$ and $\cos \pi/60$.
20. Use the inequalities of this section to determine the best approximations for $\sin \pi/30$, $\cos \pi/30$, and $\tan \pi/30$.
21. Approximate $\sin \pi/60$ and $\cos \pi/60$ by using the first three terms of the appropriate infinite series given at the close of §7.1, and compare these results with those obtained in Problems 19 and 20. [Use $\pi = 3.14159$]
22. Use (1) and (3) to verify that $\cos \theta < \dfrac{\theta}{\tan \theta} < 1$ for $0 < \theta < \dfrac{\pi}{2}$.
23. Obtain an inequality similar to (1) involving $\sin \theta$, but which does not have any square roots.
24. Solve each of the following equations for real t: (a) $\text{Arcsin } \frac{3}{5} + \text{Arccos } \frac{4}{5} = \text{Arcsin } t$; (b) $\text{Arctan } (-\frac{1}{3}) - \text{Arctan } \frac{2}{3} = \text{Arctan } t$.
25. Solve each of the following equations for real x: (a) $2 \text{ Arcsin } x/2 = \text{Arctan } x$; (b) $\text{Arctan } (x + 1) = \pi/3$; (c) $\text{Arcsin } (x^2 - 2x) = \text{Arcsin } (-\frac{1}{2})$.

CHAPTER 8

Complex Numbers

8.1 Introduction

The question "What is a number?" is quite often asked, but somewhat
less frequently answered to one's complete satisfaction. In Chapter 1 we
gave a brief sketch of the development of the system of real numbers, with
the viewpoint that a number is an element of mensuration. One could also
pursue a parallel development from the point of view of solving equations:
the integers, rational numbers, and real numbers were introduced so that
successively more complicated equations could be solved. Within the real
number system, all the common practical and theoretical mensuration
problems are solvable; the operations of addition, subtraction, multiplication, division (except by 0), and root extractions for non-negative numbers
are, at least theoretically, possible. However, with only real numbers
available, it is still not possible to measure a vector or "directed" quantity—
except as positive or negative of a certain magnitude—and such a simple
equation as $x^2 + 1 = 0$ has no solution. It is these two deficiencies in the
real number system which may be regarded as providing at least partial
motivation for an extension of this system to include "complex" numbers.
With these new numbers it is possible to give a satisfactory measure of
any vector quantity, and to solve any polynomial equation with real
coefficients. We now proceed to a description of these numbers.

An orderly construction of integers is based on a prior knowledge of
natural numbers; a development of rationals is based on integers; while a
development of real numbers is based on an earlier study of rational
numbers. An integer x may be seen to be equivalent to the ordered pair
(a, b) of natural numbers, provided we understand by this equivalence that
$x = a - b$. Moreover, a rational number r is equivalent to the ordered
pair (a, b) of integers, provided in this case we understand that $x = a/b$.

In other words, a definition of an integer involves a pair of natural numbers, and a definition of a rational number involves a pair of integers. While a careful transition from the rationals to the reals involves something much more subtle than mere *pairs* of rationals, it may still be not unreasonable to suspect that an extension of the reals can be based on ordered pairs of real numbers. This we do in our construction of the complex numbers. Of course, it is inherent in the nature of a number that an arithmetic structure is involved, and so we must make appropriate definitions of an *equality* relation, as well as the operations of addition and multiplication. This is done in the following comprehensive definition.

Definition. A *complex* number is an ordered pair of real numbers, with the pairs subject to the following conditions:

(a) *Equality.* $(a, b) = (c, d)$ if and only if $a = c$ and $b = d$.
(b) *Addition.* $(a, b) + (c, d) = (a + c, b + d)$.
(c) *Multiplication.* $(a, b)(c, d) = (ac - bd, bc + ad)$.

Before these ordered pairs with the given arithmetic structure should be accepted as "numbers," however, one should verify that they actually obey a substantial number of the usual laws of arithmetic and so resemble the more familiar real numbers. One of these laws is verified in Example 1, while the verification of others is suggested in the problems.

EXAMPLE 1.   Verify the commutative law of addition for complex numbers.

SOLUTION. $(a, b) + (c, d) = (a + c, b + d) = (c + a, d + b)$
$= (c, d) + (a, b)$.
This establishes the commutative law of addition, and we note that the commutative law of addition for real numbers was used in the proof.

Since $(a, b) + (0, 0) = (a, b)$, for any complex number (a, b), the element $(0, 0)$ is the zero of the new system, and there should be no confusion if it is designated simply as 0. Also, since $(a, b)(1, 0) = (a, b)$, for any complex number (a, b), the number $(1, 0)$ is the multiplicative identity of the system. The additive inverse $-(a, b)$ of (a, b) is $(-a, -b)$, because $(a, b) + (-a, -b) = 0$, and it is easy to check that the multiplicative inverse $(a, b)^{-1}$ of (a, b) is:

$$\left(\frac{a}{a^2 + b^2}, \frac{-b}{a^2 + b^2} \right),$$

provided $(a, b) \neq 0$. As for real numbers, we consider the operation of subtraction as inverse to addition, and so the subtraction of a complex number is the same as the addition of its additive inverse. Similarly, the operation of division is considered inverse to multiplication, and so dividing by a nonzero number is the same as multiplying by its multiplicative inverse. That is,

$$(a, b) - (c, d) = (a, b) + (-c, -d),$$

and,

$$\frac{(a, b)}{(c, d)} = (a, b)(c, d)^{-1}.$$

It is now a matter for routine checking that all the field properties listed in §1.3 are also properties of the system of complex numbers, and so this system is a field.

The complex numbers of the form $(a, 0)$, for any real a, behave just like the real numbers a in any computation involving the field properties, and so these special complex numbers are indistinguishable from real numbers— except in form. To use the technical term applied in such instances, we say that the subsystem of complex numbers of the form $(a, 0)$ is "isomorphic" to the system of real numbers. In this sense the field of complex numbers contains the real numbers as a subfield—just as the field of rational numbers contains the numbers of the form $a/1$ as integers. The complex numbers then form an *extension* of R, which we shall designate as C.

There is one important property possessed by the real numbers which is *not* shared by the complex numbers. This is the property of *order*. There is no way to order complex numbers so that the properties of §1.5 are preserved, and so the complex numbers comprise an "unordered" field. It is possible to introduce a type of "ordering" in this field, but not all of the usual properties of order are in effect, and so we do not have a *bona fide* order relation.

EXAMPLE 2. Determine the product $(2, 3)(-1, 1)$, where the indicated pairs are regarded as complex numbers.

SOLUTION. By the definition for multiplication, $(2, 3)(-1, 1) = (-2 - 3, -3 + 2) = (-5, -1)$.

EXAMPLE 3. Determine the quotient $(1, -2)/(2, -1)$, where the indicated pairs are regarded as complex numbers.

SOLUTION. By the formula for a multiplicative inverse, and the definition of multiplication, $(1, -2)/(2, -1) = (1, -2)(\frac{2}{5}, \frac{1}{5}) = (\frac{2}{5} + \frac{2}{5}, -\frac{4}{5} + \frac{1}{5}) = (\frac{4}{5}, -\frac{3}{5})$.

PROBLEMS

1. Verify the associative law of addition for complex numbers.
2. Verify the associative law of multiplication for complex numbers.
3. Verify the commutative law of multiplication for complex numbers.
4. Verify the usual distributive law for complex numbers.
5. Verify that $(1, 0)$ is the multiplicative identity for the system of complex numbers.
6. Find the sum of the following complex numbers: (a) $(1, 3), (-4, 2), (0, 2)$; (b) $(-2, 5), (3, 4), (-2, -2)$; (c) $(1, 1), (-2, 4), (3, -6), (5, 2)$.
7. Find the product of the complex numbers in each pair: (a) $(1, 2), (-2,-4)$; (b) $(5, 4), (3, -2)$; (c) $(-1, -2), (3, -2)$; (d) $(2, -5), (1, 4)$.
8. With reference to Problem 7, subtract the second member of each pair from the first.
9. With reference to Problem 7, divide the first member of each pair by the second. Check your results by multiplication.
10. Solve each of the following equations for the indicated unknowns in R: (a) $(x, 4) + (3, -4) = (6, y)$; (b) $(x, -3) - (2, y) = (3, 4)$; (c) $(3, -y) + (2x, 3) - (4, 3y) = (3, 1)$; (d) $(x, a) + (b, y) = (c, d)$, with a, b, c, d given real numbers.
11. Derive a formula for the quotient $(a, b)/(c, d)$ of two complex numbers.
12. Decide whether the identities $a0 = 0$ and $a(1) = a$, which are valid for any real number a, are also valid if a is considered to be an arbitrary complex number.
13. Show that $(0, 1)^2 = (-1, 0)$. In view of our assertion about numbers of the form $(a, 0)$, what does this equation suggest?
14. Write as a single ordered pair: (a) $(1, -2)^3$; (b) $(-2, 3)^4$.

    In Problems 15 through 17, determine the complex number (x, y), subject to the given condition.
15. $(x, y) = (2, -1)/(1, -3)$.
16. $(x, y) = (-\frac{1}{2}, \sqrt{3}/2)^3$.
17. $(3, -2) = (x, y)/(2, -1)$.
18. What is the result if you perform additions, subtractions, multiplications, and divisions in the subset of complex numbers of the form $(a, 0)$? Give your answer in generalized form.

8.2 The Normal or Rectangular Form of a Complex Number

In spite of what we have said by way of explanation in §8.1, it may seem a little strange to the student for us to define complex numbers as ordered pairs of real numbers. However, we repeat that it must be understood that these pairs are "numbers" only after they have been given an arithmetic structure, with appropriate definitions of equality, addition, and multiplication. In this section, we shall give the more common representation of these numbers. This may be regarded as the complex analogue of expressing a rational number in the conventional form a/b, after a prior definition of a rational number as an ordered pair (a, b) of integers a and b, subject to certain rules of operation.

Our definition of addition allows us to write an arbitrary complex number (a, b) in the form $(a, b) = (a, 0) + (0, b)$, and our definition of multiplication lets us write $(0, b) = (b, 0) (0, 1)$. Hence,

$$(a, b) = (a, 0) + (b, 0) (0, 1).$$

The number $(0, 1)$ plays a very important role in complex analysis, and it is customary to designate it by i (physicists and engineers often use j for this purpose). We noted in §8.1 that the numbers of the form $(a, 0)$ may be identified with their first components a, and if we make this identification, the complex number (a, b) takes the form $a + bi$.

Definition. The *normal* or *rectangular* form of the complex number (a, b) is $a + bi$, where we have designated $(0, 1)$ as i, and identified $(a, 0)$ with a and $(b, 0)$ with b. For historic reasons, a is sometimes called the *real* and b the *imaginary* component of the number, but no significance should be attached to the word "imaginary."

If we square i, by the usual rule for multiplication, we find that $(0, 1)^2 = (0, 1) (0, 1) = (-1, 0)$ or, in the new symbolism,

$$i^2 = -1.$$

It now appears that in the system of complex numbers there is a number i whose square is -1. The equation $x^2 = -1$ or $x^2 + 1 = 0$ is then solvable in this system, and herein lies its big advantage over the system of real numbers.

If we reexamine our basic definitions, with the complex numbers written in normal form, the definitions assume the following appearance:

(1) *Equality.* $a + bi = c + di$ if and only if $a = c$ and $b = d$.
(2) *Addition.* $(a + bi) + (c + di) = (a + c) + (b + d)i$.
(3) *Multiplication.* $(a + bi) (c + di) = (ac - bd) + (bc + ad)i$.

In words, these rules are tantamount to the following:

1. Two complex numbers are *equal*, if and only if their respective real and imaginary components are equal.
2. Two complex numbers are *added* by adding their respective real and imaginary components.
3. Two complex numbers are multiplied just like binomials in the symbol i, with i^2 replaced by -1 in the final result.

Some of the advantages arising from the normal form of complex numbers will be made apparent from the following examples.

EXAMPLE 1.   Express $(2 + i)^4$ as a complex number.

SOLUTION

$$(2 + i)^2 = (2 + i)(2 + i) = 4 + 4i + i^2 = 4 + 4i - 1 = 3 + 4i.$$

Hence,

$$(2 + i)^4 = (2 + i)^2 (2 + i)^2 = (3 + 4i)^2 = 9 + 24i + 16i^2$$
$$= 9 + 24i - 16 = -7 + 24i.$$

EXAMPLE 2.   Express $(2 - i)/(1 + 3i)$ in the normal form of a complex number.

SOLUTION.   We multiply numerator and denominator of the given number by $1 - 3i$, and obtain,

$$\frac{(2 - i)(1 - 3i)}{(1 + 3i)(1 - 3i)} = \frac{2 - 7i + 3i^2}{1 - 9i^2} = \frac{2 - 7i - 3}{1 + 9} = \frac{-1 - 7i}{10} = -\frac{1}{10} - \frac{7}{10}i.$$

Two complex numbers of the form $a + bi$ and $a - bi$ are said to be *conjugates of* or *conjugate to* each other. It is then apparent from Example 2 that the following rule may be used for dividing one complex number by another:

Multiply numerator and denominator of the indicated quotient by the conjugate of the denominator, and simplify the multiplications.

For it may be seen that the product of a complex number and its conjugate is always a real number, and so this procedure makes the denominator of the quotient real.

We have already noted that the complex number i is a solution of the equation $x^2 + 1 = 0$, an equation which is unsolvable in the field R of real numbers. It might be reasonable to expect that further extensions of the complex number system would be required if other more complicated equations are to be solved. However, it is a fact that any polynomial equation of the form $a_0x^n + a_1x^{n-1} + \cdots + a_{n-1}x + a_n = 0$, with n a positive integer and $a_0(\neq 0)$, $a_1, \ldots, a_{n-1}, a_n$ real numbers, can be solved completely within the system of complex numbers. This result is a consequence of the following important theorem.

THEOREM 8.21 (Fundamental Theorem of Algebra).   Any polynomial equation, with real or complex coefficients, has a complex number for a solution.

This theorem was first proved by Gauss in 1799. Since then many other proofs have been given, but they are all somewhat difficult and beyond the scope of this book. Since no new numbers are needed to solve any polynomial equation, we say that the field of complex numbers is *algebraically closed.*

An ordered pair (a, b) of real numbers has a natural geometric representation as the point in a Cartesian plane whose coordinate pair is (a, b). There is a one-to-one correspondence between the points of this plane and the complex numbers, just as there is a one-to-one correspondence between the real numbers and any algebraic scale drawn as a coordinate axis. Moreover, in this geometric environment, it is often convenient to speak of the complex numbers as if they are actual points of the plane. For example, we may speak of "the point $z = x + yi$." The horizontal axis, which contains the numbers of the form $(a, 0)$, i.e., the real numbers, is known as the *axis of reals*, while the vertical axis, which contains the numbers of the form $(0, b)$ or bi is sometimes called the *pure imaginary axis*. We shall make more use of this geometric representation of the complex numbers in the following section.

PROBLEMS

1. Write each of the following ordered pairs, regarded as complex numbers, in normal form: (a) $(-3, 5)$; (b) $(3, -2)$; (c) $(2, 6)$; (d) $(0, 1)$; (e) $(0, 0)$; (f) $(-1, -1)$.
2. Find the sum of each of the following pairs of complex numbers: (a) $2 + 3i$, $-2 - 5i$; (b) $2 + 4i$, $-2 - 6i$; (c) $6 - 5i$, $-3 - i$; (d) 5, $-2 + i$; (e) $4i$, $6i$; (f) $2i$, 6.
3. Find the product of each pair of complex numbers given in Problem 2.
4. With reference to the complex numbers given in Problem 2, express in normal form the quotient of the first number by the second in each pair.
5. Simplify each of the following: (a) $(2 + i)(-3 - 2i)(3 - 2i)$; (b) $\dfrac{(2 - 3i)^3}{(1 + 2i)}$; (c) $\dfrac{(3 - 2i)(1 + i)}{(1 + 2i)(3 - i)}$; (d) $\dfrac{2 + i - i^4}{i + i^2 + i^4}$.
6. Give the geometric representation of each of the following complex numbers: (a) $2 - 3i$; (b) $3 + i$; (c) $-4 - 3i$; (d) $3 + i/2$; (e) i; (f) $i/2$.
7. Verify that $y^3 = 1$, where $y = -\frac{1}{2} - (\sqrt{3}/2)i$.
8. Simplify $[\frac{1}{2} + \sqrt{3}/2)i]^3$, and compare the result with Problem 7.
9. Solve each of the following equations for real x and y:
   (a) $(x + 2i) + (3 - yi) = -2 + 5i$;   (b) $(2x - 3yi) + (-2 - 5i) = 1$;
   (c) $(2x + i) - (3 - 4yi) = x - 2i$;   (d) $3x + 2i = 2 + x - yi$.
10. Prove for any positive integer n: (a) $i^{4n} = 1$; (b) $i^{2n+2} = 1$ if n is odd, and $i^{2n+2} = -1$ if n is even; (c) $i^{4n+3} = -i$.
11. Prove that the sum and the product of any two conjugate complex numbers are real numbers.

12. Prove that if the sum and product of two complex numbers are real numbers, the two numbers are conjugates of each other.
13. Use the complex number i to illustrate the fact that the complex number field is not ordered as in §1.5. [Consider the "Trichotomy law" that either $i = 0$, $i > 0$, or $i < 0$.]
14. Solve each of the following equations for real or complex x:
    (a) $x/2 + 1 + 3i = 0$; (b) $3x + 4i = x - 7i$; (c) $(1 + 3i)x + 7i = 6$;
    (d) $\dfrac{3x - 2i}{x + i} = 2$.
15. Use the factoring method to solve for x (real or complex): (a) $x^2 - ix + 2 = 0$;
    (b) $x^2 + (3i - 2)x - 6i = 0$; (c) $x^4 - 1 = 0$; (d) $x^3 - 5x^2i - 6x = 0$.
16. Use the factoring method to solve for x (real or complex):
    (a) $ix^2 + 7x - 12i = 0$; (b) $2ix^2 - 5x - 2i = 0$.
17. Solve the following equation for real x and y:
$$x^2 + xi = y^2 - 2yi + 4i.$$
18. Prove that $xy = 1$, where $x = -\tfrac{1}{2} + (\sqrt{3}/2)i$ and $y = -\tfrac{1}{2} - (\sqrt{3}/2)i$.
19. Prove that the conjugate of z is a solution of the equation $2x^2 + 5x + 11 = 0$ provided z is a solution.
20. Prove the following theorem: The conjugate of the sum of two complex numbers is equal to the sum of their conjugates. If the word "sum" is replaced by the word "product" in this statement, is the new statement true? Either prove or disprove the correctness of this new statement.
21. Let f be a function on the set of all complex numbers. Determine the zeros of f [i.e., the numbers z such that $f(z) = 0$] if f is defined by:
    (a) $f(z) = 3iz + 2$;   (b) $f(z) = (1 + i)z - 2i$;
    (c) $f(z) = \dfrac{(1 - 2i)z}{1 + i}$;   (d) $f(z) = \dfrac{2iz}{1 + i} + \dfrac{2 - i}{i}$.
22. Solve the following equation for real x and y:
$$\ln (x + y) + e^y i = 1 + 3i.$$

8.3   Trigonometric Form of Complex Numbers

We have pointed out in §8.2 that it is only natural to represent the complex number $z = (a, b) = a + bi$ as the *point* (a, b) in the Cartesian plane. In this geometric representation, the "real" part a is the abscissa and the "imaginary" part b is the ordinate of the point. This is illustrated in Figure 67.

If $r \geq 0$ is the distance of the point z from the origin, this non-negative number is called the *modulus* or *absolute value* of z, and is designated by $|z|$. Thus $|z| = 0$ if and only if $z = 0$. If θ is the radian measure of any one of the angles in standard position whose terminal side passes through the point z, θ is called an *argument* of z and is usually designated as *arg z*. It may be noted that (r, θ) constitutes a pair of polar coordinates of the point

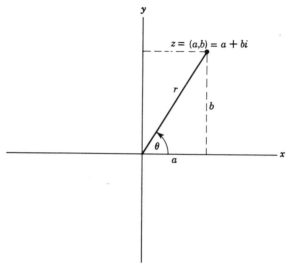

Figure 67

z. There are, of course, an infinite number of positive and negative values for *arg z*, for any given *z*, but we select the one most convenient for our purpose at hand—and this is usually the one of smallest absolute value. It follows from elementary trigonometry that, if $z = a + bi = (a, b)$, then $a = r \cos \theta$ and $b = r \sin \theta$. Hence, we can write *z* in the following *trigonometric form*:

$$z = a + bi = (r \cos \theta) + (r \sin \theta)i = r(\cos \theta + i \sin \theta)$$

If so desired, the radian *measure* θ may be replaced by the actual angle with this measure. In such a case, the angle is appropriately designated as either θ^r or $x°$, where $x = 180\, \theta/\pi$. For example, alternate forms of the complex number $z = 2(\cos \pi/4 + i \sin \pi/4)$ are:

$$z = 2(\cos \pi/4^r + i \sin \pi/4^r); z = 2(\cos 45° + i \sin 45°).$$

In most cases, however, the argument of a complex number—like its absolute value—is considered to be a real number.

EXAMPLE 1.   Express the complex number $z = 2 - 2i$ in trigonometric form.

SOLUTION.   The geometric representation of *z* is shown in Figure 68. It is clear from this diagram that $r = |z| = 2\sqrt{2}$, while θ may be taken to be $-\pi/4$.

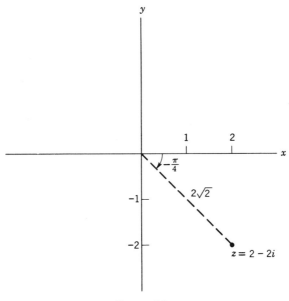

Figure 68

Hence,

$$z = 2\sqrt{2}\left[\cos\left(\frac{-\pi}{4}\right) + i\sin\left(\frac{-\pi}{4}\right)\right] = 2\sqrt{2}\left[\cos\frac{\pi}{4} - i\sin\frac{\pi}{4}\right].$$

While the addition and subtraction of complex numbers is most easily effected if we leave the numbers in normal form, it is a consequence of the following theorem that it is easier to perform multiplications and divisions of complex numbers in trigonometric form.

THEOREM 8.31. If $z_1 = r_1(\cos\theta_1 + i\sin\theta_1)$ and $z_2 = r_2(\cos\theta_2 + i\sin\theta_2)$ are any two complex numbers, the product z_1z_2 and quotient z_1/z_2 (if $z_2 \neq 0$) are given as follows:

(a) $z_1z_2 = r_1r_2[\cos(\theta_1 + \theta_2) + i\sin(\theta_1 + \theta_2)]$;

(b) $z_1/z_2 = (r_1/r_2)[\cos(\theta_1 - \theta_2) + i\sin(\theta_1 - \theta_2)]$.

· *PROOF*

$$
\begin{aligned}
z_1z_2 &= [r_1(\cos\theta_1 + i\sin\theta_1)][r_2(\cos\theta_2 + i\sin\theta_2)]\\
&= r_1r_2[(\cos\theta_1\cos\theta_2 - \sin\theta_1\sin\theta_2) + i(\sin\theta_1\cos\theta_2 + \cos\theta_1\sin\theta_2)]\\
&= r_1r_2[\cos(\theta_1 + \theta_2) + i\sin(\theta_1 + \theta_2)].
\end{aligned}
$$

If $z_2 \neq 0$, $\dfrac{z_1}{z_2} = \dfrac{r_1(\cos \theta_1 + i \sin \theta_1)}{r_2(\cos \theta_2 + i \sin \theta_2)}$

$$= \frac{r_1(\cos \theta_1 + i \sin \theta_1)\,[\cos(-\theta_2) + i \sin(-\theta_2)]}{r_2(\cos \theta_2 + i \sin \theta_2)\,[\cos(-\theta_2) + i \sin(-\theta_2)]}$$

$$= \frac{r_1[\cos(\theta_1 - \theta_2) + i \sin(\theta_1 - \theta_2)]}{r_2(\cos 0 + i \sin 0)}$$

$$= \frac{r_1}{r_2}[\cos(\theta_1 - \theta_2) + i \sin(\theta_1 - \theta_2)].$$

In words, the preceding theorem may be stated as follows:

The product (or quotient) of any two complex numbers may be effected by multiplying (or dividing) their absolute values and adding (or sub-tracting) their arguments, excluding division by zero.

EXAMPLE 2. If $z = 1 + i$, express iz and z/i in trigonometric form, and discuss both results from a trigonometric point of view.

SOLUTION. The trigonometric form of z is $\sqrt{2}(\cos \pi/4 + i \sin \pi/4)$, while the trigonometric form of i is $1(\cos \pi/2 + i \sin \pi/2)$, as may be seen from Figure 69.

Hence, by the theorem,

$$iz = \sqrt{2}\left[\cos\left(\frac{\pi}{4} + \frac{\pi}{2}\right) + i \sin\left(\frac{\pi}{4} + \frac{\pi}{2}\right)\right] = \sqrt{2}\left(\cos \frac{3\pi}{4} + i \sin \frac{3\pi}{4}\right).$$

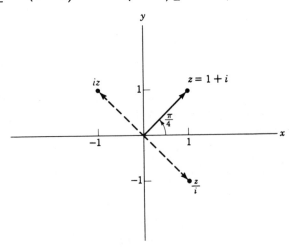

Figure 69

Similarly,

$$\frac{z}{i} = \sqrt{2}\left[\cos\left(\frac{\pi}{4} - \frac{\pi}{2}\right) + i\sin\left(\frac{\pi}{4} - \frac{\pi}{2}\right)\right] = \sqrt{2}\left[\cos\left(\frac{-\pi}{4}\right) + i\sin\left(\frac{-\pi}{4}\right)\right]$$

$$= \sqrt{2}\left(\cos\frac{\pi}{4} - i\sin\frac{\pi}{4}\right).$$

It appears from this example—and the result can be established in general—that the effect of multiplying or dividing a complex number by i is to rotate the line segment joining the number point with the origin through an angle of 90°, counterclockwise in the case of multiplication and clockwise in the case of division.

EXAMPLE 3.   If $z = 1 + i$, determine z^8.

SOLUTION.   Since $z = 1 + i = \sqrt{2}[\cos \pi/4 + i \sin \pi/4]$, it follows that $z^8 = (\sqrt{2})^8 (\cos 8\pi/4 + i \sin 8\pi/4) = 16(\cos 2\pi + i \sin 2\pi) = 16(1 + 0i) = 16$.

This example is illustrative of the ease with which integral powers of complex numbers can be determined when the trigonometric form is used for the numbers.

PROBLEMS

1. Express each of the following complex numbers in trigonometric form: (a) $1 - i$; (b) $2 + 2i$; (c) $-\frac{1}{2} + (\sqrt{3}/2)i$; (d) $\sqrt{3}/2 + i/2$; (e) $-2i$.

2. Express each of the following complex numbers in trigonometric form: (a) 3; (b) -6; (c) $-2 - 2i$; (d) $\sqrt{3} - i$; (e) $-\sqrt{3} + i$; (f) $1 - \sqrt{3}i$.

3. Use Table 2 to express each of the following complex numbers in trigonometric form: (a) $2 - 3i$; (b) $-2 - 3i$; (c) $1 + 3i$; (d) $-1 - 3i$; (e) $3 + 4i$; (f) $-3 - 4i$.

4. Simplify each of the following expressions to a complex number in normal form:

   (a) $\dfrac{[2(\cos 5\pi/6 + i \sin 5\pi/6)] [\cos \pi/5 + i \sin \pi/5]}{[4(\cos \pi/3 + i \sin \pi/3)[[\cos \pi/6 + i \sin \pi/6]}$,

   (b) $\dfrac{[2(\cos 3\pi/4 + i \sin 3\pi/4)]^3}{[4(\cos \pi/4 - i \sin \pi/4)]}$,

   (c) $\dfrac{[3(\cos \pi/6 + i \sin \pi/6)]^4}{[2(\cos \pi/3 + i \sin \pi/3)]^2}$.

5. Simplify each of the following expressions to a complex number in trigonometric form: (a) $[3(\cos 2 + i \sin 2)]^3$; (b) $[2(\cos 3 + i \sin 3)]^4$; (c) $[2(\cos 0.6 + i \sin 0.6)]^4$; (d) $[10(\cos 0.4 + i \sin 0.4)]^5$.

6. Simplify each of the following expressions to a complex number in trigonometric form:

(a) $\dfrac{[2(\cos \pi/3 - i \sin \pi/3)]^2}{[\cos 3\pi/4 - i \sin 3\pi/4]}$;

(b) $\dfrac{[5(\cos 2\pi/5 - i \sin 2\pi/5)]}{[2(\cos 3\pi/4 - i \sin 3\pi/4)]^2}$;

(c) $\dfrac{[4(\cos 5\pi/4 - i \sin 5\pi/4)]^5}{[2(\cos \pi/3 - i \sin \pi/3)]^3}$.

7. Prove, for any complex numbers z_1 and z_2, that $|z_1 z_2| = |z_1|\,|z_2|$ and $|z_1/z_2| = |z_1|/|z_2|$.

8. Use the theorem of this section to verify that the absolute value of a complex number is unaltered after the number has been multiplied or divided by i.

9. If $z_1 = a + bi$ and $z_2 = c + di$, verify that $|z_1 - z_2|$ is the actual distance between the geometric points representing z_1 and z_2.

10. Give a geometric characterization of all points which represent complex numbers z such that: (a) $|z| = 1$; (b) $|z| = 2$; (c) $|z| < 1$; (d) $|z| > 2$; (e) $z + \bar{z} = 1$, where $\bar{z}$ is the conjugate of z; (f) $z + \bar{z} < 1$.

11. If $\bar{z}$ is the conjugate of z, prove that $|z| = |\bar{z}|$.

12. If we "order" the complex numbers by the rule that $z_1 > z_2$ if and only if $|z_1| > |z_2|$, does this "ordering" of the complex numbers satisfy the requirements of an order relation as given in §1.5? If not, give an explanation.

13. Use the trigonometric form of complex numbers to simplify each of the following: (a) $(1 - i)^5$; (b) $(2 + 2i)^{10}$; (c) $(\sqrt{3}/2 - i/2)^5$; (d) $(\frac{1}{2} - \sqrt{3}i/2)^8$; (e) $(-2i)^{11}$; (f) $(\sqrt{3} + i)^7$; (g) $(1 - \sqrt{3}i)^9$.

14. Use Table 2 to determine (a) $(3 - i)^6$; (b) $(2 + 3i)^5$; (c) $(1 - 5i)^{10}$.

15. Prove that $[r(\cos \theta + i \sin \theta)]^2 = r^2(\cos 2\theta + i \sin 2\theta)$.

16. Prove that $z \cdot \bar{z} = |z|^2$, where $\bar{z}$ is the conjugate of z.

17. Prove, for any complex number $z = a + bi$, that $a \le |z|$ and $b \le |z|$.

18. Prove that the absolute value of the sum of two complex numbers is less than or equal to the sum of their absolute values. [*Hint:* write $|z_1 + z_2|^2 = (z_1 + z_2)\,(\bar{z}_1 + \bar{z}_2)$, where $\bar{z}_1 + \bar{z}_2$ is the conjugate of $z_1 + z_2$; also use the fact that $z_1 \bar{z}_2 + z_2 \bar{z}_1$ is twice the real component of $z_1 \bar{z}_2$].

8.4   DeMoivre's Theorem and Root Extractions

We have noted in §8.2 that the Fundamental Theorem of Algebra assures the existence of a complex number solution for any polynomial equation with complex coefficients. In particular, the equation $x^n - a = 0$, where a is any complex number, has a solution. (It should be understood here, of course, that a real number is a special kind of complex number.) This means that there exists in the field of complex numbers an nth root of an arbitrary complex number, and in particular of any negative real number. By the theorem of §8.3, $(\cos \theta + i \sin \theta)^2 = \cos 2\theta + i \sin 2\theta$, $(\cos \theta + i \sin \theta)^3 = \cos 3\theta + i \sin 3\theta$, etc. Indeed, for any positive integer n, it can be shown that $(\cos \theta + i \sin \theta)^n = \cos n\theta + i \sin n\theta$, and this is the Theorem of DeMoivre.

THEOREM 8.41 (De Moivre). For any positive integer n, $(\cos\theta + i\sin\theta)^n = \cos n\theta + i\sin n\theta$.

The truth of this theorem is quite evident from the preceding discussion, but a more elegant proof can be given by the Principle of Mathematical Induction, as described in Chapter 10. We shall accept the result of this theorem and proceed to show how it can be used to lead us to a procedure for the actual determination of the nth root of any complex number.

Let $z = r(\cos\theta + i\sin\theta)$, with n an arbitrary positive integer. By an nth root of z, we mean a number w such that $w^n = z$. Hence, if w exists as a complex number, $w = s(\cos\alpha + i\sin\alpha)$ and, by DeMoivre's theorem, it follows that $w^n = s^n(\cos n\alpha + i\sin n\alpha) = z = r(\cos\theta + i\sin\theta)$. If two complex numbers are equal, their absolute values must be equal, and so $s^n = r$. Since s must be a positive real number, $s = \sqrt[n]{r}$ where, as always, $\sqrt[n]{r}$ indicates the positive n^{th} root of the real number r. Moreover, from the equation connecting w and z, it also follows that:

$$\cos n\alpha = \cos\theta \text{ and } \sin n\alpha = \sin\theta.$$

These equations can be satisfied only if $n\alpha$ differs from θ by some integral multiple of 2π (the period of both the sine and cosine functions), so that $n\alpha = \theta + 2k\pi$ and $\alpha = (\theta + 2k\pi)/n$, for some integer k. If we let $k = 0, 1, 2, \ldots, n-1$ in the above formula for α, we obtain n distinct possibilities for α, whereas any other integral substitution for k will result in a repetition of a value previously obtained. These n distinct values of α are then the only possible ones, and we have obtained the following result.

THEOREM 8.42. If $z = r(\cos\theta + i\sin\theta)$ is an arbitrary complex number, there are exactly n distinct complex n^{th} roots of z, which may be expressed in the form:

$$\sqrt[n]{r}\left(\cos\frac{\theta + 2k\pi}{n} + i\sin\frac{\theta + 2k\pi}{n}\right), \quad \text{where } k = 0, 1, 2, \ldots, n-1.$$

From the point of view of geometry, the nth roots of z are n points equally spaced around a circle with center at the origin and radius $\sqrt[n]{r}$. This is illustrated in Figure 70, for the case $n = 3$.

We have emphasized in an earlier chapter that if a is a real number, $\sqrt[n]{a}$ is a well-defined real number—the principal n^{th} root—if a real n^{th} root of a exists. However, except for special cases, if z is an arbitrary complex number, it is not generally the case that $\sqrt[n]{z}$ designates a *particular* n^{th} root of z. If we wish to do so, of course, we could let this symbol designate, say, the nth root whose real component is positive and minimal, but there is no generally accepted usage of this symbol. In the case of square roots of a negative number a, however, it is customary to let $\sqrt{a}$ stand for the

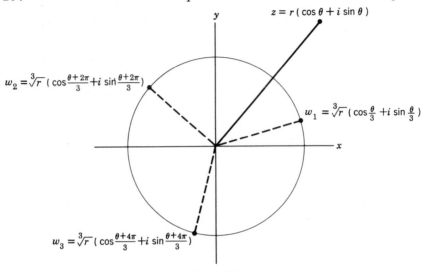

Figure 70

number $\sqrt{|a|}i$, so that $\sqrt{-4} = 2i$. In the case of the nth roots of unity, it is customary to let the one of smallest positive argument be ω, and the complete set of nth roots of unity is then $\omega, \omega^2, \omega^3, \ldots, \omega^n = 1$.

EXAMPLE 1.　Find the three cube roots of -1.

SOLUTION. The trigonometric form of -1, considered a complex number, is $1(\cos \pi + i \sin \pi)$ or, more generally, $1[\cos (\pi + 2k\pi) + i \sin (\pi + 2k\pi)]$, where k is an arbitrary positive integer. Hence, by Theorem 8.42, the three cube roots are $\cos (\pi/3 + 2k\pi/3) + i \sin (\pi/3 + 2k\pi/3)$, where $k = 0, 1, 2$. In more simple form, these three cube roots are:

$$\cos \frac{\pi}{3} + i \sin \frac{\pi}{3}, \cos \pi + i \sin \pi, \cos \frac{5\pi}{3} + i \sin \frac{5\pi}{3}.$$

Since,

$$\cos \frac{\pi}{3} = \cos \frac{5\pi}{3} = \frac{1}{2}, \text{ and } \sin \frac{\pi}{3} = \frac{\sqrt{3}}{2}, \sin \frac{5\pi}{3} = \frac{-\sqrt{3}}{2},$$

the three desired cube roots, in rectangular form, are:

$$\frac{1}{2} + \left(\frac{\sqrt{3}}{2}\right)i, \; -1, \frac{1}{2} - \left(\frac{\sqrt{3}}{2}\right)i.$$

In Figure 71, we have given a graphical representation of these three cube roots, which we note are equally spaced on the unit circle.

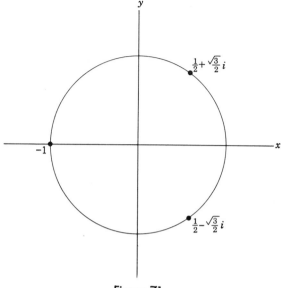

Figure 71

EXAMPLE 2.   Find the two square roots of $2 + 2i$.

SOLUTION.   The trigonometric form of $2 + 2i$ is $2\sqrt{2}(\cos \pi/4 + i \sin \pi/4)$. Hence the two square roots of the given number are:

$$\sqrt[4]{8}\left(\cos \frac{\pi}{8} + i \sin \frac{\pi}{8}\right); \; \sqrt[4]{8}\left(\cos \frac{9\pi}{8} + i \sin \frac{9\pi}{8}\right).$$

Now $\cos 9\pi/8 = -\cos \pi/8$ and $\sin 9\pi/8 = -\sin \pi/8$, while

$$\cos \frac{\pi}{8} = \sqrt{\frac{1 + \cos \pi/4}{2}} = \sqrt{\frac{1 + \sqrt{2}/2}{2}} = \frac{\sqrt{2 + \sqrt{2}}}{2},$$

and

$$\sin \frac{\pi}{8} = \sqrt{\frac{1 - \cos \pi/4}{2}} = \frac{\sqrt{2 - \sqrt{2}}}{2}.$$

Hence the two square roots of $2 + 2i$ are:

$$\sqrt[4]{8}\left(\frac{\sqrt{2 + \sqrt{2}}}{2} + \frac{\sqrt{2 - \sqrt{2}}}{2}i\right)$$

and

$$-\sqrt[4]{8}\left(\frac{\sqrt{2 + \sqrt{2}}}{2} + \frac{\sqrt{2 - \sqrt{2}}}{2}i\right).$$

EXAMPLE 3.   Find the five fifth roots of $1 + \sqrt{3}i$.

   SOLUTION.   The trigonometric form of $1 + \sqrt{3}i$ is $2(\cos \pi/3 + i \sin \pi/3)$. Hence the five fifth roots of $1 + \sqrt{3}i$ may be expressed as:

$$\sqrt[5]{2}\left[\cos\left(\frac{\frac{\pi}{3} + 2k\pi}{5}\right) + i \sin \frac{\frac{\pi}{3} + 2k\pi}{5}\right], \qquad \text{for } k = 0, 1, 2, 3, 4.$$

These roots may be expressed as $\sqrt[5]{2}[\cos \pi/15 + i \sin \pi/15]$, $\sqrt[5]{2}[\cos 7\pi/15 + i \sin 7\pi/15]$, $\sqrt[5]{2}[\cos 13\pi/15 + i \sin 13\pi/15]$, $\sqrt[5]{2}[\cos 19\pi/15 + i \sin 19\pi/15]$, and $\sqrt[5]{2}[\cos 5\pi/3 + i \sin 5\pi/3]$. The geometric representation of these numbers is given in Figure 72. If we need to know the rectangular form of the numbers, it is a simple matter to convert them with the help of Table 2. For example, $\pi/15 = 0.2094$, and from Table 2, $\cos 0.2094 = 0.9781$ while $\sin 0.2094 = 0.2079$. Hence, $\cos \pi/15 + i \sin \pi/15 = 0.9781 + 0.2079i$. The other fifth roots could be converted to decimal form in a similar manner, with a use of the Reduction Principle.

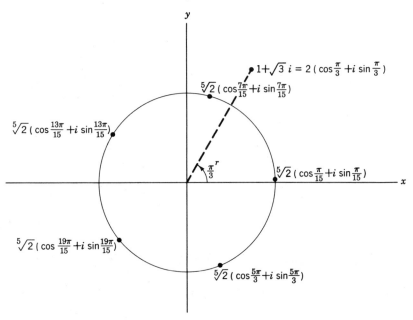

Figure 72

PROBLEMS

1. If ω is the nth root of unity with smallest positive argument, verify that the other n^{th} roots are $\omega^2, \omega^3, \ldots, \omega^n = 1$.

2. Use the symbolism of Problem 1 to express the five fifth roots of 32.
3. Find, in rectangular form, the four fourth roots of -1.
4. Find the four fourth roots of $-i$ and express in rectangular form.
5. Find the three cube roots of $\sqrt{3} + i$, and represent this number and its cube roots on a graph.
6. Find the five fifth roots of i, and represent this number and its fifth roots on a graph.
7. Use Table 2 to approximate in rectangular form the three cube roots of $2 - 3i$.
8. Use Table 2 to approximate in rectangular form the three cube roots of $3 + 4i$.
9. Determine the five complex solutions of the equation $x^5 = 1$.
10. If z is a solution of the equation $x^6 = 1$, prove that the conjugate $\bar{z}$ of z is also a solution.
11. Without any arithmetic analysis, use a diagram to construct the sixth roots of z, where: (a) $z = -1$; (b) $z = -i$; (c) $z = 64$; (d) $z = 1 + i$.
12. Write each of the following numbers in the form bi, where b is real: (a) $\sqrt{-16}$; (b) $\sqrt{-36}$; (c) $\sqrt{-12}$.
13. If we designate one square root of a complex number as $\sqrt{z}$, would it be correct to designate the other one as $-\sqrt{z}$? Give a reason for your answer.
14. Extend the proof of DeMoivre's theorem to the case where n is a negative integer.
15. Extend DeMoivre's theorem to the case where n is any rational number.
16. What is the geometric effect of multiplying a complex number by either square root of i?
17. Decide if the following indicated equalities are true or false: (a) $|z|^2 = |z^2|$; (b) $\sqrt{|a|} = |\sqrt{a}|$, where $a < 0$, and $\sqrt{a}$ is either square root of a.
18. If $f(z)$ is defined to be the real component of $\bar{z}$, the conjugate of z, determine each of the following: (a) $f(2 + i)$; (b) $f(z + w)$, where $z = 1 - i$ and $w = 2 + 3i$; (c) $f(zw)$, where z and w are given by (b).
19. If z is any complex number, prove that $1 + z + z^2 + z^3 = (1 - z^4)/(1 - z)$.
20. Use the result of Problem 19 to prove that $1 + \cos \theta + \cos 2\theta + \cos 3\theta = \dfrac{1}{2} + \dfrac{\sin 7\theta/2}{2 \sin \theta/2}$.
21. Solve the equation $x^3 + i$, and express each solution in the form $a + bi$.
22. Factor $x^3 - 64$ into linear factors.
23. Verify that the rules for multiplication and division of numbers of the form $re^{i\theta}$, with r and θ real, are identical with the corresponding rules for numbers of the form $r(\cos \theta + i \sin \theta)$, provided we assume that the usual laws of exponents hold for complex exponents.
24. If we were to identify the number $re^{i\theta}$ with the number $r(\cos \theta + i \sin \theta)$, determine the trigonometric form of $e^{\pi i}$. [This identification is justified in more advanced courses.]
25. How would *you* now answer the question "What is a Number?"

CHAPTER 9

Theory of Equations

9.1   Polynomials

Previously, we used the word "polynomial" to refer to an expression of the form $a_0x^n + a_1x^{n-1} + \cdots + a_{n-1}x + a_n$. While the nature of x depends on the context, the *coefficients* $a_0(\neq 0), a_1, \ldots, a_{n-1}, a_n$ are from some number system, usually a field, and the nonnegative integer n is called the *degree* of the polynomial. In our discussions, the coefficient field will be either the field R of real numbers or the field C of complex numbers. We note that elements from the field of coefficients are themselves considered to be polynomials of degree 0, since $a = ax^0$, for any field element $a \neq 0$. The number 0 is also considered a polynomial, but no degree is assigned to it. The additive parts of a polynomial, i.e., $a_0x^n, a_1x^{n-1}, \ldots, a_{n-1}x$, and a_n are called its *terms*. We shall always use $P[x]$ to designate a polynomial in x, with $\deg P[x]$ indicating its degree.

If the rule of mapping of a function f is given by an equation of the form $f(x) = P[x]$, for any x in the domain of f, then f is said to be a *polynomial function*. For example, the function f, defined on R by $f(x) = 3x^4 - x + 4$, is a polynomial function.

The algebraic operations of a number system are the operations of addition, subtraction, multiplication, division, and the extraction of roots. We have already seen that, in the field C, it is possible to perform all these operations except division by 0. (We recall, however, that before an expression such as $\sqrt[n]{1 - i}$ has an unambiguous meaning, we must make clear which of the n n^{th} roots is to be understood.) If we include along with the set of complex numbers a symbol x, and *formally* perform any sequence of these operations on the enlarged system, we obtain what are called *algebraic expressions* in x. Examples of such algebraic expressions are:

$$2x - 1, \sqrt{3 + 2x}, \frac{1 - 3x}{1 + 2x}, (2i - 1)x^2 + \frac{1}{(i - 1)x}.$$

It may be worthwhile to point out that, if other processes are permitted, it is possible to obtain nonalgebraic, or "transcendental," expressions, such as $e^{\sin x}$, $\cos(1 + x)$, and $\ln(2x - 1)$. A polynomial in x is, of course, a special kind of algebraic expression, and it is with polynomials that we are to be mostly concerned in this chapter.

There is an arithmetic of polynomials, just as there is for any number system and for functions. As a matter of fact, the arithmetic of polynomials with coefficients in a field is very much like the arithmetic of integers. In both of these systems, it is possible to perform additions, subtractions, and multiplications without exceptions. However, in order to obtain a system closed under division (except by 0), it was necessary to extend the integers to the field of rational numbers; for the same reason we must extend the system of polynomials to the field of all "rational functions" of x, which means that we must include all quotients $P[x]/Q[x]$ of polynomials $P[x]$ and $Q[x]$ ($\neq 0$). In order to obtain root extractions, it is necessary to extend the field of rational functions still further to fields of so-called "algebraic functions," but we shall not discuss this type of field extension here.

The student is probably familiar with the pertinent definitions of the relations and operations in the system of all polynomials with coefficients in C. However, we shall review them briefly, using the polynomials $P_1[x]$ and $P_2[x]$, where $P_1[x] = \sum_{k=0}^{m} a_k x^{m-k}$ and $P_2[x] = \sum_{k=0}^{n} b_k x^{n-k}$, $n \geq m$. We may assume that coefficients which do not appear are zero.

Equality

$$P_1[x] = P_2[x] \text{ if and only if } a_k = b_k, \quad k = 0, 1, 2, \ldots, n.$$

That is, two polynomials are "equal" if corresponding coefficients are equal. For example, if $ax^3 + bx^2 + cx + d = 3x^2 - 2x - 1$, it follows that $a = 0, b = 3, c = -2, d = -1$.

Addition and Subtraction

$$P_1[x] \pm P_2[x] = \sum_{k=0}^{n} (a_k \pm b_k)x^k.$$

This means that we add (or subtract) polynomials by formally adding (or subtracting) corresponding coefficients of the polynomials. For example,

$$(3x^3 + 2x - 5) + (x^3 - 2x^2 + x + 4) = 4x^3 - 2x^2 + 3x - 1.$$

Multiplication

$$P_1[x] \cdot P_2[x] = \sum_{k=0}^{n+m} c_k x^k, \text{ where } c_k = \sum_{i=0}^{k} a_i b_{k-i}, \quad k = 0, 1, 2, \ldots, n+m.$$

This means, in effect, that we multiply two polynomials, by multiplying each term of one by each term of the other, according to the rule that $(ax^r)(bx^s) = abx^{r+s}$, and then collect terms having like powers of x. For example,

$$(2x^2 - x + 1)(3x^2 + 2) = 6x^4 + 4x^2 - 3x^3 - 2x + 3x^2 + 2$$
$$= 6x^4 - 3x^3 + 7x^2 - 2x + 2.$$

Division.   We have already pointed out that while the division of one polynomial by another can always be formally indicated, the quotient is not always a polynomial. In the system of integers it is the *Division Algorithm* which asserts that for two integers $m, n > 0$, there exist integers q and r, $0 \leq r < n$, such that $m = nq + r$ or $m/n = q + r/n$. In this division process, q is the *quotient* and r is the *remainder*. In the system of polynomials with complex coefficients, there is a similar algorithm which we now state as a theorem without proof.

THEOREM 9.11.   If $P[x]$ and $D[x]$ ($\neq 0$) are two polynomials, there exists polynomials $Q[x]$ and $R[x]$, where $0 \leq \deg R[x] < \deg D[x]$, such that $P[x] = D[x] \cdot Q[x] + R[x]$, or $P[x]/D[x] = Q[x] + R[x]/D[x]$.

The actual procedure for determining the quotient and remainder for two polynomials is much like long division in ordinary arithmetic, and we merely illustrate with an example.

EXAMPLE.   Find the quotient and remainder when $3x^4 + x^2 - x + 1$ is divided by $x^2 - 2$.

SOLUTION

$$
\begin{array}{r|ll}
x^2 - 2 & 3x^4 + x^2 - x + 1 & \underline{3x^2 + 7} \\
& \underline{3x^4 - 6x^2} & \\
& 7x^2 - x & \\
& 7x^2 - 14 & \\
& \overline{-x + 15.} &
\end{array}
$$

Thus,

$$3x^4 + x^2 - x + 1 = (x^2 - 2)(3x^2 + 7) + (15 - x),$$

or

$$\frac{(3x^4 + x^2 - x + 1)}{x^2 - 2} = 3x^2 + 7 + \frac{15 - x}{x^2 - 2}.$$

In this case, $Q[x] = 3x^2 + 7$ and $R[x] = 15 - x$.

In a later section we shall give an abbreviated method, known as "synthetic division," which is applicable to a very special type of divisor.

Our principal concern in this chapter is with *polynomial equations* of the form $P[x] = 0$. In such an equation x is no longer to be considered a formal symbol but is understood to be a variable whose universe is C. Hence, a polynomial equation does not express an equality of polynomials, as discussed earlier, but is rather an open sentence which becomes an equality between complex numbers after a proper replacement of x from C. The two notions of equality become the same in case the polynomial equation is in fact an identity—and is then true for any complex substitution for x. By a "solution" of a polynomial equation we mean a complex number r which, when substituted for x in the equation, reduces it to a true equality. We then write that $P[r] = 0$. The *complete solution* or the *solution set* of the equation is, of course, the set of all such complex number solutions. It is easy to see that 2 is a solution of the equation $x^4 - 2x^3 + x^2 - 4 = 0$, for $2^4 - 2(2^3) + 2^2 - 4 = 0$. It is a much more difficult job to start with the equation and discover the solution 2. However, the theory of equations is for the most part devoted to this project of discovery for a given polynomial equation.

PROBLEMS

1. Classify the following expressions as algebraic or nonalgebraic in x: (a) $1 + 2x$; (b) $(1 - x^2)/(1 + x^2)$; (c) $2^{\sin x}$; (d) 3^x; (e) $2 + 3x - x^2$; (f) $\sqrt{2} - x + x^2$; (g) $(1 + x)^{2/3}$.
2. Find the sum of the indicated polynomials: (a) $x^3 - 2x + 3$, $2x - 4$; (b) $3x^4 + x^2 - 2x + 1$, $3x^3 - 3x^2 + x - 5$; (c) $3 + 2x$, $2 + 5x - 2x^2 + x^3$.
3. Subtract the first polynomial from the second for each pair of polynomials in Problem 2.
4. Find the product of each pair of polynomials in Problem 2.
5. With reference to the polynomials in Problem 2, divide the one of least degree into the other member of each pair, using the long division process.
6. Given the two polynomials, $2x^2 - (1 - i)x + 1$, $(1 - i)x^3 + 3ix - 4$: (a) Find their sum; (b) Subtract the first from the second; (c) Find their product.
7. Find the quotient and remainder when the first polynomial of Problem 6 is divided into the second.
8. Give the degree of each of the following polynomials: (a) $3x^4 - 1$; (b) $2x^3 - 3x + 2$; (c) $ix^2 + (1 + i)x - 2$; (d) $2 - ix + ix^5$.
9. Use the long division process to divide $3x^4 - 2x^2 + 2x - 5$ by $x^2 + x - 1$.
10. By $nP[x]$, we mean $P[x] + P[x] + \cdots + P[x]$, with n summands. If $P[x] = 2x^3 + 3x - 2$, $Q[x] = x^2 - 1$, $R[x] = 2x - 1$, find each of the following in polynomial form: (a) $P[x] + 2Q[x]$; (b) $3P[x] + 2R[x]$; (c) $(P[x])^2(Q[x])^2$; (d) $P[x] + 2Q[x] - 4R[x]$.

11. With reference to the polynomials of Problem 10, find the degree of each of the following: (a) $(P[x])^3(R[x])$; (b) $2P[x] - 3(Q[x])^2$; (c) $Q[x] + 3(P[x] - 2)^2$.
12. If $P[x] = 3x^3 - 2x^2 + x + 1$, find: (a) $P[1]$; (b) $P[-1]$; (c) $P[2]$; (d) $P[c]$; (e) $P[x + h] - P[x]$; (f) $P[c] + P[-c]$.
13. Use the Division Algorithm for integers to determine integers q and $r \geq 0$, $r < d$, such that $p = qd + r$, where: (a) $p = 17$, $d = 4$; (b) $p = 435$, $d = 13$; (c) $p = 146$, $d = 39$.
14. If $P[x] = D[x] \cdot Q[x] + R[x]$, with deg $R[x] <$ deg $D[x]$, find $Q[x]$ and $R[x]$ where:
    (a) $P[x] = 4x^3 - 2x + 1$, $D[x] = 2x - 1$;
    (b) $P[x] = x^6 + 4x^4 - 3x^2 + 6$, $D[x] = x^2 + 2$;
    (c) $P[x] = 3x^4 - 2x^3 + x^2 + x - 2$, $D[x] = x - 3$.
15. A polynomial function is defined on R by $f(x) = 3x^3 - 2x + 1$, for any x in R. Determine: (a) $f(-1)$; (b) $f(2)$; (c) $f(0)$; (d) $f(\frac{1}{2})$.
16. If $(x - 2)(x + 2) = 0$, we can conclude that $x - 2 = 0$ or $x + 2 = 0$. On the other hand, if $(x - 2)(x + 2) = 4$, why can we not conclude that $x - 2 = 4$ or $x + 2 = 4$? What property are we using in the first case?
17. Explain why it is evident that the equation $2x^4 + x^2 + 6 = 0$ has no real solution.
18. If we wish to solve the equation $P[x] = 0$ for complex solutions, explain the difference between this usage of the equality sign $(=)$ and that defined for polynomials in this section.
19. If g is a polynomial function defined on C by $g(z) = iz^3 - 2iz + 1$, determine: (a) $g(-1)$; (b) $g(1)$; (c) $g(1 + 2i)$; (d) $g(1/i)$.

9.2 Linear and Quadratic Equations

In this section we shall be concerned with equations of the form $ax^2 + bx + c = 0$, where the coefficients a, b, c are most frequently real numbers. If $a \neq 0$, the equation is quadratic, while if $a = 0$ and $b \neq 0$, the equation is linear. We have already used these words in connection with functions in Chapter 4, and it is likely that the student is familiar with equations of these two types. If not, a brief review is included in the Appendix, but in addition it may be in order at this time to take a somewhat more critical look at these types of equations.

The most general linear equation in one unknown with either real or complex coefficients is of the form $bx + c = 0$. Its only complex solution is $-c/b$, and this leads us to the following simple case of a more general result to be given in the next section.

THEOREM 9.21. If $P[x] = bx + c$ and $P[r] = 0$, then $P[x] = b(x - r)$.

PROOF. Since we have seen that $r = -c/b$, it follows that $b(x - r) = b[x - (-c/b)] = b(x + c/b) = bx + c = P[x]$.

Whether the solution $-c/b$ is to be accepted, in any given case, depends on the nature of the solution desired. For example, if we are interested only in integral solutions and $-c/b = \frac{2}{3}$, the equation has effectively no solution.

If f is a function defined on R by $f(x) = bx + c$, with b, c real, we noted in Chapter 4 that the graph of f is a straight line, and for this reason f is said to be a "linear" function. (It should be pointed out, however, that in more advanced mathematics it is preferred to restrict the use of the word "linear" to cases where $c = 0$. In such cases, the graphs must include the origin.) In a more geometric environment, it is customary to replace $f(x)$ by y, and refer to $y = bx + c$ as "the equation of the line" described as the graph of f. We are then emphasizing that the line consists of all points (x, y) such that $y = bx + c$. The solution $-c/b$ is the abscissa of the point where the line crosses the x-axis. It is not difficult to show that any equation of the form $ax + by + c = 0$ is the equation of some straight line in the Cartesian plane.

EXAMPLE 1.   Express $2x - 3$ in the factored form of Theorem 9.21.

SOLUTION.   If $2x - 3 = 0$, $2x = 3$, and so $x = \frac{3}{2}$. Hence, by Theorem 9.21,

$$2x - 3 = 2(x - \tfrac{3}{2}).$$

We now turn to quadratic equations of the form $ax^2 + bx + c = 0$, where $a \neq 0$, and all coefficients are considered to be real numbers. In the Appendix Review we have outlined two methods of solving such equations: (a) factoring; (b) completing the square. The method of factoring is based on the property that the product of two field elements can be 0 only if at least one of them is 0. The method of completing the square leads us to the Quadratic Formula and, since we shall be referring to this formula again, we repeat the result in the form of a theorem.

THEOREM 9.22.   If $P[x] = ax^2 + bx + x$, with $a(\neq 0)$, b, c real, the equation $P[x] = 0$ has two solutions r_1, r_2 (which may be equal) given by
$$r_1 = \frac{-b + \sqrt{b^2 - 4ac}}{2a}, r_2 = \frac{-b - \sqrt{b^2 - 4ac}}{2a}.$$

The number $b^2 - 4ac$ appearing under the radical sign is called the *discriminant d* of the equation, and it is this number which determines the nature of the solutions r_1, r_2. In terms of d, these solutions may be expressed in the form:

$$r_1 = \frac{-b + \sqrt{d}}{2a}, r_2 = \frac{-b - \sqrt{d}}{2a}.$$

We recall that, if d is a negative number, the symbol $\sqrt{d}$ has been defined as $\sqrt{|d|}\,i$, but we have not established any such convention if the coefficients and d are allowed to be general complex numbers. It is possible to establish a convention for this and derive a result which corresponds to Theorem 9.22 for the cases where a, b, c are complex numbers. However, we shall not pursue this matter here. It is now easy to see the validity of the relationship between d and the solutions of a general quadratic equation $ax^2 + bx + c = 0$, as described in the following table.

d	Solutions
$d = p^2$, p an integer	real, rational, unequal
$d = 0$	real, rational, equal
$0 < d \neq p^2$, p an integer	real, irrational, unequal
$d < 0$	complex conjugates

EXAMPLE 2.   Describe the nature of the solutions in C of the equation:

$$2x^2 + 2x + 5 = 0.$$

   SOLUTION.   In this case, $a = 2$, $b = 2$, $c = 5$. Hence, $d = 2^2 - 4(2)(5) = -36$, and we see that the solutions of the equation are complex conjugates. Since $\sqrt{-36} = 6i$, the actual solutions are $(-2 \pm 6i)/4$ or, more simply, $-\frac{1}{2} \pm 3i/2$.

   If a function f is defined on R by $f(x) = ax^2 + bx + c$, with a, b, c real, we have seen in Chapter 4 that the graph of f is called a "parabola," which opens up or down according as $a > 0$ or $a < 0$. The real solutions of $ax^2 + bx + c = 0$ are the abscissas of the points where the parabola crosses the x-axis. (If the parabola touches the axis at only one point, the equation has a unique real solution.) It is customary to refer to $y = ax^2 + bx + c$ as "the equation" of the parabola, the curve being regarded as the set of points (x, y) which satisfy the equation.

   If r_1 and r_2 are the two solutions of $ax^2 + bx + c = 0$, it is a matter of elementary computation to verify that:

$$r_1 + r_2 = \frac{-b}{a} \quad \text{and} \quad r_1 r_2 = \frac{c}{a}.$$

It is now possible to obtain the result analogous to Theorem 9.21 for quadratic equations.

THEOREM 9.23. If r_1 and r_2 are the complex (or real) solutions of $P[x] = ax^2 + bx + c = 0$, then $P[x] = a(x - r_1)(x - r_2)$.

SOLUTION. By direct multiplication, we see that $a(x - r_1)(x - r_2)$
$= a[x^2 - (r_1 + r_2)x + r_1r_2] = a[x^2 - (-b/a)x + c/a] = ax^2 + bx + c$
$= P[x]$.

EXAMPLE 3. Factor the polynomial $2x^2 - 3x + 1$.

SOLUTION. Since $a = 2$, $b = -3$, $c = 1$, it follows that $d = 9 - 8 = 1$. Hence $r_1 = (3 + 1)/4 = 1$ and $r_2 = (3 - 1)/4 = \frac{1}{2}$. It then follows, by Theorem 9.23, that $2x^2 - 3x + 1 = 2(x - \frac{1}{2})(x - 1)$.

EXAMPLE 4. Factor the polynomial $2x^2 + 2x + 5$.

SOLUTION. We discovered in Example 2 that the two complex solutions of the equation $2x^2 + 2x + 5 = 0$ are $r_1 = -\frac{1}{2} + 3i/2$ and $r_2 = -\frac{1}{2} - 3i/2$. By Theorem 9.23 we then have $2x^2 - 3x + 1 = 2(x + \frac{1}{2} - 3i/2)(x + \frac{1}{2} + 3i/2) = (\frac{1}{2})(2x + 1 - 3i)(2x + 1 + 3i)$.

In Example 4, we note that the coefficients of the factors are not all real numbers, although the original polynomial has only real coefficients. It is only because we now accept complex (and not necessarily real) coefficients that the given polynomial can be factored into linear factors.

PROBLEMS

Unless otherwise stated, the universe of each variable in any equation to be solved will be assumed to be C.

1. Solve each of the following equations for x: (a) $3x - 2 = 0$; (b) $4x + 3 = 0$; (c) $kx + t = 0$; (d) $sx - t = 0$; (e) $3x - 2 = x + 5$; (f) $x - 2 = -5x + 7$; (g) $2x/3 = \frac{7}{2}$; (h) $3x/2 - \frac{5}{3} = 0$.
2. Factor each of the following linear polynomials as outlined in Theorem 9.21: (a) $3x + 2$; (b) $5x - 3$; (c) $7x + 2$; (d) $kx + t$; (e) $3x/2 + \frac{5}{3}$; (f) $\frac{2}{5} - x/3$.
3. Solve each of the following equations for x: (a) $2x^2 - 3x + 1 = 0$; (b) $3x^2 + x - 3 = 0$; (c) $4x^2 + 2x + 3 = 0$; (d) $x^2 - 5x + 1 = 0$.
4. Use the form outlined in Theorem 9.23 to factor the left member of each of the equations given in Problem 3.
5. Without solving the equations, determine the sum and product of the solutions of each of the following equations: (a) $3x^2 - 2x + 1 = 0$; (b) $4x^2 + x + 3 = 0$; (c) $2x^2 - 3x + 1 = 0$; (d) $x^2 - 3x + 9 = 0$; (e) $3x^2 + px + q = 0$; (f) $rx^2 - 2x + t = 0$.
6. Find an equation, with integral coefficients, the sum and product of the solutions of which are, respectively: (a) $\frac{2}{3}$, $-\frac{3}{4}$; (b) 2, $-\frac{2}{3}$; (c) $\frac{3}{2}$, $\frac{3}{4}$; (d) $-4, 3$; (e) π, $\pi/4$; (f) π/c, $2\pi/c^2$.

7. Use a graph to approximate the real solutions of the equation:
(a) $2x^2 + 3x - 1 = 0$; (b) $x^2 - 5x + 5 = 0$; (c) $x^2 + 3x + 1 = 0$.

8. Solve each of the following equations for x:

(a) $\dfrac{x-2}{2} + \dfrac{x-1}{3} = \dfrac{3x+1}{6} - 5$;   (b) $t^2 - bx = a^2 + cx$;

(c) $xy + ix - (y+1) = 2 + 3i$.

9. Use the method of linear equations to solve each of the following equations for x: (a) $2x^2 + 5 = 0$; (b) $4x^2 - 3t = 0$; (c) $x^2 + k^2t^2 = 0$.

10. Use the method of linear equations to solve each of the following equations for x: (a) $2 \ln x - 3 = 7$; (b) $\ln x^2 - 2 = 0$; (c) $\ln x^4 = 16$; (d) $\dfrac{3^x - 1}{2} = \dfrac{3^x + 1}{3}$; (e) $2(10)^x - 3 = 5(10^x - 2)$.

11. Graph the line whose equation is: (a) $2x - 3y + 1 = 0$; (b) $3x + y - 6 = 0$; (c) $2x + y = 0$; (d) $3y + 7 = 0$.

12. A bottle contains a gallon of solution which is 30 per cent alcohol by volume. How much alcohol should be added to obtain a solution which is 40 per cent alcohol, assuming the capacity of the bottle is ample?

13. Draw the graph whose equation is $|x| + |y| = 1$.

14. It takes Jones three hours and Smith four hours to do a certain job. If both men work on the job, with neither interfering with the other, how long will it take for the job to be completed?

15. A man forty years of age has a son aged fourteen. In how many years will the son be half as old as his father?

16. Solve each of the following equations for the indicated variable:
(a) $S = (a - rh)/(1 - r)$ for h; (b) $S = n(a + b)/2$ for b; (c) $R = v_0 t + gt^2/2$ for v_0; (d) $y/(\sin \theta_1) = (2 + y)/(\sin \theta_2)$ for y.

17. Find two consecutive positive integers whose product is 72.

18. Determine the limitations on real k if the solutions of the following equations are real: (a) $x^2 + kx - 1 = 0$; (b) $2x^2 + x - k = 0$; (c) $kx^2 - 3x + 5k = 0$.

19. A plane takes $1\frac{1}{2}$ hours to fly to a certain spot against a constant head wind, while the return flight takes only one hour. If the wind velocity is 30 mph, determine the (assumed constant) air speed of the plane during the flight.

20. Solve for x: (a) $x^4 - 2x^2 + 1 = 0$; (b) $x^4 + 2x^2 - 15 = 0$; (c) $3x + 2\sqrt{x} = 2$; (d) $x^4 + 3ix^2 + 2 = 0$; (e) $x^2 - 4 + 3/x^2 = 0$; (f) $3x^{2/3} + 5 = 8x^{1/3}$.

21. Solve each of the following equations for real x: (a) $\sqrt{x-3} = \sqrt{8-2x}$; (b) $\sqrt{x-1} = \sqrt{2x-3} + 1$; (c) $\sqrt{x+2} + 2 = \sqrt{4x+8}$.
Be sure to check your solutions in the respective equations, because extraneous "solutions" may occur.

22. In solving the equation $x(x - 1) = x$, why is it not permitted to divide both members of the equation by x?

23. Solve $4 \sin^2 2\theta + 2 \cos^2 2\theta - 3 = 0$ for all θ such that $0 \le \theta \le 2\pi$.

24. Solve the equation $2 \sin^2 \theta + 3 \cos \theta = 0$ for all θ such that $0 \le \theta \le 2\pi$.

25. Determine k if $P[x] = 2x^2 - 3x - (k - 2)$ and: (a) 2 is a solution of $P[x] = 0$; (b) the two solutions of $P[x] = 0$ are reciprocals of each other; (c) the product of the solutions of $P[x] = 0$ is -5.

9.3   The Remainder and Factor Theorems

We now consider several theorems which will be of use in determining the solution set of a polynomial equation $P[x] = 0$, the coefficients of $P[x]$ being complex (or real) numbers. It will be convenient sometimes to speak of the *zeros* of the polynomial rather than the *solutions* of the polynomial equation, but the notions are the same. The first theorem is a consequence of the Division Algorithm theorem discussed in §9.1.

THEOREM 9.31   (Remainder Theorem).   If a polynomial $P[x]$ is divided by a binomial of the form $x - a$, where a is any complex number, until a remainder r free of x is obtained, then $r = P[a]$.

PROOF.   Theorem 9.11 implies the existence of a polynomial $Q[x]$ and a complex number r such that $P[x] = (x - a)Q[x] + r$. This equation is an identity, valid for every real number x, and is valid in particular if $x = a$. Hence, on substituting a for x we obtain $P[a] = 0 + r = r$.

EXAMPLE 1.   Use the Remainder Theorem to determine the remainder when $P[x] = 3x^4 - x^2 + x - 2$ is divided by $x + 2$.

SOLUTION.   Since $x + 2 = x - (-2)$, the desired remainder is $P[-2]$, or $3(-2)^4 - (-2)^2 + (-2) - 2 = 48 - 4 - 2 - 2 = 40$. This result can be verified by actual division.

THEOREM 9.32   (Factor Theorem).   If a is a zero of $P[x]$, then $x - a$ is a factor of $P[x]$.

PROOF.   The assertion that a is a zero of $P[x]$ implies that $P[a] = 0$, and so, by the Remainder Theorem, $r = P[a] = 0$. It is then a consequence of Theorem 9.11 that there exists a polynomial $Q[x]$ such that $P[x] = (x - a)Q[x]$, and so $x - a$ is a factor of $P[x]$.

It is an immediate consequence of this theorem that linear factors of $P[x]$ are determined as zeros of $P[x]$ are discovered. The converse of the Factor Theorem is also immediate: If $x - a$ is a factor of $P[x]$, it is quite clear that a is a zero of $P[x]$. That every polynomial of degree $n \geq 1$ has a zero is the statement of the following theorem which we have previously listed as Theorem 8.21.

THEOREM 9.33   (Fundamental Theorem of Algebra).   Any polynomial equation $P[x] = 0$ of degree $n \geq 1$, with complex coefficients, has a complex number as a solution.

As indicated earlier, many proofs of this theorem are available, but they are all beyond the scope of this book.

It is now easy to use the Fundamental Theorem and the Factor Theorem to find the complete solution set—at least theoretically— of any polynomial equation. The Fundamental Theorem asserts the existence of *one* solution for such an equation, but the proof of the following theorem illustrates a procedure for finding *all* solutions—i.e., the procedure actually terminates. By the "multiplicity" of a zero *a* of $P[x]$, we shall mean the number of times $x - a$ occurs as a factor of $P[x]$.

THEOREM 9.34.   The number of zeros of a polynomial $P[x]$ of degree n is s, where $s \leq n$. If n_i is the multiplicity of the zero a_i, then

$$\sum_{i=1}^{s} n_i = n.$$

PROOF.   The Fundamental Theorem asserts the existence of a zero a_1 of $P[x]$, and by the Factor Theorem we may write $P[x] = (x - a_1)Q_1[x]$, where $Q_1[x]$ is a polynomial of degree $n - 1$. If we apply the Fundamental Theorem to $Q_1[x]$, we know there exists a zero a_2 of $Q_1[x]$, and by the Factor Theorem $Q_1[x] = (x - a_2)Q_2[x]$, where $Q_2[x]$ is a polynomial of degree $n - 2$. But then $P[x] = (x - a_1)(x - a_2)Q_2[x]$. This procedure may be continued, but it is clear that it must terminate after n stages, for otherwise the degree of the product of the factors would exceed n. Hence, $P[x] = (x - a_1)(x - a_2) \cdots (x - a_n)a_0$, where a_0 is some complex number (a polynomial of degree 0). By multiplication, it is evident that a_0 must be the leading coefficient of $P[x]$, i.e., the coefficient of x^n. It may happen, of course, that not all of $a_1, a_2, \ldots , a_n$ are distinct, but if s of these solutions are distinct it must be the case that $s \leq n$, as stated in the theorem. Moreover, the manner in which the zeros were obtained implies that, if a_i occurred n_i times, then $\sum_{i=1}^{s} n_i = n$.

Theorem 9.34 is the generalization of Theorems 9.21 and 9.23 which was promised in §9.2.

EXAMPLE 2.   Find a polynomial equation of degree 3 whose solution set is $\{-1, 2, -3\}$.

SOLUTION.   The Factor Theorem implies that $x + 1, x - 2$, and $x + 3$ are factors of the desired polynomial, and no more than three linear factors are permitted by Theorem 9.34. Hence, $P[x] = a_0(x + 1)(x - 2)(x + 3)$, where $a_0 (\neq 0)$ may be chosen at random. If we let $a_0 = 1$, we obtain $(x + 1)(x - 2)(x + 3) = 0$ or, equivalently, $x^3 + 2x^2 - 5x - 6 = 0$ as a satisfactory polynomial equation.

The converse of the Factor Theorem, referred to above, along with Theorem 9.34 lead us to an important result in the solution of polynomial equations: Each linear factor of $P[x]$ provides us with a zero of $P[x]$, and Theorem 9.34 guarantees that no more zeros are possible. Hence, we obtain the complete solution set of a polynomial equation by determining the set of zeros of the various linear factors of the polynomial.

EXAMPLE 3. Solve the equation $x^3 - 27 = 0$.

SOLUTION. Since 3 is an evident solution of the equation, $x - 3$ is a factor of $x^3 - 27$. By actual division, we find that $x^3 - 27 = (x - 3)(x^2 + 3x + 9)$. We can use the Quadratic Formula to find the zeros of $x^2 + 3x + 9$, and we find them to be $(-3 \pm \sqrt{9 - 36})/2$, i.e., $(-3 \pm 3\sqrt{3}i)/2$. The desired set of solutions is then $\{3, (-3 \pm 3\sqrt{3}i)/2\}$.

EXAMPLE 4. Determine the complete solution set of the equation $(2x - 1)(x - 1)(x^2 + 1) = 0$.

SOLUTION. Since the zeros of the individual factors are $\frac{1}{2}$, 1, $\pm i$, the solution set of the given equation is $\{\frac{1}{2}, 1, \pm i\}$.

We remark that the Quadratic Formula makes it unnecessary to factor every quadratic factor of a polynomial into linear factors, in order to obtain the zeros of the polynomial. It is clear that this can be done, however, if we so desire.

PROBLEMS

1. Determine the polynomial with lowest degree and leading coefficient 1, having the following zeros: (a) $1, -2, 3$; (b) $0, 3, -3$; (c) $3, 2$; (d) $-1, 3, -2, 4$; (e) $0, 1, 2, -3, 4$.
2. Use the directions of Problem 1 for the following: (a) $2, i, -i, 1$; (b) $1 + i$, $1 - i, 3, 2$; (c) $2 - 3i, 2 + 3i, i, -i$; (d) $\frac{1}{2} + i, \frac{1}{2} - i, \frac{2}{3}$.
3. Use the directions of Problem 1 for the following: (a) $1 + i, i, -2$; (b) $3 - i, 2 + i, 4, -2$; (c) $0, i, 1 + i, -2$; (d) $0, 2 + 3i, 3 - 2i$.
4. Determine the polynomial with leading coefficient 1, having the following zeros, each of multiplicity 1 except as indicated: (a) $0, -1, 2$, with 2 a zero of multiplicity 3; (b) $-1, 2$, with 2 a zero of multiplicity 2; (c) $i, -1, 1$, with i a zero of multiplicity 3 and 1 a zero of multiplicity 2; (d) $1 - i, i$, with $1 - i$ a zero of multiplicity 2.
5. If $P[x] = 4x^3 - 2x^2 + x - 5$, use the Remainder Theorem to find: (a) $P[-2]$; (b) $P[1]$; (c) $P[i]$; (d) $P[-i/3]$.
6. If $P[x] = 2x^4 + x^2 - i$, use the Remainder Theorem to find: (a) $P[i]$; (b) $P[1 - 2i]$; (c) $P[i/2]$.
7. Determine the complete solution set of each of the following equations:

(a) $(x - 2)(x + 3)(x^2 + x + 1) = 0$; (b) $(x - 3)(x + 2)(x - 7)(x + 4) = 0$;
(c) $(x^2 - 5x + 6)(x^2 - x + 2) = 0$; (d) $(x - 4)(x^2 + x - 30)(x^2 - 1) = 0$.

8. Determine the complete solution set of each of the following equations:
   (a) $(x - 2)(x + 5)^3(x - 3) = 0$;   (b) $(x^2 + x + 1)^2(x^2 + 1)^3 = 0$;
   (c) $(x - 3)^2(x + 2)^3(x^2 - 1)^3(x^2 + 4)^2 = 0$.

9. With reference to Problem 8 and Theorem 9.34, in each case determine n, s, and n_i, and check that $\sum_{i=1}^{s} n_i = n$.

10. Determine the solution set of each of the following equations: (a) $3x^2 - 2ix + 3 + i = 0$; (b) $2ix^2 - 3x + 2 - i = 0$; (c) $x^2 + (i - 1)x - 1 = 0$;
    (d) $x^2 + ix - i = 0$.

11. Use the Remainder Theorem to find the remainder when: (a) $2x^3 - 3x + 1$ is divided by $x - 3$; (b) $2x^4 + x^2 - 5$ is divided by $x - \sqrt{2}$; (c) $x^3 - ix^2 + 3x - 1 + 2i$ is divided by $x + i/2$.

12. Use the Factor Theorem to verify that $x - a$ is a factor of $x^n - a^n$, for any positive integer n.

13. Use the Factor Theorem to verify that $x + y$ is a factor of $x^n + y^n$, for any odd positive integer n.

14. Determine the number k if: (a) $x + 1$ is a factor of $3x^3 - kx + 5$; (b) $x - 2$ is a factor of $2x^4 + k^2x^2 + 1$; (c) $x + 2$ is a factor of $2x^2 - 3k^2x + 3k$.

15. Express each of the following polynomials as a product of linear factors:
    (a) $x^4 - 16$; (b) $16x^4 - 1$; (c) $x^3 + x^2 - x - 1$; (d) $3x^3 - 2x^2 + x - 2$, given that 1 is a zero.

16. Find the polynomial of degree 6 with leading coefficient 1 which has 1 and -2 as its only zeros, and each occurs with the same multiplicity.

17. Is $x - 2$ a factor of $x^7 - 2x^4 - 30x - 36$? If so, give the multiplicity of 2 as a zero of the polynomial.

18. Find the complete solution set of $4x^3 - x - 3 = 0$, and express the left member of the equation as a product of linear factors.

19. Determine a and b so that: (a) $3x^3 + ax^2 - 5x + b$ is divisible by $x + 1$ and $x - 2$; (b) $x^4 + ax^3 + bx^2 - x + 2$ is divisible by $x^2 - 1$.

20. Use Theorem 9.34 to show that if $P[x]$ is a polynomial of formal degree n, but with $n + 1$ zeros, each of its coefficients must be 0.

21. Use the result of Problem 20 to show that if the zeros of $P[x]$ and $Q[x]$ are the same, and each with the same multiplicity, then $Q[x] = cP[x]$, for some complex number c.

9.4   Synthetic Division

The division of a polynomial by a binomial of the form $x - c$ can be abbreviated to a process known as *synthetic division*. The process is essentially that of ordinary long division, but with the omission of all but the essential numbers. While it is possible to use the method with nonreal coefficients, we shall restrict our illustrations to polynomials with real—and usually integral—coefficients. We shall demonstrate the method by means of an example. If the polynomial $2x^5 - x^4 + 12x^2 - 10x + 2$ is divided by $x + 2$, the steps of the long division process are shown below.

$$
\begin{array}{r}
x + 2\,\big|\,2x^5 - x^4 + 0x^3 + 12x^2 - 10x + 2\,\big|\,2x^4 - 5x^3 + 10x^2 - 8x + 6. \\
\underline{2x^5 + 4x^4} \\
- 5x^4 + 0x^3 \\
\underline{- 5x^4 - 10x^3} \\
10x^3 + 12x^2 \\
\underline{10x^3 + 20x^2} \\
- 8x^2 - 10x \\
\underline{- 8x^2 - 16x} \\
6x + 2 \\
\underline{6x + 12} \\
- 10
\end{array}
$$

Thus, $2x^5 - x^4 + 12x^2 - 10x + 2 = (2x^4 - 5x^3 + 10x^2 - 8x + 6)(x + 2) - 10$.

In the above arithmetic process, the powers of x play no important role except to keep the coefficients in order. It is then possible to omit the powers of x from the computation provided we are careful to keep the coefficients of these powers in distinct vertical columns. This has been done in the display below, *where we have been careful to include the coefficients 0 and 1.*

$$
\begin{array}{r}
1 + 2\,\big|\quad 2 \quad -1 \qquad 0 \qquad 12 \quad -10 \qquad 2 \quad\big|\,2 \quad -5 \quad 10 \quad -8 \quad 6. \\
\underline{2 \qquad 4} \\
-5 \qquad 0 \\
\underline{-5 \quad -10} \\
10 \qquad 12 \\
\underline{10 \qquad 20} \\
- 8 \quad -10 \\
\underline{- 8 \quad -16} \\
6 \qquad 2 \\
\underline{6 \qquad 12} \\
-10
\end{array}
$$

The above array of numbers can be simplified still further, because there are needless duplications. Two occurrences each of 2, -5, 0, 10, 12, -8, -10, 6, and 2 may be observed in the same vertical column, and with no intervening numbers as we examine the array of columns from left to right, and in each case the lower number can safely be omitted. If we then "project" the remaining numbers into three horizontal rows, the result will be as follows:

$$\underline{1+2|} \quad \begin{array}{rrrrrr} 2 & -1 & 0 & 12 & -10 & 2 \\ & 4 & -10 & 20 & -16 & 12 \\ \hline -5 & & 10 & -8 & 6 & -10 \end{array} \qquad \underline{|2 \quad -5 \quad 10 \quad -8 \quad 6.}$$

The coefficient 1 of x in the divisor is always 1, for the type of division under consideration, and so it may be omitted. If we copy the leading 2 of the dividend on the third row, the numbers on this row will be the coefficients of the quotient in their proper order, followed by the remainder -10. The original listing of the quotient may then be omitted, and we have simplified the arithmetic process to the abbreviated display below:

$$\underline{2|} \quad \begin{array}{rrrrrr} 2 & -1 & 0 & 12 & -10 & 2 \\ & 4 & -10 & 20 & -16 & 12 \\ \hline 2 & -5 & 10 & -8 & 6 & -10 \end{array}.$$

In this simplified form, we note that any number on the second row can be obtained by multiplying by 2 (the "divisor") the number on the third row in the column preceding it on the left; any number on the third row can be obtained by subtracting, in order, those on the second row from those on the first. Hence, by starting with the first number on the third row—which was merely copied from the first row—we can alternately produce the successive numbers of the second and third rows. After one further slight change we obtain the process known as *synthetic division*: We replace the divisor 2 by -2 (in general, change the sign of the divisor), and obtain the third row by the orderly *addition* of the numbers on the second row with those on the first. It is clear that the subtraction of any number is equivalent to the addition of its negative. The final computation would then have the following appearance:

$$\underline{-2|} \quad \begin{array}{rrrrrr} 2 & -1 & 0 & 12 & -10 & 2 \\ & -4 & 10 & -20 & 16 & -12 \\ \hline 2 & -5 & 10 & -8 & 6 & -10 \end{array}.$$

EXAMPLE 1.   Use synthetic division to divide $3x^4 - 2x^2 + x - 5$ by $x - 1$.

SOLUTION.   In this case, $c = 1$, and the computation by synthetic division will have the indicated form.

$$\underline{1|} \quad \begin{array}{rrrrr} 3 & 0 & -2 & 1 & -5 \\ & 3 & 3 & 1 & 2 \\ \hline 3 & 3 & 1 & 2 & -3 \end{array}$$

The quotient is then $3x^3 + 3x^2 + x + 2$ and the remainder is -3.

The process of synthetic division can be used to advantage in the checking of a possible zero of a polynomial. For if c is a zero of $P[x]$, the remainder, when $P[x]$ is divided by $x - c$, must be 0 as a consequence of the Remainder Theorem.

EXAMPLE 2.   Use synthetic division to show that -2 is a zero of

$$x^5 - 3x^3 + 4x^2 - 8.$$

SOLUTION.   The synthetic division computation, for the division of the polynomial by $x + 2$ [i.e., by $x - (-2)$] is shown below.

$$
\begin{array}{r|rrrrrr}
-2 & 1 & 0 & -3 & 4 & 0 & -8 \\
   &   & -2 & 4 & -2 & -4 & 8 \\
\hline
   & 1 & -2 & 1 & 2 & -4 & 0
\end{array}
$$

Since the remainder is 0, the number -2 is a zero of the given polynomial.

In our search for the real solution set of an equation, it will be found useful to establish upper and lower bounds to the magnitudes of these solutions. Our process of synthetic division provides us with two results which are very useful in this connection.

THEOREM 9.41 (Upper Bound).   Let $P[x]$ be a polynomial with real coefficients (not all 0), and $c > 0$ a real number. Then, in the process of synthetic division of $P[x]$ by $x - c$, if the numbers on the third row are all of the same sign—with a suitable sign for 0—the number c is an upper bound of the set of real zeros of $P[x]$.

PROOF.   We can write $P[x] = (x - c)Q[x] + r$, where $Q[x]$ is the quotient polynomial and r the real number remainder. The uniformity in sign of the numbers on the third row of the synthetic division computation implies that both r and $Q[x]$ have the same sign for any $x > 0$. More-over, if $x > c$, the number $x - c > 0$ and $P[x]$ will exceed r in absolute value, so that $P[x]$ can not be 0. Thus every real positive zero of $P[x]$ must be less than c, which is to say that c is an upper bound to its set of real zeros.

THEOREM 9.42 (Lower Bound).   Let $P[x]$ be a polynomial with real coefficients (not all 0), and $c < 0$ a real number. Then, in the process of synthetic division, if the numbers on the third row alternate in sign—with a suitable sign given to 0—the number c is a lower bound to the set of real zeros of $P[x]$.

PROOF. The proof of this theorem resembles that of Theorem 9.41, and depends on the fact that the alternating nature of the signs in the third row implies that $Q[x]$ and r are of opposite sign for any $x > 0$. If $x < c$, we then note that $x - c < 0$, and so $|P[x]| > |r|$, whence $P[x] \neq 0$ for any $x < c$. We leave the further details of the proof to the student.

EXAMPLE 3. Show by synthetic division that 4 is an upper bound and -2 is a lower bound of the set of real zeros of $x^4 - 3x^3 - 4x^2 + 3x - 7$.

SOLUTION. The computation below shows the division of the given polynomial by $x - 4$ and $x + 2$.

4		1	-3	-4	3	-7		-2		1	-3	-4	3	-7
			4	4	0	12					-2	10	-12	18
		1	1	0	3	5				1	-5	6	-9	11

Since the numbers on the third row of the left computation are all positive (with 0 being given a positive sign), and $4 > 0$, it follows from Theorem 9.41 that 4 is an upper bound of the set of zeros of the polynomial. Since $-2 < 0$, and the numbers on the third row of the right computation alternate in sign, it is a result of Theorem 9.42 that -2 is a lower bound of the sets of zeros. Hence, all real zeros t of the polynomial must satisfy the inequality $-2 < t < 4$.

When bounds are obtained in this way for the set of real zeros of a polynomial, they are, of course, in no way unique unless they are required to be integers. Moreover, it may happen that the best integral bounds can not be obtained by this method. It should be pointed out that the above theorems provide *sufficient* but not always *necessary* conditions for bounds of the set of real zeros of a polynomial.

PROBLEMS

1. Use synthetic division to divide $2x^3 - x^2 + 5x - 10$ by: (a) $x - 1$; (b) $x + 1$; (c) $x - 2$; (d) $x + 2$.
2. Use synthetic division to divide $4x^4 - 2x^2 + 5x - 2$ by: (a) $x - 3$; (b) $x + 3$; (c) $x - 4$; (d) $x + 4$.
3. Use synthetic division to divide $3x^3 - x^2 + 2x + 5$ by: (a) $x - \frac{1}{2}$; (b) $x + \frac{1}{2}$; (c) $x - \frac{2}{3}$; (d) $x + \frac{2}{3}$.
4. Use synthetic division to divide $4x^4 + x^2 - 8$ by: (a) $x - \frac{2}{3}$; (b) $x + \frac{1}{3}$; (c) $x - \frac{1}{2}$.
5. If $P[x] = 2x^3 + x - 5$, use synthetic division to compute: (a) $P[1]$; (b) $P[-1]$; (c) $P[2]$; (d) $P[-3]$.
6. If $P[x] = x^4 + x^2 + 6$, use synthetic division to compute: (a) $P[-3]$; (b) $P[-2]$; (c) $P[\frac{1}{2}]$; (d) $P[-\frac{1}{3}]$.

7. Use synthetic division to verify that 5 is an upper bound and -3 is a lower bound of the real zeros of $x^4 - 2x^3 - 9x^2 + 2x + 8$.

8. A polynomial function f is defined on R by $f(x) = 2x^4 - 3x + 5$. Use synthetic division to determine: (a) $f(1)$; (b) $f(-1)$; (c) $f(2)$; (d) $f(-\frac{1}{2})$.

9. Use the direction of Problem 8 if $f(x) = x^3 + x^2 - 2x + 1$.

10. Verify that the complete solution set of the equation $2x^3 - 5x^2 - 4x + 3 = 0$ is $\{-1, \frac{1}{2}, 3\}$. Use synthetic division, and apply the process to *successive* quotients, rather than reverting to the original polynomial each time. Why is this procedure valid?

11. Use the directions of Problem 10 for the polynomial equation $2x^4 + 3x^3 - 4x^2 - 3x + 2 = 0$ and the solution set $\{-2, -1, 1, \frac{1}{2}\}$.

12. Use synthetic division with random divisors to discover integral bounds for the real zeros of the following polynomials: (a) $2x^3 - 5x^2 + 6$; (b) $4x^4 + 2x^2 - 6x - 5$; (c) $3x^4 - 2x^2 + 8$.

13. Use synthetic division with random divisors to discover integral bounds for the real zeros of the following polynomials: (a) $4x^5 - x^2 + 2x - 6$; (b) $x^4 - 3x^3 + 2x^2 - x - 6$.

14. If $2x^2 - 3x + 1$ is divided by $x - c$, the remainder is 3. What are the possible values of c?

15. If $3x^2 - 5x - 1$ is divided by $x - c$, the remainder is 2. What are the possible values of c?

16. Use synthetic division to verify that, if $ax^2 + bx + c$ is divided by $x - 1$, the remainder is $a + b + c$. Also check this result with the Remainder Theorem.

17. Fill in the details of the proof of Theorem 9.42.

18. Determine k if: (a) the remainder is 5 when $3x^3 - x^2 + kx + 2$ is divided by $x - 2$; (b) the remainder is 2 when $kx^4 - x^3 + x - 6$ is divided by $x + 1$; (c) the remainder is -4 when $x^4 - 2kx^2 + x - 2$ is divided by $x + 2$.

19. Use synthetic division to compute a table of values of the function f, where f is defined on R by $f(x) = 2x^3 - 9x^2 + x + 1$, using all integral x satisfying $-2 \le x \le 4$. Use these values to sketch the function.

20. Use the directions of Problem 19 if $f(x) = 2x^4 - 10x^2 + x - 8$, $-3 \le x \le 3$.

21. If $x^3 - 2x^2 + kx - 4$ yields the same remainder when divided by $x - 2$ and $x + 2$, determine k.

22. Use the directions of Problem 21 if the given polynomial is $2x^4 + kx - 3x + 2$.

23. Make a slight modification of the synthetic division process to divide $3x^3 - x^2 + x - 6$ by: (a) $2x - 1$; (b) $3x + 2$; (c) $4x - 3$.

9.5   Real Polynomial Equations

In this and the final sections of the chapter, we shall consider the general problem of finding solutions for a polynomial equation with real coefficients. We shall find that, in general, the problem is a very difficult one.

It is possible, of course, that every complex number is a solution of an equation, and in such a case the equation is said to be an *identity*, a notion which we have discussed more carefully at an earlier time. For example, the equation $(x + 1)(x - 1) = x^2 - 1$ is an identity, and its solution set is C. Our first theorem is of interest in connection with identities.

THEOREM 9.51.   If a polynomial of degree n in x has more than n complex zeros, the coefficient of each power of x must be 0, and so the polynomial is identically 0.

PROOF.   Let $P[x]$ be the given polynomial, so that $P[x] = a_0 x^n + a_1 x^{n-1} + \cdots + a_{n-1}x + a_n$. By Theorem 9.34, we know that $P[x]$ has n complex zeros (possibly not all distinct), which we may designate as $c_1, c_2, \ldots, c_n$. The Factor Theorem then allows us to write:

$$P[x] = a_0(x - c_1)(x - c_2) \cdots (x - c_n).$$

If c is a zero of $P[x]$, with $c \neq c_i, i = 1, 2, \ldots, n$, then

$$a_0(c - c_1)(c - c_2) \cdots (c - c_n) = 0.$$

But, $c - c_i \neq 0, i = 1, 2, \ldots, n$, and so the absence of divisors of 0 in a field requires that $a_0 = 0$. But then, $P[x] = a_1 x^{n-1} + a_2 x^{n-2} + \cdots + a_{n-1} + a_n$, and our hypothesis is that $P[x]$ has more than n, and so *a fortiori* more than $n - 1$, zeros. A repetition of the previous argument then requires that $a_1 = 0$, and in like manner we can show that $a_2 = a_3 = \cdots = a_n = 0$. This completes the proof.

COROLLARY 9.51.   If the equation, formed by equating two polynomials of degree n or less, has more than n complex solutions, the two polynomials are identical.

PROOF.   Let the two polynomials be $a_0 x^n + a_1 x^{n-1} + \cdots + a_n$ and $b_0 x^n + b_1 x^{n-1} + \cdots + b_n$, where we are assuming that at least one of a_0, b_0 is not 0. Then any zero of both polynomials will also be a solution of

$$(a_0 - b_0)x^n + (a_1 - b_1)x^{n-1} + \cdots + (a_{n-1} - b_{n-1})x + a_n - b_n = 0,$$

and so this equation has more than n complex solutions. By the theorem it then follows that, $a_0 - b_0 = a_1 - b_1 = \cdots = a_n - b_n = 0$, and so $a_0 = b_0$, $a_1 = b_1, \ldots, a_n = b_n$. The two polynomials are then identical.

EXAMPLE 1.   Prove   that $\dfrac{(x - a)(x - b)}{(c - a)(c - b)} + \dfrac{(x - b)(x - c)}{(a - b)(a - c)} + \dfrac{(x - c)(x - a)}{(b - c)(b - a)} = 1$ is an identity for distinct, but otherwise arbitrary, complex numbers a, b, c.

PROOF. The above equation has degree 2 and it is immediate that a, b, c are 3 solutions. It then follows from Theorem 9.51 that the equation is an identity.

EXAMPLE 2. Without expanding, show that $(x - 1)^2 + 3(x + 1)^2$ and $4(x + 1)^2 - 4x$ are identical polynomials.

PROOF. If $x = 0$, both polynomials equal 4; if $x = 1$, both polynomials equal 12; if $x = -1$, both polynomials equal 4. Since the degree of each polynomial is 2, and the polynomials are equal for at least 3 distinct x, it follows from the Corollary that the polynomials are identical.

EXAMPLE 3. Determine real numbers A and B such that $A(2x + 1) + B(x - 2) = 5x - 5$ is to be an identity.

SOLUTION. The above equation may also be written $(2A + B)x + A - 2B = 5x - 5$ so that, by the Corollary, $2A + B = 5$ and $A - 2B = -5$. If we solve these equations for A and B we obtain $A = 1$ and $B = 3$.

It is clear that if an equation is known to be an identity, the problem of its solution presents no difficulty! Hence, let us return to a consideration of equations which are not identities, otherwise known as *conditional equations*. Since we have precise methods for determining the (real or complex) solutions of a linear or quadratic equation, it is clear that we can solve any polynomial equation $P[x] = 0$ if we can express $P[x]$ as a product of linear and quadratic factors. That such a factorization is at least theoretically possible is the result of the two following theorems.

THEOREM 9.52. Nonreal complex zeros of a real polynomial occur in conjugate pairs: if $a + bi$ is a zero, so is $a - bi$.

SOLUTION. We first assume that $a + bi$ is a nonreal zero of $P[x]$, and form the real product $(x - a - bi)(x - a + bi) = x^2 - 2ax + a^2 + b^2$ which we shall designate $D[x]$. If we now apply Theorem 9.11 to $P[x]$, with $D[x]$ as divisor, we obtain $P[x] = D[x]Q[x] + R[x]$, for polynomials $Q[x]$ and $R[x]$, where $R[x] = rx + s$ is of the first degree. Since $P[a + bi] = 0 = D[a + bi]$, it follows that $R[a + bi] = 0 = r(a + bi) + s = ra + s + rbi$. Hence, $ra + s = 0$ and $rb = 0$. Since $a + bi$ is assumed to be nonreal, $b \neq 0$, and so $r = s = 0$. Hence $R[x] = 0$ and $P[x] = D[x]Q[x]$. But $a + bi$ and $a - bi$ are the two conjugate complex zeros of $D[x]$, and so these numbers also appear as zeros of $P[x]$, as asserted.

THEOREM 9.53.   Any real polynomial can be written as a product of real linear and quadratic factors.

PROOF.   By Theorem 9.52, the nonreal zeros of a real polynomial $P[x]$ occur in conjugate pairs, and there is a quadratic real factor of $P[x]$ associated with each such pair of zeros. The zeros of any remaining factor must be all real, and if these are $a_1, a_2, \ldots, a_k$, this factor may be written as $a_0(x - a_1)(x - a_2) \cdots (x - a_k)$, with $a_0 \in R$, according to the Factor Theorem. Hence, if $D_1[x], D_2[x], \ldots, D_t[x]$ are the quadratic factors previously obtained, we may express $P[x]$ in the factored form:

$$P[x] = a_0(x - a_1)(x - a_2) \cdots (x - a_k)D_1[x]D_2[x] \cdots D_t[x],$$

a form which exhibits only real factors.

The two preceding theorems give us information about the nature of the zeros of a real polynomial, but they are of little practical use in an actual determination of these zeros. For no algorithm is provided for the factoring of $P[x]$, as is asserted by Theorem 9.53, and it is possible that the coefficients of the factors are irrational. There is one final result, which is sometimes of help in finding the solutions of a real polynomial equation. This is known as Descartes' Rule of Signs, a result which we state without proof. If the terms of a polynomial are arranged in order of descending powers of x, with all 0 terms omitted, we say there is a *variation in sign* when two adjacent coefficients are of opposite sign. For example, there are three variations in sign in $2x^5 - 4x^4 + 2x^2 - x - 2$ and one variation in sign in $2x^4 + x^2 - 5$.

THEOREM 9.54   (Descartes' Rule of Signs).   The number of positive real zeros of a polynomial $P[x]$ is equal to the number of variations in sign of the coefficients of $P[x]$, or less than this number by a positive even integer.

It is stated that the Rule gives information about *positive* real zeros only and gives no precise information even then. However, $P[c] = P[-(-c)]$, and so c is a negative zero of $P[x]$ if and only if $-c$ is a positive zero of $P[-x]$. Hence, we are able to consider the negative zeros of $P[x]$ by a consideration of the positive zeros of $P[-x]$.

EXAMPLE 4.   Use Descartes' Rule to examine the real solutions of the equation $3x^5 - 2x^3 + x^2 + 5x - 2 = 0$.

SOLUTION.   There are three variations in sign in the coefficients of the given polynomial, and so the number of positive real solutions is either 3 or 1. If we replace x by $-x$ in the polynomial, we obtain

$-3x^5 + 2x^3 + x^2 - 5x - 2 = 0$. Since there are two variations in sign in the coefficients of the polynomial on the left, there are either 2 or 0 negative solutions to the original equation. The various possibilities for the solutions of the equation are then as follows:

> 3 positive, 2 negative, no nonreal;
> 3 positive, no negative, 2 conjugate complex;
> 1 positive, 2 negative, 2 conjugate complex;
> 1 positive, no negative, 2 pairs of conjugate complex.

We note in closing this section that any polynomial equation with real coefficients, and with an odd degree, has at least one real solution.

PROBLEMS

1. Verify the following identity in C, for distinct numbers a, b, c:
$$\frac{(x-a)(x-b)}{(c-a)(c-b)}c^2 + \frac{(x-b)(x-c)}{(a-b)(a-c)}a^2 + \frac{(x-c)(x-a)}{(b-c)(b-a)}b^2 = x^2.$$

2. Verify, without expansion, that the following are identities in C:
(a) $(x+1)(x+2)(x-1) = (x-2)^3 + 8x(x-1) - 5x + 6$;
(b) $(x-2)(x+1) - (x-1)^2 = x - 3$.

3. Verify, without expansion, that the following are identities in C:
(a) $2(x-1)(x+2) - 3(x+1)(x-2) + (x-1)^2 = 3(x+1)$;
(b) $(x+1)(x-2)(x+2) = (x+1)^3 - 2(x+1)^2 - 3(x+1)$.

4. Determine real numbers A and B so that the following equations are identities in C:
(a) $A(x-1)^2 - B(x-2)^2 = 2(2x-3)$;
(b) $A(x-2)^2 + B(x+2)^2 = x^2 + 6x + 4$.

5. Determine real numbers A, B, C so that the following equations are identities in the field of complex numbers:
(a) $A(x-1)(x+2) + B(x+1)(x-1) + C(x-2)(x+1) = x^2 + x + 1$;
(b) $A(x-1)^2 + B(x-2)^2 + C(x+2)^2 = 4x^2 + 2x + 13$.

6. Determine real numbers A, B, C, D so that the following equations are identities in the field of complex numbers:
(a) $(A-1)x^3 + (B+2)x^2 + Cx - D = x^3 + x^2 + x - 2$;
(b) $Ax^3 + B(x-1)^2 + C(x+1)^2 + D(x-2) = 3x^2 + x + 5$.

7. Find a polynomial of the same degree, but with zeros the negatives of the zeros of the polynomial:
(a) $2x^3 - 3x^2 + 5x - 2$;   (b) $3x^4 - 2x^3 + x^2 - 5x + 1$;
(c) $x^4 + 2x^2 + 6$;   (d) $x^4 - 2x^3 + x^2 + 1$.

8. Without actually finding the solution sets, what can you say about the solutions of: (a) $3x^4 + 5x^2 - 2 = 0$; (b) $x^6 - 4x^4 + x^2 + 2 = 0$?

9. Use Descartes' Rule of Signs to obtain information about the real zeros of the polynomials in Problem 7.

10. Use Descartes' Rule of Signs to obtain information about the zeros of each of the following polynomials:

(a) $3x^3 - x^2 + 2x - 5$;   (b) $4x^4 + x^2 - 3x + 1$;
(c) $4x^4 + 2x^2 + 5$;   (d) $-3x^6 - 6x^4 + x^2 + 2x - 1$.

11. Write down an equation of degree n with real coefficients and with the indicated solutions c_1, c_2:

(a) $n = 2$, $c_1 = 1 - i$;   (b) $n = 3$, $c_1 = 1$, $c_2 = i$;
(c) $n = 4$, $c_1 = 1 + i$, $c_2 = 3 - i$;   (d) $n = 4$, $c_1 = i$, $c_2 = 2 + 2i$.

12. Write down an equation of degree n, with real coefficients, with solutions c_1, c_2, c_3, where:

(a) $n = 4$; $c_1 = 1$, $c_2 = 2 - 3i$;
(b) $n = 4$; $c_1 = -1$, $c_2 = 2$, $c_3 = 3 - i$;
(c) $n = 5$; $c_1 = 0$, $c_2 = 1 - i$, $c_3 = 2 - i$;
(d) $n = 6$; $c_1 = i$, $c_2 = 2i$, $c_3 = 1 + i$.

13. Factor the following polynomial into linear or quadratic factors with real coefficients, given that the number shown is a zero:

(a) $2x^3 + 5x^2 - 2x - 15$, $-2 + i$; (b) $x^4 - 7x^3 + 21x^2 - 37x + 30$, $1 - 2i$.

14. Use De Moivre's theorem to express the following polynomials as products of linear or quadratic polynomials: (a) $x^4 + 1$; (b) $x^4 + 16$; (c) $x^3 - 1$.

15. If $a + bi$ is a solution of $x^3 + px^2 + qx + r = 0$, verify by actual substitution that $a - bi$ is also a solution.

16. Explain why it is immediately evident that $2x^4 + 5x^2 + 1$ has no real zeros.

17. Show, without solving, that the real solutions (if any) of the equation $3x^4 - 2x^3 + x^2 - 2x + 4 = 0$ lie between 0 and 1.

18. If $P[x] = x^n + a_1x^{n-1} + a_2x^{n-2} + \cdots + a_{n-1}x + a_n$, and $M = \max |a_i|$, $i = 1, 2, \ldots, n$, show that $1 + M$ is an upper bound to the real zeros of $P[x]$.

19. Find the solutions of the equation $x^4 + x^3 - 2x^2 - 6x - 4 = 0$, given that $-1 + i$ is one solution.

20. Determine the numbers a and b such that $-2i$ is a zero of the polynomial $x^3 + 3x^2 + bx + c$.

21. Why is it true that no straight line can intersect the graph of a polynomial function in more than n points, if n is the degree of the defining polynomial?

9.6   Rational Zeros of Rational Polynomials

While the discussions of §9.5 are sometimes useful in solving polynomial equations, the results there were largely theoretical in nature and frequently of little help in solving a given equation. So we are still faced with the practical problem of determining the solutions of a polynomial equation. In view of the difficulty of the problem, we shall make a simplification and assume that the coefficients are rational numbers. In this case there is a finite—though sometimes tedious—procedure for finding the rational solutions, if there are any of this kind. In many cases, we shall see that the method actually gives us the complete complex solution set of the equation.

It is clear that the solutions of an equation are unchanged if each coefficient is multiplied by the same nonzero number. We may then assume that the coefficients of the rational polynomial equation have been "cleared" of fractions, so that the resulting equation has only integral coefficients. The following theorem is then very useful for determining the rational solutions.

THEOREM 9.61.   Let $P[x] = a_0x^n + a_1x^{n-1} + \cdots + a_{n-1}x + a_n$, where $a_0, a_1, \ldots, a_{n-1}, a_n$ are integers. Then, if p/q is a rational zero of $P[x]$, with p/q a fraction in reduced form, p is an integral divisor of a_n and q is an integral divisor of a_0.

PROOF.   Since p/q is a zero of $P[x]$,

$$a_0\left(\frac{p}{q}\right)^n + a_1\left(\frac{p}{q}\right)^{n-1} + \cdots + a_{n-1}\left(\frac{p}{q}\right) + a_n = 0.$$

If we multiply both members of this equality by q^n, we obtain:

$$a_0p^n + a_1p^{n-1}q + \cdots + a_{n-1}pq^{n-1} + a_nq^n = 0$$

or, in equivalent form,

$$a_0p^n + a_1p^{n-1}q + \cdots + a_{n-1}pq^{n-1} = -a_nq^n.$$

Since p may be factored out of the left member, p must be an integral divisor of the right member. But p and q are relatively prime, by our assumption, and so p must divide a_n, as asserted. If we write the above equality in the form

$$a_0p^n = -a_1p^{n-1}q - \cdots - a_{n-1}pq^{n-1} - a_nq^n,$$

it may be seen by a similar argument that q is an integral divisor or factor of a_0.

The theorem then supplies us with a complete list of possibilities for rational zeros of a polynomial, from a mere inspection of its first and last coefficients. It is apparent, of course, that if the leading coefficient of a polynomial is 1, the rational zeros of the polynomial are integers.

EXAMPLE 1.   From an inspection of the coefficients, determine the set of possible rational zeros of $2x^5 - 4x^3 + 2x - 9$.

SOLUTION.   Using the symbolism of a general polynomial, we see that $a_0 = 2$ and $a_5 = -9$. Hence, if p divides -9 and q divides 2, the choices for p are $\pm 1, \pm 3, \pm 9$, while the choices for q are $\pm 1, \pm 2$. After duplicates have been eliminated, the remaining possible solutions of the form p/q, as required by the theorem, are:

$$\pm 1, \ \pm 3, \ \pm 9, \ \pm \tfrac{1}{2}, \ \pm \tfrac{3}{2}, \ \pm \tfrac{9}{2}.$$

After we have obtained the set of possible rational solutions of an equation, there remains the problem of checking each of these numbers. Of course, there may be no rational solutions, but the checking may be accomplished by means of synthetic division. In this connection, it may be useful to note that if a fraction ever appears on the third row of a synthetic division computation, the rational number being checked may be immediately discarded.

EXAMPLE 2.   Determine the rational solutions of the equation:

$$2x^4 - 5x^3 + 7x^2 - 10x + 6 = 0.$$

SOLUTION.   An application of the above theorem shows that the rational solutions are contained in the set $\{\pm 1, \pm 2, \pm 3, \pm 6, \pm \tfrac{1}{2}, \pm \tfrac{3}{2}\}$. If we now make a systematic check of these numbers, we find that $\tfrac{3}{2}$ and 1 are solutions. The computation for these two cases is shown below, the "reduced" or quotient polynomial being used for the second check.

$\tfrac{3}{2}$	2	-5	7	-10	6		1	2	-2	4	-4
		3	-3	6	-6				2	0	4
	2	-2	4	-4	0			2	0	4	0

We now observe that the final quotient, after the removal of the factors $x - \tfrac{3}{2}$ and $x - 1$, is $2x^2 + 4$. The zeros of this polynomial are clearly $\pm \sqrt{2}i$, and so the solution set of the original equation is $\{\tfrac{3}{2}, 1, \pm \sqrt{2}i\}$.

In checking the candidates for rational solutions of an equation, it is often the case that the work may be reduced by taking advantage of some of the results which we obtained in earlier sections. For example, it may happen that upper or lower bounds to the solutions are apparent from the synthetic division computation, and if so, certain of the candidates may be eliminated from further consideration. Moreover, as in Example 2, we could use Descartes' Rule of Signs to observe that the equation can have no negative real solutions. This observation by itself would reduce by one-half the number of checks to be made.

We close this section and chapter with a very modest appraisal of what we have accomplished. The problem of solving a general polynomial equation has been left unsolved, for we have considered principally the rational solutions of rational equations. If we have been able to get the complete complex solution set of an equation, we have been lucky on account of the low degree of the "reduced" equation. But, as a matter of fact, the occurrence of polynomial equations with rational solutions is quite rare outside of "textbook" problems: most equations which are encountered in practice have only irrational or nonreal solutions. There are methods for attacking the more general problem which we have left undone, but they are beyond the scope of this book. (One somewhat common method of this type is known as "Newton's Method," but this involves a knowledge of differential calculus and is available only for the real solutions.) With the advent of modern, high-speed computers, however, by means of which it is possible to set up "programs" for the solution of an equation, the importance of these longhand methods of solution appears to have diminished.

It may be useful to point out that graphical methods may be used to *approximate* the real—and in particular the irrational—solutions of an equation. For the real solutions of an equation $y = f(x)$ are the abscissas of the points of intersection of the graph of f with the x-axis. If a careful graph of f is constructed it may be possible to use this method to obtain a satisfactory rational approximation to any real solution. The property described in Problem 11 may be very useful for this purpose. As a matter of fact, with unlimited time and patience, it is possible to obtain a graphical approximation to any real solution of any polynomial equation to any desired degree of accuracy. Without adequate tables of logarithms and circular functions, however, there is a limit to the accuracy with which one can solve a transcendental equation involving these nonalgebraic functions.

PROBLEMS

1. By inspection of the coefficients, determine the set of possible rational solutions of each of the following equations:
   (a) $2x^4 - 4x^3 + x - 6 = 0$;   (b) $4x^3 - 3x^2 + 2x + 3 = 0$;
   (c) $3x^5 - 3x^3 + 4x^2 - 2x + 8 = 0$;   (d) $8x^4 - 3x^2 + 5x - 8 = 0$.
2. Inspect the coefficients and apply Descartes' Rule, if useful, to determine the set of possible rational zeros of each of the following polynomials:
   (a) $3x^5 - 2x^4 + x^3 - 5x + 9$; (b) $5x^4 + 2x^2 + 12$; (c) $5x^4 - 3x^2 + 6x - 8$;
   (d) $2x^4 + x^3 + x^2 + 1$.
3. Use the direction of Problem 2 for each of the following polynomials:
   (a) $3x^4 + 2x^3 + x^2 + 5$; (b) $5x^5 - 7x^3 + 2x - 1$; (c) $2x^4 - 5x^2 + 8$;
   (d) $1 + 2x + 3x^2 + 4x^3 + x^5$.
4. Use the method of this section to discover any rational solutions of the equation $3x^2 - 5 = 0$. Since $\sqrt{\frac{5}{3}}$ is a solution, comment on the nature of this number.
5. Find the rational solutions of each of the following equations and, if the reduced equation is quadratic, complete the complex solution set:
   (a) $2x^4 - 5x^3 + 4x^2 - 5x + 2 = 0$;
   (b) $6x^4 - x^3 - 8x^2 + x + 2 = 0$;
   (c) $x^4 - 2x^3 + x^2 + 2x - 2 = 0$;
   (d) $3x^6 - 16x^5 + 26x^4 + 2x^3 - 33x^2 + 10x = 0$.
6. Use the direction of Problem 5 for each of the following equations:
   (a) $6x^3 - 35x^2 + 19x + 30 = 0$;

(b) $3x^3 + 13x^2 + 2x - 8 = 0$;
(c) $x^4 + 2x^3 - 13x^2 + 10x = 0$;
(d) $x^4 - 9x^3 + 30x^2 - 44x + 24 = 0$.

7. Write down an equation of degree 4 which will have: (a) no positive solutions; (b) no negative solutions; (c) no real solutions.

8. Determine all rational zeros of the following polynomials, or show that none exist:
(a) $x^4 - x^3 + 5x^2/9 + 4x/9 - \frac{4}{9}$;
(b) $x^4 + 3x^3/2 + x^2 - \frac{1}{2}$;
(c) $x^6 + 3x^3/2 + x/2$.

9. Show that the polynomial equation $x^3 + 3x - 5 = 0$ has no rational solution.

10. Determine the complete complex solution set of: (a) $4x^3 - 3x^2 + 4x - 3 = 0$; (b) $x^3 + 3x^2/2 + x + \frac{3}{2} = 0$.

11. If $P[a]$ and $P[b]$ are of opposite sign, there is at least one real zero of the polynomial $P[x]$ between a and b. Use this fact to isolate between integers the real zeros of the following polynomials: (a) $x^3 - 3x + 1$; (b) $x^3 + 2x^2 - 6x + 3$; (c) $x^3 - x^2 - 11x + 14$; (d) $x^4 - 11x - 50$.

12. Use the statement of fact in Problem 11 to isolate between integers the real zeros of $x^4 - 2x^3 - 3x^2 + 2x + 1$.

13. For what value of k will $2x^2 + x - k$ and $x^2 + 3x + 2$ have a common factor?

14. If c_1 and c_2 are the zeros of $x^2 + bx + c$, find: (a) $c_1^2 + c_2^2$; (b) $c_1^4 + c_2^4$; (c) $1/c_1 + 1/c_2$.

15. When synthetic division is used to check a rational number as a possible zero of a polynomial, explain why the presence of a fraction on the third row of the computation shows immediately that the tested number is not a zero of the polynomial (whose coefficients are assumed to be integers).

16. Use the method suggested in Problem 11 to isolate the real solutions of the equation $x^3 - x^2 - 11x + 14 = 0$ between integers, and continue the same procedure to show that approximations to the three real solutions of the equation are 1.324, 3.093, and -3.417.

CHAPTER 10

The Binomial
Theorem and Sequences

10.1 The Fundamental Counting Principle

The topics to be discussed in this chapter are of importance in many different phases of mathematics, as well as being of interest in themselves. Some of them are of basic importance in a study of probability and statistics, a study which the student may pursue at some later time. The Principle of Mathematical Induction, which we give in §10.6, is used in almost every branch of pure mathematics, and it would be difficult to overemphasize its importance. We lead up to the main idea of this first section with some examples.

If a college student has three pairs of shoes, three pairs of slacks, and five sport shirts, in how many different outfits can he appear on the campus? He can wear any one of the five shirts with any one of the three slacks, and this combination can be selected in $5 \cdot 3$ or 15 different ways. In addition, with any choice of shirt and slacks, he may select any one of three pairs of shoes. Since he can choose his shoes in three ways, there are $15 \cdot 3$ or 45 ways in which he can select his three-piece outfit. As another example, suppose there are three candidates for President, two for Vice-President, and three for Secretary of the student body of your college. In how many ways can the three offices be filled? Since any one of the three candidates for President can be associated with either of the two candidates for Vice-President, these two offices together can be filled in $3 \cdot 2$ or 6 different ways. Since a secretary can be chosen in three ways, and may be associated with any one of the six choices for the other offices, the three positions can be filled in $6 \cdot 3$ or 18 ways. These two examples are illustra-

235

tive of the following principle, which is basically just a matter of ordinary common sense.

Fundamental Counting Principle.   If there are m possible outcomes of one event and, after it has occurred, a second event can happen in any one of n ways, the *sequence* of two events can occur in mn ways.

We emphasize that it is the "sequence" or "ordered pair" of the two events which is of interest here and not the individual events. It is of course easy to extend the Counting Principle to include more than two events.

EXAMPLE 1.   How many three-letter code words can be formed from the letters of the alphabet?

SOLUTION.   In this problem, three events are involved: a selection of the first, second, and third letters of a word. There are 26 letters in the alphabet, and so each event has 26 possible outcomes. Since each choice is independent of what the preceding choice has been, an application of an extension of the Fundamental Counting Principle gives us $26 \cdot 26 \cdot 26$ or 17,576 different possibilities for three-letter code words.

EXAMPLE 2.   Three men wish to stay overnight in a certain city but, for business reasons, each wishes to stay in a different hotel from the other two. If five hotels can accommodate them, in how many ways can they take up quarters for the night?

SOLUTION.   For the purposes of the problem, let us call the men A, B, and C. Then A can stay in any one of the five hotels and, after he has made his selection, B can stay in any one of the remaining four, with a choice of three left for C. (We note in this case, unlike the situation in Example 1, that the outcome of each event affects the outcome of the subsequent event.) By an extension of the Fundamental Counting Principle, we then see that the men can be housed for the night in $5 \cdot 4 \cdot 3$ or 60 different ways which are satisfactory to them.

EXAMPLE 3.   If $A = \{1, 3, 5, 7\}$ and $B = \{2, 4, 6\}$, determine the number of elements in $A \cup B$ and in $A \times B$.

SOLUTION.   Since $A \cap B = \varnothing$, the number of elements in $A \cup B$ is the sum of the numbers in A and B separately, and this sum is $4 + 3$ or 7. The elements of $A \times B$, on the other hand, are ordered pairs of elements from A and B in this order. The first member of a pair can be selected from A in four ways, while the second member can be selected from B in three ways. By the Fundamental Counting Principle, the two members can be selected in $4 \cdot 3$ or 12 ways, and so there are 12 elements in $A \times B$.

PROBLEMS

1. How many four-letter code words can be made if the first and fourth letters must be consonants and the second and third vowels?
2. If four colors are available, in how many ways can a map of four countries be colored, with no two countries in the same color?
3. If $S = \{1, 2, 3, 4\}$ and $T = \{3, 5, 7\}$, determine the number of elements in $S \cup T$ and in $S \times T$.
4. How many five-digit numbers can be written down, if 0 is to be excluded as a first digit for any number except the number 0?
5. A student has six shirts and three ties, the colors of three of the shirts and two of the ties being shades of green, while the colors of the other articles are various shades of blue. How many shirt-tie combinations are possible for him if: (a) all color combinations are acceptable; (b) blue and green combinations are not acceptable?
6. If there are three major routes from Jacksonville to Atlanta, three from Atlanta to Chicago, and two from Chicago to Minneapolis, how many major routings are possible for a trip from Jacksonville to Minneapolis?
7. In how many ways can eight girls and nine boys be seated on a row of 17 chairs, if each girl is to be between two boys?
8. In a certain college, mathematics courses are offered at periods 1, 2, 6, physics at periods 2, 5, 7, and English at periods 1, 7, 9. In how many different ways can a college student make up his class schedule if he wishes to take one course from each of the three subject areas?
9. In how many different ways can the letters of the word MONDAY be arranged?
10. The inscriptions on car license plates of a certain state consist of two letters of the alphabet followed by a four-digit nonzero number. How many different license plates are possible if: (a) the letters may not be repeated on any one plate, and the first digit of the number may not be 0; (b) no further restrictions are imposed on the choice of letters and digits?
11. Determine how many four-digit numbers can be formed out of the digits 1, 2, 3, 4 if: (a) no digit is repeated; (b) repetitions of digits are permitted.
12. If there are six chairs in a reception room, in how many ways can four people be seated?
13. A signal device consists of three rows of lights, each with a red, a green, and an amber light. Determine how many signals can be sent from this device, if at least one light is to be lit in each row for every signal.
14. It is possible to record information on "punched" cards by punching holes at the proper locations. If a card has 80 columns and 12 locations in each column, how many theoretically different lines of information can be punched on any one card if exactly one hole is to be punched in each column?
15. A signalman can hold a flag in each hand, and each flag can be put in any one of four positions. If each pattern represents a signal, how many different signals

can be sent? If two successive patterns are needed for a signal, how many signals are available to the signalman?

10.2   Permutations and Combinations

A special application of the Fundamental Counting Principle arises when we consider the different possible *ordered* arrangements or "permutations" of a set of elements. Such arrangements can be broken down into sub-patterns, each of which is equivalent to a permutation of elements either in a straight line or on a circle. These basic permutations are called *linear* or *circular*, according to the type of arrangement. It sometimes happens that, while the elements of a set may be all distinct in one sense they are nonetheless indistinguishable from each other. For example, the four letters A, A, A, A which appear in the word *ALABAMA* are indistinguishable from each other, but they are distinct letters in the sense that they occupy distinct positions in the word. In this section, we shall be concerned only with *distinguishable* elements and all permutations will be *linear*, which may then be considered arranged in a linear array.

The basic problem in permutations is the following: In how many ways can n objects be arranged in a straight line? If we think of the objects as occupying the first, second, third, . . . , n^{th} positions in the linear array, the arranging of the objects can be broken down into the primary events of filling the first position, filling the second position, filling the third position, etc. Since there are n objects, the first position can be filled in n ways, the second in $n - 1$ ways, the third in $n - 2$ ways, etc., with only one way of filling the final position. Hence, by the Fundamental Counting Principle, the n positions can be filled in $n(n - 1)(n - 2) \cdots 3 \cdot 2 \cdot 1$ ways. This is then the number of permutations of n objects in a linear arrangement.

Products of the form $n(n - 1)(n - 2) \cdots 3 \cdot 2 \cdot 1$ occur frequently in mathematics and are designated $n!$ (read "*n* factorial"). Thus $n!$ is the product of all integers from 1 to n, inclusive. We also make the *definition* that $0! = 1$. If we designate the number of permutations of n objects in a linear array by $P(n)$, we have shown above that:

$$P(n) = n!.$$

EXAMPLE 1.   Express $8 \cdot 7 \cdot 6 \cdot 5$ in terms of factorials.

SOLUTION. $8 \cdot 7 \cdot 6 \cdot 5 = \dfrac{8 \cdot 7 \cdot 6 \cdot 5 \cdot 4 \cdot 3 \cdot 2 \cdot 1}{4 \cdot 3 \cdot 2 \cdot 1} = \dfrac{8!}{4!}$

EXAMPLE 2. In how many ways can 6 students be seated on a row of six chairs?

SOLUTION. This is precisely the number of permutations of six objects in a linear array, and so the desired number is 6! or 720.

A slightly different problem arises if we ask for the number of ways in which r objects can be selected from a set of n objects $(r \leq n)$ and then arranged in a linear array. This is called the "number of permutations of n objects taken r at a time," and is designated $P(n, r)$. Since the first position can be filled in n ways, the second in $n - 1$ ways, . . . , and the rth in $n - r + 1$ ways, we obtain the following formula for $P(n, r)$:

$$P(n, r) = n(n - 1)(n - 2) \cdots (n - r + 1) = \frac{n!}{(n - r)!}.$$

In case $r = n$, this formula gives $P(n) = P(n, n) = n!$, as before.

If the order of the objects is of no interest in an array, we are concerned with mere *subsets* or "combinations" of objects. The "number of combinations of n objects taken r at a time," designated $C(n, r)$ or $\binom{n}{r}$, is then the number of ways in which r objects can be selected from a set of n $(\geq r)$ objects; this can also be phrased as the "number of r-subsets of an n-set." Both notations are useful, and will be used. The notation $C(n, r)$ is more suggestive if the elements of the subsets are being "combined" in some way, while $\binom{n}{r}$ is probably to be preferred in purely set-theoretic circumstances, but we emphasize that both symbols have the same meaning. Inasmuch as order is not of importance in subsets, it follows immediately that $C(n, r) = \binom{n}{r} \leq P(n, r)$. In fact, since each subset of r objects can be permuted in $r!$ ways, there are $r!$ times as many permutations of r objects as there are r-subsets or combinations of r objects. Hence, $P(n, r) = r! C(n, r)$ $= r! \binom{n}{r}$, and so $C(n, r) = \binom{n}{r} = \dfrac{P(n, r)}{r!} = \dfrac{n!}{(n - r)! r!}$. Inasmuch as $0! = 1$, this formula remains valid even when $r = n$; and in this case $C(n, n) = \binom{n}{n} = 1$, which is simply the assertion that there is only 1 subset of n elements in a set of n elements.

EXAMPLE 3. How many five-digit integers can be formed from the numbers of the set $\{1, 2, 3, 4, 5, 6, 7, 8\}$.

SOLUTION. This is a matter of choosing five of the eight given digits, and arranging them to form numbers. Symbolically, this can be done in $P(8, 5)$ ways, and so the desired number is $8!/3!$ or 6,720.

EXAMPLE 4.   In how many ways can a committee of three boys and two girls be chosen from a class of twelve boys and eight girls?

SOLUTION.   Since order is not involved in committee member-ship, this is a problem involving subsets of a set. There are $\binom{12}{3}$ possible subsets of three boys and $\binom{8}{2}$ possible subsets of two girls, obtainable from the given class. An application of the Fundamental Counting Principle then gives us $\binom{12}{3} \cdot \binom{8}{2} = \frac{12!}{3!9!} \cdot \frac{8!}{2!6!} = \frac{12 \cdot 11 \cdot 10}{3 \cdot 2 \cdot 1} \cdot \frac{8 \cdot 7}{2 \cdot 1} = 6,160$ ways of forming the committee.

EXAMPLE 5.   The Directions of an examination specify that the student is to answer four of the first six, and six of the remaining nine questions. In how many ways can a student complete the examination?

SOLUTION.   The student may select four questions from the first six, and this can be done in $C(6, 4)$ ways. He must then select six from the remaining nine questions, and this can be accomplished in $C(9, 6)$ ways. By the Fundamental Counting Principle, the student can do his examination in $[C(6, 4)] [C(9, 6)] = \frac{6!}{4!2!} \cdot \frac{9!}{6!3!} = \frac{6 \cdot 5}{2 \cdot 1} \cdot \frac{9 \cdot 8 \cdot 7}{3 \cdot 2} = 15 \cdot 84 = 1,260$ ways.

PROBLEMS

1. Determine the number represented by each of the following factorials: (a) 3!; (b) 8!; (c) 5!; (d) 0!; (e) 10!.
2. Evaluate each of the following: (a) 3(4!); (b) 6(5!); (c) 2(5!) + 3!; (d) 4(5!) − 2(3!); (e) 3(4!) + 4(5!) + 6(2!).
3. Evaluate each of the following: (a) 5!/3!; (b) 10!/5!; (c) 7!/4!; (d) [(12!) (6!)]/[(7!) (3!)].
4. Find the number represented by each of the following symbols: (a) $\binom{5}{2}$; (b) $P(6, 3)$; (c) $P(8, 4)$; (d) $\binom{10}{5}$; (e) $P(6)$; (f) $P(9)$.
5. Express each of the following as a multiple of the largest possible factorial: (a) 9(8!); (b) 10(6!) − 7(5!); (c) (3!) (6!) + 6!.
6. In how many ways can a working party of six soldiers be selected from a platoon of 15?

7. How many different "singles" tennis matches (involving two players) can be arranged with a group of: (a) ten players; (b) six players? For the purposes of the problem, assume that not all matches are to be played simultaneously.

8. A plane is determined by three points. How many planes can be determined by five points in space, no four of which are coplanar?

9. If there are two possible catchers but only one pitcher in a group of nine ball players, how many baseball teams can be formed, assuming that all positions other than catcher and pitcher can be filled by any player?

10. In how many different ways can ten books be arranged on a shelf, if the books of a certain three-volume set are to be kept together in the proper order?

> For Problems 11 and 12 the following information is relevant. A deck of playing cards has four suits, each suit containing an ace, nine cards numbered from 2 to 10, and three "face" cards (king, queen, jack). Two cards with the same number or picture are said to have the same "rank."

11. A poker hand consists of five cards; a "pair" is a set of two cards with the same rank; a "full house" is a hand consisting of three cards of equal rank and a "pair" of some other rank.
    (a) How many different poker hands are possible from a deck of playing cards?
    (b) How many different poker hands are possible with at least one "pair" in each?
    (c) In how many different ways is it possible for a poker player to get a hand consisting of a "full house"?

12. A bridge "deal" is four hands of 13 cards from one deck of playing cards, the order of the hands relative to the dealer being of importance.
    (a) How many different bridge "deals" are possible from a deck of playing cards?
    (b) How many different bridge "deals" are possible from a deck of playing cards, if the dealer gets all the aces, kings, and queens?

13. A man has one penny, one nickel, one dime, one quarter, and one half-dollar in his pocket. If he reaches into his pocket and pulls out three coins, how many different sums are possible?

14. Three civic clubs have memberships of 40, 50, and 60 people. In how many different ways can a steering committee for a certain drive be constituted if three members are to be selected from each club?

15. In Problem 14, if the 60-member club consists of 30 couples, and man-wife combinations are not to be permitted on the committee, in how many ways can the committee be formed?

16. A baseball squad of 15 men is to make a trip in two conveyances—a station wagon and a car. If the station wagon will take ten and the car will take five players, in how many different ways can the squad make the trip?

17. In how many ways can the wife of a college President entertain: (a) 3; (b) 4; (c) 3 or more of a total of 10 faculty wives at tea?

18. Solve the following equation for n: $\dbinom{n+2}{4} = 6\dbinom{n}{2}$.

19. Prove that $r\dbinom{n}{r} = n\dbinom{n-1}{r-1}$.

10.3   More on Permutations and Combinations

Our primary purpose in discussing permutations and combinations in this chapter is to provide a foundation for a proof of the simplest case of the Binomial Theorem. The preceding two sections are adequate for this purpose, but we are inserting one more section on permutations and combinations to round off this study more satisfactorily. We shall now relax the assumption that our permutations are always linear and that the elements are always distinguishable.

If the elements of a set are considered arranged in a circular array, we have called the arrangement a "circular" permutation. (It is of no consequence, of course, whether the geometric form of the array is actually a circle, but the ordered set must be closed with no "first" or "last" member.) For such a permutation, a displacement of each element the same number of positions in either direction (i.e., all clockwise or all counterclockwise), will produce a permutation which is indistinguishable from the original. These indistinguishable permutations are said to be *cyclic* permutations of the given array. For example, the beads on a string or the keys on a ring may be displaced in this way without effecting any real change in the arrangement.

If there are n distinguishable objects in a circular array, there are n possible cyclic permutations which are not to be distinguished from the original. (It should be noticed that any cyclic permutation in a counterclockwise direction is equivalent to a certain cyclic permutation in a clockwise direction, and so both types do not have to be considered.) Inasmuch as the linear permutations of the same n objects are all distinguishable, the number of linear permutations of these objects is n times as great as the number of circular permutations. There are $P(n)$ or $n!$ permutations of n objects in a linear array, and so there must be $n!/n$ or $(n - 1)!$ permutations of n objects in a circular array. A similar argument will show that the number of permutations of n distinguishable objects, taken r at a time, in a circular array, is $P(n, r)/r$ or $n!/[(n - r)!r]$.

EXAMPLE 1.   In how many ways can eight people be seated at a round table?

SOLUTION.   The solution to this problem is a direct application of the above result for circular permutations. Hence the desired number is 7! or 5,040.

Let us now return to linear permutations, but we shall no longer insist that the objects be all distinguishable. If we permute n objects, s of which are indistinguishable, the permutations which arise from these s objects will not be distinguishable. Since there are $s!$ possible arrangements of this kind, there will be $s!$ times as many permutations of n distinguishable objects as there are if s of the objects are indistinguishable. It follows that the number of permutations of n objects, s of which are indistinguishable, is $n!/s!$. If there are an additional t objects which are not to be distinguished from each other, a similar argument will give the number of distinguishable permutations as $n!/[s!t!]$, and it is easy to extend the argument. There is no *general* formula for the number of permutations of n objects, taken r at a time, $r < n$, if some of the objects are indistinguishable.

EXAMPLE 2.   How many distinguishable permutations can be made of the letters of the word *MISSISSIPPI?*

SOLUTION.   The word contains 11 letters, four of which are I, four are S, and two are P. Hence, the number of distinguishable permutations is $11!/[4!4!2!]$ or 34,650.

Many problems which arise in permutations and combinations cannot be solved by the direct application of any formula. Such problems must be broken down into basic subproblems in some way consistent with common sense. The following problem illustrates the method for one such problem.

EXAMPLE 3.   From a group of four Americans, three Canadians, and two Mexicans, a committee is to be formed. Find the number of different committees possible if: (a) any number of people may comprise a committee; (b) each of the three nationalities must be represented on a committee.

SOLUTION

(a) For this case, there are two possibilities which confront each person: Either he is selected or he is not selected. Since there are nine persons involved, the number of possible outcomes of this selection process is 2^9 or 512. This includes the possibility that none are selected, however, and so there are 511 committees of one or more persons.

(b) In this case, there may be selected 1, 2, 3, or 4 Americans, 1, 2, or 3 Canadians, and 1 or 2 Mexicans. The Americans can be selected in $\binom{4}{1} + \binom{4}{2} + \binom{4}{3} + \binom{4}{4} = 4 + 6 + 4 + 1 = 15$ ways; the Canadians can be selected in $\binom{3}{1} + \binom{3}{2} + \binom{3}{3} = 3 + 3 + 1 = 7$ ways; and the Mexicans can be selected in $\binom{2}{1} + \binom{2}{2} = 2 + 1 = 3$ ways. Hence, by the

Fundamental Counting Principle, the number of possible committees under the given circumstances is $15 \cdot 7 \cdot 3 = 315$.

PROBLEMS

1. In how many ways can six keys be arranged on a key ring?
2. In how many ways can six keys be selected from a collection of ten keys and arranged on a key ring?
3. A party of six men and six women are to be seated at two round tables. In how many ways can this be done if: (a) the men and women are to be at different tables; (b) no two men or women are to sit together; (c) any arrangement of men and women is permissible?
4. How many distinguishable permutations are possible with all letters of the words: (a) *SYZYGY;* (b) *ALABAMA;* (c) *ARRANGEMENT;* (d) *LLAMA?*
5. A selection of fruit is to be made from three apples, four oranges, and two grapefruit. If we assume that all pieces are distinguishable, how many selections are possible with: (a) at least one piece taken; (b) at least one piece of each kind of fruit taken?
6. In how many ways can a committee of at least two and not more than four people be chosen from a group of eight people?
7. If $P(n, r) = 24$ and $\binom{n}{r} = 4$, determine n and r.
8. In how many ways can a man invite one or more of his six local friends to dinner?
9. How many different numbers can be formed by using all of the six following digits: 1, 1, 2, 2, 3, 3?
10. In how many ways can five prizes be given away to eight boys, if each boy is eligible for all of the prizes.
11. A jeweler wishes to make a bracelet by linking together six different sections of linkages. In how many ways can he do this if he has ten different kinds of linkages available?
12. Determine the number of ways in which it is possible to: (a) select; (b) select and arrange four letters from the word PARALLEL?
13. Use the directions of Problem 12 for the letters of the word KENNEDY.
14. A squad of baseball players consists of seven outfielders, six infielders, three pitchers, and five catchers. How many baseball teams of nine men can be chosen?
15. In how many ways can three men and three women be seated at a round table if: (a) there are no restrictions on seating; (b) men and women are to be seated in alternate chairs?
16. The families of Smith, Jones, and Robinson are to be seated on a bench. If there are five members to each family, how many arrangements of family names are possible after they have been seated?
17. In how many ways can a committee of five be chosen from a group of ten people if two particular people agree to serve only if both are chosen?

10.4   The Binomial Theorem

If a and b are arbitrary real numbers, it is well known that $(a + b)^2 = a^2 + 2ab + b^2$, $(a + b)^3 = a^3 + 3a^2b + 3ab^2 + b^3$, and $(a + b)^4 = a^4 + 4a^3b + 6a^2b^2 + 4ab^3 + b^4$. The corresponding formal sum of products of powers of a and b equal to $(a + b)^n$, for any real number n, is known as its *binomial expansion*. The theorem which establishes its validity is known as the *Binomial Theorem*.

The various terms in the expansion of $(a + b)^2 = (a + b)(a + b)$ arise from the multiplication of each term of the first factor by each term of the second factor. The expansion then consists of the four terms a^2, ab, ba, and b^2, and on combining ab with ba we obtain the familiar result $a^2 + 2ab + b^2$. In a similar way, if we consider $(a + b)^3 = (a + b)(a + b)(a + b)$, there are eight terms which arise from the multiplication of one and only one term from each factor. These eight products are a^3, a^2b, ab^2, bab, b^2a, aba, ba^2, and b^3, and on combining equal terms we obtain $a^3 + 3a^2b + 3ab^2 + b^3$.

More generally, the terms of the expansion of $(a + b)^n$, where n is any positive integer, arise from the multiplication of exactly one term from each of the n factors of $(a + b)^n$. There is a choice of either a or b as a multiplier from each factor and, if we select b from r of the factors and a from the remaining $n - r$ factors, each such product will be $a^{n-r}b^r$. But the r choices of b (and automatically the associated $n - r$ choices of a) can be made in $C(n, r)$ or $\binom{n}{r}$ ways, and so there are $\binom{n}{r}$ products equal to $a^{n-r}b^r$. If we allow r to assume all integral values from 0 to n, inclusive, the expansion of $(a + b)^n$ can be written down as follows:

$$(a + b)^n = a^n + \binom{n}{1}a^{n-1}b + \binom{n}{2}a^{n-2}b^2 + \cdots + \binom{n}{n-1}ab^{n-1} + b^n.$$

The coefficients $1, \binom{n}{1}, \binom{n}{2}, \ldots, \binom{n}{n-1}, 1$ of this expansion are known as the *binomial coefficients*. It is clear that if we know these coefficients, for any n, we can write down the corresponding binomial expansion. It is possible to obtain these coefficients from what is known as "Pascal's Triangle," displayed in the configuration below. The rows of the "Triangle," each of which is formed from the preceding in an obvious way, are the binomial coefficients for successive positive integral exponents n, beginning with $n = 0$. Although it has some interest, Pascal's Triangle has little practical value, since all rows prior to a given row must be reproduced before this row can be obtained. The theoretical basis for the Triangle is contained in Problem 19.

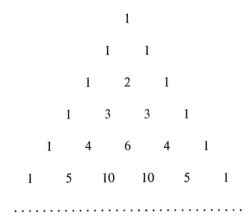

$$1$$
$$1 \quad 1$$
$$1 \quad 2 \quad 1$$
$$1 \quad 3 \quad 3 \quad 1$$
$$1 \quad 4 \quad 6 \quad 4 \quad 1$$
$$1 \quad 5 \quad 10 \quad 10 \quad 5 \quad 1$$

$\cdots\cdots\cdots\cdots\cdots\cdots\cdots\cdots\cdots\cdots$

EXAMPLE 1. Write out the complete binomial expansion for $(\frac{1}{2} + 2x)^5$.

SOLUTION. This expansion is the case of the general result with $a = \frac{1}{2}, b = 2x, n = 5$. Hence,

$$\left(\frac{1}{2} + 2x\right)^5 = \left(\frac{1}{2}\right)^5 + \binom{5}{1}\left(\frac{1}{2}\right)^4 (2x)^1 + \binom{5}{2}\left(\frac{1}{2}\right)^3 (2x)^2$$

$$+ \binom{5}{3}\left(\frac{1}{2}\right)^2 (2x)^3 + \binom{5}{4}\left(\frac{1}{2}\right)^1 (2x)^4 + (2x)^5 = \frac{1}{32} + 5\left(\frac{1}{16}\right)(2x)$$

$$+ 10\left(\frac{1}{8}\right)(4x^2) + 10\left(\frac{1}{4}\right)(8x^3) + 5\left(\frac{1}{2}\right)(16x^4) + 32x^5$$

$$= \frac{1}{32} + 5x/8 + 5x^2 + 20x^3 + 40x^4 + 32x^5.$$

If we examine the $(r + 1)^{st}$ term of the binomial expansion of $(a + b)^n$, we notice that this term involves the number r in a conspicuous way. For this term is $\binom{n}{r} a^{n-r} b^r$, i.e., $n!/[r!(n - r)!]a^{n-r}b^r$ or, more simply,

$$\frac{n(n - 1)(n - 2)\cdots(n - r + 1)}{r!} a^{n-r}b^r,$$

and we make the following general observations:

1. The numerator of the coefficient formally contains the product of r consecutive descending integers, beginning with n.
2. The denominator of the coefficient formally contains the factor $r!$.
3. The exponent of b is r and the exponent of a is $n - r$. With these three observations as a memory device, it is easy to write down any particular term of a binomial expansion without the complete expansion, or

even the terms which precede it. This is often useful in problems in probability and statistics.

EXAMPLE 2. Determine the fifth term of the binomial expansion of:

$$\left(\frac{1}{\sqrt{2}} - \frac{x^2}{3}\right)^{10}.$$

SOLUTION. The conspicuous number formally associated with the fifth term is 4. Hence, an application of the above memory device gives us the fifth term as:

$$\frac{10\cdot9\cdot8\cdot7}{4!}\left(\frac{1}{\sqrt{2}}\right)^{10-4}\left(\frac{-x^2}{3}\right)^4 = \frac{10\cdot9\cdot8\cdot7}{4\cdot3\cdot2\cdot1}\left(\frac{1}{2^3}\right)\left(\frac{x^8}{81}\right) = \left(\frac{35}{108}\right)x^8.$$

PROBLEMS

In Problems 1 through 8, give the complete binomial expansion as indicated.

1. $(3x + 5)^3$.   **2.** $(1 - 3x^2)^5$.
3. $(\frac{1}{2} - 2x)^4$.   **4.** $(x - \frac{3}{2})^5$.
5. $(1 + 2x^2)^6$.   **6.** $(\frac{2}{3} + 3x)^6$.
7. $(1 - x)^8$.   **8.** $(2 - xy)^5$.
9. Find the sixth term of the binomial expansion of $(2x - 3y/2)^{12}$.
10. Find the seventh term of the binomial expansion of $(1 + 2x^3)^{10}$.
11. Find the two middle terms of the binomial expansion of $(\sqrt{2} + x^2/2)^9$.
12. Find the term involving x^6 in the binomial expansion of $(y - x^2/2)^8$.
13. Find the term which is independent of x in the binomial expansion of $(2x - 3/x)^{12}$.
14. Write out the general binomial expansion of $(x + h)^n$.
15. Give a proof of the fact that $\dbinom{n}{1} + \dbinom{n}{2} + \cdots + \dbinom{n}{n-1} + \dbinom{n}{n} = 2^n - 1$,

without merely adding the indicated terms.
16. As in Problem 15, prove that

$$1 - \binom{n}{1} + \binom{n}{2} - \binom{n}{3} + \cdots + (-1)^n\binom{n}{n} = 0.$$

17. Prove that $\dbinom{n}{r+1} = \dfrac{n-r}{r+1}\dbinom{n}{r}$, and then derive a rule for determining the successive binomial coefficients beginning with $\dbinom{n}{1} = n$.

18. Write out the complete binomial expansion for $[2x^3 - 1/(2\sqrt{x})]^9$.
19. Prove Pascal's Rule, which is responsible for the validity of Pascal's Triangle:

$$\binom{n+1}{r} = \binom{n}{r} + \binom{n}{r-1}, \qquad 0 < r \le n.$$

10.5   Extension of the Binomial Theorem

While the Binomial Theorem was developed primarily for the expansion of binomials, it is possible to extend the result to other polynomials by a proper grouping of the terms. For example, we can apply the Binomial Theorem to obtain the "trinomial" expansion of $(1 + x + y)^8$, if we write this expression in the form $[1 + (x + y)]^8$. We may then treat it as the case of $(a + b)^n$ where $a = 1$, $b = x + y$, and $n = 8$. The proof of the validity of such an expansion is known as the Trinomial Theorem, and it is possible to extend it to polynomials in general with the Multinomial Theorem.

The proof which we gave of the Binomial Theorem in the preceding section was based on the theory of permutations and combinations and so is valid only if the exponent n is a positive integer. An alternate proof, based on mathematical induction, is suggested in Problem 7 of §10.6, but this proof also assumes that n is a positive integer. It can be shown by methods of more advanced mathematics that the Binomial Theorem is actually valid under more general conditions. However, if n is not a positive integer, the expansion does not terminate with a finite number of terms, and its usefulness depends on the "convergence" of the expansion—a matter to be discussed briefly in §10.9. The following result will be sufficient for our purposes here, but we omit the proof of it:

The binomial expansion of $(1 + x)^n$, where the coefficient of the $(r + 1)^{\text{st}}$ term is $\dfrac{n(n - 1)(n - 2) \cdots (n - r + 1)}{r!}$, is valid for any real number n, provided $|x| < 1$.

By the "validity" of the above expansion, we mean that $(1 + x)^n$ can be approximated *to any desired degree of accuracy* by taking a sufficiently large (but finite) number of terms. In writing down the expansion with n not an integer, it is necessary to discard the notation $\binom{n}{r}$ of subsets. Hence, as indicated above, we must write the expansion as follows:

$$(a + b)^n = a^n + na^{n-1}b + \frac{n(n - 1)}{2!}a^{n-2}b^2 + \cdots$$
$$+ \frac{n(n - 1) \cdots (n - r + 1)}{r!}a^{n-r}b^r + \cdots .$$

In particular, it is useful to observe that:

$$(1 + x)^n = 1 + nx + \frac{n(n - 1)}{2!}x^2 + \frac{n(n - 1)(n - 2)}{3!}x^3 + \cdots ,$$

and, if $n = -1$,

$$(1 + x)^{-1} = 1 - x + x^2 - x^3 + \cdots.$$

Since $(a + b)^n = [a(1 + b/a)]^n = a^n(1 + b/a)^n$, it follows from the result that was stated without proof above, that $(a + b)^n$ can also be expressed by a satisfactory binomial expansion provided $|b/a| < 1$.

EXAMPLE 1.   Find the first four terms of the binomial expansion of:

$$(1 + 2x)^{1/2}.$$

SOLUTION.   This the case of $(a + b)^n$ where $a = 1, b = 2x, n = \frac{1}{2}$. Hence,

$$(1 + 2x)^{1/2} = 1^{1/2} + \left(\frac{1}{2}\right)(1)^{-1/2}(2x) + \frac{(1/2)(-1/2)}{2!}(1)^{-3/2}(2x)^2$$

$$+ \frac{(1/2)(-1/2)(-3/2)}{3!}(1)^{-5/2}(2x)^3 + \cdots = 1 + x - \frac{x^2}{2} + \frac{x^3}{2} - \cdots.$$

As more terms are included, this will approximate $(1 + 2x)^{1/2}$, provided $|2x| < 1$, i.e., $|x| < \frac{1}{2}$.

EXAMPLE 2.   Use a binomial expansion to find a 3-digit approximation for $\sqrt[3]{65.1}$.

SOLUTION

$$\sqrt[3]{65.1} = (65.1)^{1/3} = (64 + 1.1)^{1/3} = \left[64\left(1 + \frac{1.1}{64}\right)\right]^{1/3}$$

$$= 4\left(1 + \frac{1.1}{64}\right)^{1/3} = 4\left[1 + \left(\frac{1}{3}\right)\left(\frac{1.1}{64}\right) + \frac{(1/3)(-2/3)}{2!}\left(\frac{1.1}{64}\right)^2 + \cdots\right]$$

$$= 4(1 + 0.0057 - 0.00003 + \cdots) \doteq 4(1.00567) \doteq 4.023.$$

It may be well to point out, in connection with binomial approximations such as that in Example 2, that the number of terms required for a given degree of accuracy depends upon the size of $|x|$ (<1) in $(1 + x)^n$, as well as upon n.

PROBLEMS

In Problems 1 through 8, write out the first four terms of the indicated binomial expansion, and state the conditions for convergence.

1. $(1 + 3x)^{1/2}$.   2. $(1 - 3/x)^{2/3}$.
3. $(2 + 5x^2)^{1/3}$.   4. $(5 - 3/x)^{-2}$.

5. $(1 - 2x)^{-1}$.

6. $(4 + 2x^3)^{-1/2}$.

7. $(4 + 5a)^{1/3}$.

8. $(2 + 3/x)^{-2/3}$.

9. Use a "binomial" expansion to expand $(1 + a - b)^3$.

10. Use a "binomial" expansion to expand $(2x - 2 + x^2)^4$.

In Problems 11 through 16, use a binomial expansion to approximate each of the indicated quantities, correct to 4 decimal places.

11. $(1.01)^{-2}$.

12. $(8.63)^{1/3}$.

13. $1/\sqrt{2.2}$.

14. $1/(1.05)^3$.

15. $\sqrt[3]{120}$.

16. $\sqrt[4]{17}$.

17. Establish the validity of the following approximation formulas, where $|x| < 1$:
(a) $\sqrt{1 + x} \doteq 1 + x/2$; (b) $(1 + x)^{-2/3} \doteq 1 - 2x/3$; (c) $(1 - x)^{-1} \doteq 1 + x$.

18. Determine the approximate percentage increase in the: (a) surface area; (b) volume of a sphere, if its radius is increased from 100 inches to 101 inches.

19. The period of a simple pendulum of length L inches is T seconds where $T \doteq 0.3198\sqrt{L}$, and it may be calculated that the pendulum beats seconds $(T = 2)$ if $L \doteq 39.10$. If the length of the pendulum is increased by 0.16 inches, determine the approximate increase in period. [*Hint:* Apply the binomial expansion to $\sqrt{L + h}$, where $h = 0.16$].

20. Determine the approximate change in period if the pendulum in Problem 19 is decreased in length to 38.5 inches.

21. Assume the earth is a sphere of radius 3,960 miles, and find an approximation formula for the maximum range of unobstructed vision from a point h feet above the surface of the earth.

22. Use the formula that was found in Problem 21 to determine the maximum range of unobstructed vision from a point 50 yards above the surface of the earth.

10.6   Mathematical Induction

An early attempt was made by G. Peano (1858–1932) to reduce the theory of natural numbers to a minimal set of postulates and undefined terms. Although his set has been shown by later investigators not to be minimal, nor even to define the natural numbers uniquely, these so-called "Peano postulates" have nonetheless been regarded as standard characterizing postulates for the natural numbers. We shall not list all the postulates here, but will be content with giving the one of present interest to us—the postulate of *Induction*. It should be recalled that we have not included 0 in the set N of natural numbers.

THE POSTULATE OF INDUCTION.   Let S be a subset of N with the following properties:

(1) $1 \in S$

(2) $k + 1 \in S$ provided $k \in S$, for an arbitrary $k \in N$.
Then $S = N$.

From the Postulate of Induction, we are able to derive quite easily

THE PRINCIPLE OF MATHEMATICAL INDUCTION.   Let $P(n)$ be a statement involving an arbitrary natural number n. Then if
   (1) $P(1)$ is true, and
   (2) $P(k + 1)$ is true whenever $P(k)$ is true,
it follows that $P(n)$ is true for every natural number n. (We often refer to (2) as our "inductive assumption.")

   PROOF.   Let S be the subset $\{n|n \in N,\ P(n)$ is true$\}$. By (1), we know that $P(1)$ is true, and so $1 \in S$. From (2) we know that $k + 1 \in S$ whenever $k \in S$, for any natural number k. But then the Postulate of Induction asserts that $S = N$, which is to say that $P(n)$ is true for every natural number n.

   A word of caution should possibly be given that mathematical induction is quite different from empirical induction—frequently called "induction"—in the natural sciences. Empirical induction is a type of reasoning which allows one to proceed from a number of observations to a statement of a physical law, the degree of certainty of the "law" depending on the frequency of the observations on which it was based. This kind of "inductive" reasoning is often quite convincing—as for instance the prediction that the sun will rise in the east tomorrow—but the statement has its origin in experience rather than logic. The proof of an assertion by mathematical induction, on the other hand, follows essentially from the inductive postulate of Peano—the accepted truth of which lies at the very foundation of mathematics.
   It is often the case that even the mathematical novice feels that if enough examples of a certain proposition are established, the truth of the general proposition must follow. But in reality this is equivalent to empirical induction. It can happen that many cases of a proposition are true, but the proposition is not true in its complete generality. The mathematical statement $n^2 - 40n - 41 \neq 0$ is true for $n = 1, 2, 3, \ldots, 40$, but it is easily seen to be false for $n = 41$. We now illustrate the use of the Principle of Mathematical Induction with a few examples.

   EXAMPLE 1.   If $a > 1$, use mathematical induction to prove that $a^n > 1$ for every positive integer n.

   PROOF.   The assertion $P(n)$ to be established for every natural number n is: $a^n > 1$.
   (1) Since $a^1 = a > 1$, $P(1)$ is true.
   (2) Let us assume that $P(k)$ is true for an arbitrary natural number k,

i.e., $a^k > 1$. Then $a^{k+1} = (a^k)a > 1$, since $a^k > 1$ and $a > 1$, whence $P(k + 1)$ is true.

It follows, by the Principle of Mathematical Induction, that $P(n)$ is true, i.e., $a^n > 1$, for any natural number n.

EXAMPLE 2.   The sum of the interior angles of a convex polygon of $n + 2$ sides is $180n°$.

PROOF.   We shall let $P(n)$ stand for the assertion to be proved.

(1) If $n = 1$, the polygon is a triangle, and it is well known from elementary geometry that the sum of the interior angles of any triangle is $180°$. Hence, $P(1)$ is true.

(2) Let us assume that $P(k)$ is true for an arbitrary, but fixed, natural number k, i.e., a polygon of $k + 2$ sides has interior angles which total $180k°$. Now any convex polygon of $k + 3$ sides may be broken up into a triangle and a convex polygon of $k + 2$ sides, by joining the first and third of any three consecutive vertices of the given polygon. By our inductive assumption, the sum of the angles of the polygon with $k + 2$ sides is $180k°$, while the sum of the angles of the triangle is $180°$. The sum of the angles of both—which make up the angles of the given polygon of $k + 3$ sides— is then $180(k + 1)°$. But this means that $P(k + 1)$ is true.

By the Principle of Mathematical Induction, it then follows that $P(n)$ is true for every natural number n, and the assertion has been verified.

It may appear to the somewhat careless reader that our proofs by mathematical induction are circular. Our inductive assumption that $P(k)$ is true for an arbitrary natural number k seems to differ only in notation from the assertion to be proved—that $P(n)$ is true for every natural number n. However, the inductive assumption is not that $P(k)$ is in fact true, but rather that *if* $P(k)$ is true *then* $P(k + 1)$ is also true. This is quite different from the statement that $P(n)$ *is* true for every natural number n.

EXAMPLE 3.   Use mathematical induction to prove that $x^n - y^n$ is divisible by $x - y$, for every natural number n.

SOLUTION.   We let $P(n)$ be the proposition to be established.

(1) Since $x^1 - y^1 = x - y$ is certainly divisible by $x - y$, $P(1)$ is true.

(2) Let us assume that $P(k)$ is true, for an arbitrary natural number k, i.e., $x^k - y^k$ is divisible by $x - y$. But $x^{k+1} - y^{k+1} = x^{k+1} - xy^k + xy^k - y^{k+1} = x(x^k - y^k) + y^k(x - y)$, where both terms are divisible by $x - y$. Hence, $x^{k+1} - y^{k+1}$ is divisible by $x - y$, which means that $P(k + 1)$ is true.

It follows by mathematical induction that $P(n)$ is true for any natural number n, as desired.

PROBLEMS

Use the Principle of Mathematical Induction to establish the truth of the assertions in Problems 1 through 6. More problems involving mathematical induction will be suggested in subsequent sections.

1. $x^{2n} - y^{2n}$ is divisible by $x - y$, for every natural number n.

2. $2^n \geq 2n$, for every natural number n.

3. $2^{n-1} \leq n!$, for every natural number n.

4. Any set of $n + 1$ points in a plane, no three of which are collinear, determines $n(n + 1)/2$ lines in the plane.

5. If $a > 1$, $(a + 1)^n \geq 1 + na$, for every natural number n.

6. $n^3 + 2n$ is divisible by 3 for every natural number n.

7. Use mathematical induction to prove the Binomial Theorem, for any positive integer n:

$$(a + b)^n = a^n + \binom{n}{1}a^{n-1}b + \binom{n}{2}a^{n-2}b^2 + \cdots + \binom{n}{n-1}ab^{n-1} + b^n.$$

[*Hint:* Assume the theorem for $n = k$, and multiply both members of this equality by $a + b$. Then compute the $(r + 1)$st term of the product and show that it is $\dfrac{(k + 1)!}{r!\,(k + 1 - r)!}\, a^{k+1-r}b^r$, which may be seen to be the $(r + 1)$st term of the binomial expansion with $n = k + 1$.]

8. Find the error in the following "proof" by mathematical induction that "All numbers in a set of n numbers are equal."

Proof. Let $P(n)$ be the given assertion.

(1) Since every number is equal to itself, it is apparent that $P(1)$ is true.

(2) Let us assume that $P(k)$ is true, and consider an arbitrary set of $k + 1$ numbers $a_1, a_2, \ldots, a_k, a_{k+1}$. Then, since $a_1, a_2, \ldots, a_k$ and $a_2, a_3, \ldots, a_k, a_{k+1}$ are both sets of k numbers, our inductive assumption implies that $a_1 = a_2 = \cdots = a_k$ and also $a_2 = a_3 = \cdots = a_k = a_{k+1}$, so that $P(k + 1)$ is true.

It follows by mathematical induction (!) that $P(n)$ is true for any natural number n, as asserted.

9. It is well known that there exists an integer n such that $x + n = y$, for arbitrary integers x and y. Can you prove this statement by mathematical induction? If so, give the proof; if not, explain why such a proof is not possible.

10. Use mathematical induction to prove that $1! + 2! + \cdots + n!$ is an integer for every positive integer n.

11. Use mathematical induction to prove that $|\sin n\theta| \leq n|\sin \theta|$, for any given real number θ and every positive integer n.

12. Use mathematical induction to prove, for every positive integer n: (a) $n^2 - n + 2$ is an even integer; (b) $2n^3 + 3n^2 + n$ is divisible by 6.

13. Extend the proof given in Problem 5 to include any $a > -1$. Discover where the "proof" would break down if $a < -1$.

10.7   Sequences

If the elements of a set are arranged in a definite order, the ordered set may be called a *sequence*, this notion having been introduced earlier in simple cases. It is customary to enclose the elements of a sequence in parentheses rather than braces, as we have been doing for sets in general. Thus $(a_1, a_2, a_3, \ldots)$ is a sequence whose first member or *term* is a_1, second is a_2, third is a_3, etc. Such a sequence may also be designated $(a_n), n = 1, 2, 3, \ldots$, or even abbreviated to (a_n), with a_n indicating the general or n^{th} term. In earlier chapters we have referred to a finite sequence such as $(a_1, a_2, \ldots, a_n)$, with a finite number n of terms, as an *n-tuple*, and when $n = 2$ as an ordered *pair*. These are then special cases of the more general concept under present discussion. The sequences to be discussed here will always be infinite, and in every case the terms will be in one-to-one correspondence with the natural numbers.

We saw in Chapter 4 that a function is basically a mapping of the members of one set—the *domain*—onto the members of another set—the *range* of the function. It is then natural to regard a sequence as a function on the set N of natural numbers. For the sequence $(a_1, a_2, \ldots, a_n, \ldots)$ is essentially a mapping $n \rightarrow a_n$ of the natural numbers N, where each number n is mapped onto the nth term a_n of the sequence. The domain of the sequence (regarded as a function) is N, and its range is the set of terms. However, even though we may consider a sequence as a special kind of function, it is usually preferred not to use the notation of functions, but rather to write a_n instead of $f(n)$ for the nth term of (a_n).

One common method of defining a sequence (a_n) is to write a formula for a_n in terms of n.

EXAMPLE 1.   Write the first three terms of the sequence (a_n) where:

$$a_n = 3n^2 - 2n + 1.$$

SOLUTION.   A replacement of n by $1, 2, 3$, respectively, in the formula for a_n, gives the following:

$$a_1 = 3 \cdot 1^2 - 2 \cdot 1 + 1 = 3 - 2 + 1 = 2;$$
$$a_2 = 3 \cdot 2^2 - 2 \cdot 2 + 1 = 12 - 4 + 1 = 9;$$
$$a_3 = 3 \cdot 3^2 - 2 \cdot 3 + 1 = 27 - 6 + 1 = 22.$$

Another method of describing a sequence is by means of a *recursion* formula, which allows us to determine any term from the preceding term. If such a formula is to be adequate, it is necessary, of course, to be given the first—or some other—term.

EXAMPLE 2.   Let (a_n) be a sequence for which $a_1 = 1$, and $a_n = 2a_{n-1} + 3$, $n = 2, 3, 4, \ldots$. Find the first three terms of the sequence.

SOLUTION.   Since $a_1 = 1$, $a_2 = 2a_1 + 3 = 2 \cdot 1 + 3 = 5$, $a_3 = 2a_2 + 3 = 2 \cdot 5 + 3 = 13$. The desired terms are then 1, 5, 13.

It is sometimes possible to manipulate a recursion formula and either derive or guess from it an expression for the nth term in terms of n. For example, it is easy to verify by mathematical induction that $a_n = 2^{n+1} - 3$, for the sequence in Example 2. If we let $P(n)$ represent the statement of this formula, it is immediate that $a_1 = 2^2 - 3 = 1$, and so $P(1)$ is true. Now let us assume that $P(k)$ is true, for an arbitrary positive integer k. Then, $a_{k+1} = 2a_k + 3 = 2(2^{k+1} - 3) + 3 = 2^{k+2} - 6 + 3 = 2^{k+2} - 3$, and we have shown that $P(k + 1)$ is true. Hence, $P(n)$ is true for every positive integer n.

While most sequences are defined by either an explicit formula for a_n or by means of a recursion formula, there are other ways to define a sequence. For example, we can define the sequence (a_n) to be the sequence whose terms in order are the digits in the decimal representation of $e = 2.71828 \cdots$. Thus, $a_1 = 2$, $a_2 = 7$, $a_3 = 1$, $a_4 = 8$, etc., and while it is possible to obtain any desired term, there is no formula available for the nth term.

On many occasions we wish to know the sum of certain or all terms of a sequence. However, it should be recognized that what we mean by the "sum" of a sequence must be clarified before it is possible to perform the addition. For example, if we attempt to determine the "sum" of the terms of the sequence $(1, -1, 1, -1, \ldots)$, by adding *pairs* of terms in the order of occurrence, the result is consistently 0, and we might conclude that the sum of the sequence is then 0. However, if we try to obtain the sum by adding the terms individually in their natural order, the successive partial sums which we encounter are $1, 0, -1, 1, 0, -1, \ldots$, and so we obtain no definite answer. Different methods of summation are used for different purposes, but the most common method is the one which we now describe. The sum S_n of n terms of the sequence (a_n) is defined so that:

$$S_1 = a_1$$
$$S_k = S_{k-1} + a_k.$$

This method of summation requires that we start with the first term, add the second to it, and successively add each term to the sum of the preceding terms as already computed. Hence, $S_1 = a_1$, $S_2 = a_1 + a_2$, $S_3 = (a_1 + a_2) + a_3$, $S_4 = [(a_1 + a_2) + a_3] + a_4$, etc. It can be shown that this recursion formula does define S_n, the sum of n terms of the sequence, for any positive integer n. (See Problem 7.) The sequence (S_n), associated in this way with

(a_n), is called the *sequence of partial sums* of (a_n). When we write $S_n = a_1 + a_2 + \cdots + a_n$, it will be understood that the addition is to be performed in the manner described above, but the sum of a *finite* number of terms is, of course, independent of the manner of summation. The manner of summation is of importance only when we are trying to obtain the "sum" of the terms of an infinite sequence. We touch on this topic very briefly in §10.9, for a very special type of sequence. We shall use the Greek letter Σ, introduced in an earlier problem set, to designate a summation, and in particular $\sum_{i=1}^{n} a_i$ will be frequently used as an abbreviation for $a_1 + a_2 + \cdots + a_n$.

PROBLEMS

1. Find the first five terms of the sequence (a_n) where a_n is: (a) $2n + 1$; (b) $3 - (-1)^n$; (c) $2(\frac{1}{2})^n$; (d) $n^2 + 1/n$.

2. Find the first five terms of the sequence (a_n) where:
   (a) $a_1 = 2$ and $a_n = 3a_{n-1} + 1$;   (b) $a_1 = -1$ and $a_n = -a_{n-1}$;
   (c) $a_1 = 3$ and $a_n = (n/2)a_{n-1}$;   (d) $a_1 = 0$ and $a_n = a^2_{n-1} + 2$.

3. Find the next two terms of the sequence (a_n) if:
   (a) $a_1 = 1$, $a_2 = 3$, and $a_n = (\frac{1}{2})(a_{n-1} + a_{n-2})$;
   (b) $a_1 = -1$, $a_2 = 1$, and $a_n = 2a_{n-1} + 3a_{n-2}$.

4. Find the first four terms of the sequence (S_n) of partial sums of the sequence (a_n) where: (a) $a_n = (-1)^n$; (b) $a_n = 3 - (-1)^{n+1}$; (c) $a_1 = 1$, $a_n = 2a_{n-1}/(n - 1)$; (d) $a_1 = -2$, $a_n = 2^n - 3a_{n-1}$.

5. If a_n is the nth digit in the decimal expansion of $\pi/4$, determine the first three terms of (a_n) and also of its associated sequence of partial sums.

6. Use the directions of Problem 5 where a_n is the nth digit in the decimal expansion of $\frac{3}{7}$.

7. Use mathematical induction to prove that S_n is defined for every positive integer n, if S_1 is given and $S_k = S_{k-1} + a_k$, for any positive integer k.

8. Let the sequence of partial sums of (a_n) be defined so that $S_1 = a_1 + a_2$, $S_2 = (a_1 + a_2) + (a_3 + a_4)$, $S_3 = [(a_1 + a_2) + (a_3 + a_4)] + (a_5 + a_6)$, etc., i.e. the terms are paired off in order, and each pair is added successively to the sum of the preceding pairs. Determine the first five terms of (S_n) where $a_n = 2n - 1$.

9. Use the directions of Problem 8 where $a_n = 2n^2 - 3n$.

10. If $a_1 = 2$ and $a_n = a^2_{n-1}$, $n > 1$, use mathematical induction to prove that $a_n = 2^{2^{n-1}}$, for every positive integer n.

11. Determine the first five terms of the sequence of partial sums of (a_n) where $a_n = 1/[n(n + 1)]$. Make an "educated guess" for S_n, and try to prove it correct by mathematical induction.

12. If $a_2 = 6$ and $a_n = na_{n-1}$, $n > 2$, use mathematical induction to prove that $a_n = 3n!$, for any positive integer $n \geq 2$. [*Hint:* In this case it is appropriate to ignore a_1, and define the proposition $P(n)$ to be the following: $a_{n+1} = 3(n + 1)!$, for every positive integer n.]

13. Use mathematical induction to prove that $\sum_{k=1}^{n} k = n(n+1)/2$, for every positive integer n.

14. Use mathematical induction to prove that $\sum_{k=1}^{n} k^2 = n(n+1)(2n+1)/6$, for every positive integer n.

15. Use mathematical induction to prove that $\sum_{k=1}^{n} 2^k = 2(2^n - 1)$, for every positive integer n.

16. If $P(n)$ is the proposition that $1 + 3 + 5 + \cdots + 2n - 1 = n^2 + 1$, show that $P(k+1)$ is true if $P(k)$ is true, whereas the proposition is actually false. Where does an induction "proof" fail?

10.8 Arithmetic Sequences

Among the many types of sequences are two of common occurrence. These are the "arithmetic" and "geometric" sequences, also known as "progressions." In this section we shall discuss arithmetic sequences.

An arithmetic sequence is distinguished by the fact that successive terms differ by the same amount—called the *common difference*. For example, $(1, 2, 3, \ldots)$ is an arithmetic sequence with common difference 1, because $2 - 1 = 3 - 2 = 4 - 3 = \cdots = 1$. Another arithmetic sequence is $(1, 3, 5, \ldots)$, the common difference in this case being $3 - 1 = 5 - 3 = \cdots = 2$. More generally, if the common difference of an arithmetic sequence (a_n) is d, we must have $a_2 - a_1 = a_3 - a_2 = \cdots = d$, so that $a_2 = a_1 + d, a_3 = a_2 + d = a_1 + 2d, a_4 = a_3 + d = a_2 + 2d = a_1 + 3d$, etc. It is easy to see in general—and we suggest an induction proof of this in Problem 2—that $a_n = a_1 + (n-1)d$, for any natural number n. We restate this result as follows:

The nth term of an arithmetic sequence (a_n) is given by

$$a_n = a_1 + (n-1)d.$$

EXAMPLE 1. Find the first five terms of the arithmetic sequence (a_n), where $a_1 = 8$ and $d = -3$.

SOLUTION. From the formula for a_n, we obtain $a_2 = a_1 + d = 8 + (-3) = 5, a_3 = a_2 + d = 5 + (-3) = 2, a_4 = a_3 + d = 2 + (-3) = -1, a_5 = a_4 + d = -1 + (-3) = -4$.

EXAMPLE 2. Find the nineteenth term of the arithmetic sequence whose first three terms, in order, are $3, 4\frac{1}{2}, 6$.

SOLUTION.   We see from the characteristic property of arithmetic sequences that $d = 4\frac{1}{2} - 3 = 6 - 4\frac{1}{2} = \frac{3}{2}$. Since $a_1 = 3$, $a_n = a_1 + (n - 1)d = 3 + (n - 1)\frac{3}{2}$, and so $a_{19} = 3 + 18(\frac{3}{2}) = 30$.

EXAMPLE 3.   If the third and seventh terms of an arithmetic sequence are 1.4 and 2.2, respectively, determine the twentieth term.

SOLUTION.   Since $a_n = a_1 + (n - 1)d$, we have $a_3 = a_1 + 2d = 1.4$ and $a_7 = a_1 + 6d = 2.2$. If we solve these two equations simultaneously, we obtain $a_1 = 1$ and $d = 0.2$. Hence, $a_{20} = a_1 + 19d = 1 + 19(0.2) = 1 + 3.8 = 4.8$.

It is easy to find a formula for the sum of n terms of an arithmetic sequence (a_n), if we notice that $a_{n-1} = a_n - d$, $a_{n-2} = a_n - 2d$, etc., where d is the common difference. The determination of this formula is suggested in Problem 1, but we shall prove its validity by mathematical induction.

THEOREM 10.81.   The sum of n terms of the arithmetic sequence (a_n) is given by the following formula:

$$S_n = a_1 + a_2 + \cdots + a_n = n\frac{(a_1 + a_n)}{2}.$$

PROOF.   Let $P(n)$ represent the formula to be established.
(1) If we let $n = 1$, the formula becomes $S_1 = 1(a_1 + a_1)/2 = a_1$, which is clearly the "sum" of the first n terms where $n = 1$. Hence $P(1)$ is true.
(2) Let us suppose that the formula is valid for $n = k$, i.e., $S_k = k(a_1 + a_k)/2$, for an arbitrary fixed natural number k. Then $S_{k+1} = S_k + a_{k+1} = k(a_1 + a_k)/2 + a_{k+1} = k[a_1 + a_{k+1} - d]/2 + a_{k+1} = k(a_1 + a_{k+1})/2 - kd/2 + a_{k+1}$. But, $a_{k+1} = a_1 + kd$, and so $kd/2 = (a_{k+1} - a_1)/2$. Hence, $S_{k+1} = k(a_1 + a_{k+1})/2 + (a_1 - a_{k+1})/2 + a_{k+1} = k(a_1 + a_{k+1})/2 + (a_1 + a_{k+1})/2 = (k + 1)(a_1 + a_{k+1})/2$. Hence, $P(k + 1)$ is true, and by mathematical induction $P(n)$ is true for any natural number n.

COROLLARY.   If d is the common difference in the arithmetic sequence (a_n), we also have the alternate formula:

$$S_n = \frac{n}{2}[2a_1 + (n - 1)d].$$

PROOF.   Because $a_n = a_1 + (n - 1)d$, and if we replace a_n by this equal expression, we obtain $S_n = n[a_1 + a_1 + (n - 1)d]/2 = (n/2)[2a_1 + (n - 1)d]$.

EXAMPLE 4. Find the sum of the first 50 odd positive integers.

SOLUTION. The odd positive integers comprise a sequence (a_n) for which $a_1 = 1$ and $d = 2$. Hence, for this sequence, $S_{50} = (50/2)[2(1) + (50 - 1)2] = 25(2 + 98) = 2,500$.

The *arithmetic mean* $(x + y)/2$ of two numbers x and y is probably a familiar notion. If we observe that x, $(x + y)/2$, y are three successive terms of an arithmetic sequence, it is easy to extend the notion of one mean to include any number of arithmetic means. Thus, if one or more numbers are inserted between any two given numbers so that the combined ordered set are in the sequential order of an arithmetic sequence, the numbers inserted are called *arithmetic means* of the given numbers.

EXAMPLE 5. Insert three arithmetic means between 4 and 16.

SOLUTION. . The given numbers and the three means must comprise five ordered terms of an arithmetic sequence (a_n) for which $a_1 = 4$ and $a_5 = 16$. Then, $a_5 = a_1 + 4d = 4 + 4d = 16$, and so $4d = 12$, $d = 3$. Hence, $a_2 = 7$, $a_3 = 10$, $a_4 = 13$, and these numbers are the desired arithmetic means.

PROBLEMS

1. Using the suggestion given immediately prior to the Theorem, write $S_n = a_1 + a_2 + \cdots + a_{n-1} + a_n$ as a sum in reverse order, and by adding the two expressions for S_n, obtain the formula for S_n as given in the Theorem.

2. Use mathematical induction to prove that $a_n = a_1 + (n - 1)d$ for an arithmetic sequence (a_n) with common difference d.

3. Find the twelfth term and the sum of the first 12 terms of the arithmetic sequence whose first term is 2 and common difference is 3.

4. The second term of an arithmetic sequence is 5 and the seventh term is 20. Determine the first term and the sum of the first seven terms.

5. Find the twentieth term of the arithmetic sequence whose first three terms are $-2, -5, -8$, in this order.

6. If the first term of an arithmetic sequence is 19 and its common difference is -2, find the sixty-first term and the sum of the first 61 terms.

7. For an arithmetic sequence (a_n), determine: (a) S_7, if $a_1 = 3$ and $d = -4$; (b) S_9, if $a_1 = -6$ and $d = 3$.

8. For an arithmetic sequence (a_n), determine: (a) S_{10}, if $a_7 = 13$ and $a_{12} = 28$; (b) S_{15}, if $a_4 = 15$ and $d = 2$.

9. Use the method of Problem 1 to discover the formula for the sum of the first n odd natural numbers.

10. Use the method of Problem 1 to discover the formula for the sum of the first n even natural numbers.

11. Determine the indicated sums: (a) $\sum\limits_{r=1}^{10} 5r$; (b) $\sum\limits_{r=1}^{27} (2r + 1)$; (c) $\sum\limits_{r=1}^{50} (r + 3)$;

(d) $\sum\limits_{r=1}^{60} (5 - r)$.

12. Insert three arithmetic means between 3 and –17.
13. Insert six arithmetic means between 2 and 23.
14. Find the first term of an arithmetic sequence whose fifteenth term is 59 and common difference is 4.
15. If $300 is invested at 6 per cent simple interest, use a formula from this section to determine the amount of the investment after 10 years.
16. For how many years must $100 be invested at 6 per cent simple interest if the final amount is to exceed $500?
17. Find a_1 and a_8 for the arithmetic sequence (a_n) where $d = -2$ and $S_8 = 72$.
18. How many feet of rung material is required for the construction of a ladder of 31 rungs, if the rungs taper from 29 inches in length at the bottom to 19 inches at the top?
19. If logs are stacked so that there are 20 logs on the bottom row and 1 less on each successive row, how many rows are needed to stack 155 logs?
20. A slide of uniform slope is to be built on a level piece of land. If there are to be 15 equally spaced supports, the lengths of the longest and shortest being 5 and 47 feet, respectively, find the length of each intermediate support.
21. The force of gravity causes a body near the surface of the earth to fall (in a vacuum) so that its velocity at the end of 1 second is 32.2 feet/sec. and its increase in velocity for each successive second is also 32.2 feet/sec. Use a formula from this section to obtain its theoretical velocity after 10 seconds of fall.
22. A new piece of machinery costs $30,000. If the machinery depreciates 5 per cent of its original cost each year, determine its value at the end of 10 years.
23. A man buys a car for $3,000, making a down payment of $1,000. If he agrees to pay the remainder in 20 equal monthly payments of $100 plus 6 per cent of the unpaid balance, determine the total amount of his interest payments.

10.9   Geometric Sequences

A sequence whose successive terms are 1, 2, 4, 8, ⌄.. has the feature that each term (after the first) may be found from the preceding by multiplying the latter by 2. This is an example of a "geometric" sequence, which can be described more generally as a sequence (a_n) such that $a_k = ra_{k-1}$, for $k = 2, 3, 4, \ldots$ and some real number $r \neq 0$. The number r is known as the *common ratio*, and gives the ratio of any term to the preceding term, r being comparable to d of an arithmetic sequence. It is customary to express the successive terms of a geometric sequence, whose first term is a_1 and common ratio is r, in the form $a_1, ra_1, r^2a_1, \ldots$. As for arithmetic sequences, we are interested in formulas for the nth term and for the sum of

n terms. It is clear, from the preceding array of terms, that the nth term of that general sequence has the following form:

$$a_n = r^{n-1}a_1.$$

A formal proof of this result can be given quite easily by mathematical induction, and this proof is suggested in Problem 2.

EXAMPLE 1. Find the tenth term of the geometric sequence whose first term is 2 and common ratio is $\frac{3}{2}$.

  SOLUTION

$$a_{10} = \left(\frac{3}{2}\right)^9 (2) = \frac{3^9}{2^8} = \frac{19683}{256}.$$

If we let $S_n = a_1 + a_2 + \cdots + a_n$, in Problem 1 we suggest an elementary method (similar to that in Problem 1 of §10.8) for obtaining a formula for S_n. The following theorem establishes the validity of this result by mathematical induction.

THEOREM 10.91. If S_n is the sum of n terms of the geometric sequence (a_n), whose common ratio is r, $S_n = a_1(1 - r^n)/(1 - r)$.

  PROOF. We let $P(n)$ represent the assertion of the formula.
  (1) If $n = 1$, the formula gives $S_1 = a_1(1 - r^1)/(1 - r) = a_1$, a trivially correct statement, and so $P(1)$ is true.
  (2) Let us assume $P(k)$ is true, so that $S_k = a_1(1 - r^k)/(1 - r)$, for an arbitrary but fixed natural number k. Then

$$S_{k+1} = S_k + a_{k+1} = \frac{a_1(1 - r^k)}{1 - r} + r^k a_1 = \frac{a_1(1 - r^k) + r^k a_1(1 - r)}{1 - r}$$

$$\frac{a_1(1 - r^k + r^k - r^{k+1})}{1 - r} = \frac{a_1(1 - r^{k+1})}{1 - r}.$$

Hence, $P(k + 1)$ is true, and it follows by mathematical induction that $P(n)$ is true for every natural number n.

For convenience in case $r > 1$, it should be observed that the formula can also be expressed in the form:

$$S_n = \frac{a_1(r^n - 1)}{r - 1}.$$

EXAMPLE 2. Find the sum of the first 12 terms of the geometric sequence whose first term is 2 and common ratio is $\frac{1}{2}$.

SOLUTION

$$S_{12} = \frac{2[1 - (1/2)^{12}]}{1 - 1/2} = 4\left(1 - \frac{1}{2^{12}}\right)$$

$$= 4 - \frac{1}{2^{10}} = 4 - \frac{1}{1024} = \frac{4095}{1024}.$$

With geometric sequences it is sometimes possible to define what we call the "sum" of all terms of the sequence, even when the number of these terms is infinite. It is in connection with such infinite sums that the manner of summation becomes critical, and we use the summation convention adopted for S_n in §10.8. But first we must introduce the concept of a "limit," a notion of basic importance in the calculus.

Intuitively, the "limit" of a sequence (a_n) is a number L—if such a number exists—to which the terms of the sequence get arbitrarily close if a sufficiently large number of terms are considered. Thus, for sufficiently large index n—say $n > M$, for some real number M—the difference $|a_n - L|$ will be arbitrarily close to 0. Formally, we write this as follows:

lim $a_n = L$ if, for arbitrary $\epsilon > 0$, there exists a real
number M such that $|a_n - L| < \epsilon$, provided $n > M$.

To illustrate the notion of limit, consider the sequence $(1, \frac{1}{2}, \frac{1}{3}, \ldots,$ $1/n, \ldots)$. It should be apparent that $1/n$ is arbitrarily close to 0, if n is sufficiently large. To be precise, if $\epsilon > 0$ is given, it is sufficient to choose $M = 1/\epsilon$, and we are then able to assert that $1/n - 0 = 1/n < 1/(1/\epsilon) = \epsilon$, provided $n > 1/\epsilon = M$. Hence, by our definition of limit of a sequence, the limit of this sequence is 0.

As another, and rather "homey," illustration, consider the case of an easily tired frog that jumps halfway to the opposite bank of a 30-foot creek in each of a sequence of jumps. If $S_1, S_2, S_3, \ldots$ designates the *total* distance jumped by the frog in 1, 2, 3, $\ldots$ jumps, respectively, it is evident that S_n will get as close to 30 as we wish. Indeed, while S_n never equals 30 for any index n, S_n will actually exceed any real number less than 30. Under these circumstances, lim $S_n = 30$.

We now adopt the summation convention for S_n, as we did in §10.8, for the sum of the first n terms of a sequence (a_n). If the sequence (S_n) of partial sums, associated with (a_n), has a limit, we *define* this limit to be the *sum* S_∞ of the whole sequence. That is, to restate this definition:

$$S_\infty = \lim S_n.$$

In particular, let us consider the geometric sequence (a_n) and the formula for S_n given in the theorem above. We may write $S_n = a_1/(1 - r) + a_1 r^n/(1 - r)$, and note that n occurs only in the second term of this expression. If $|r| < 1$, it is intuitively evident that the numerator of this second term gets arbitrarily close to 0, for an n sufficiently large, while the denominator is independent of n. Hence the limit of this second term is 0, so that $\lim S_n = a_1/(1 - r)$. We have obtained the following result:

$$S_\infty = \frac{a_1}{(1 - r)}, \qquad \text{provided } |r| < 1.$$

EXAMPLE 3.   Determine the sum of the infinite geometric sequence whose terms in order are $1, \frac{1}{2}, \frac{1}{4}, \frac{1}{8}, \ldots, \dfrac{1}{2^{n-1}}, \ldots$.

SOLUTION.   In this case, the sequence is geometric with $a_1 = 1$ and $r = \frac{1}{2}$. Hence $S_\infty = 1/(1 - \frac{1}{2}) = 1/(\frac{1}{2}) = 2$.

EXAMPLE 4.   Express the "repeating" decimal number $0.7121212\cdots$ as the quotient of two integers.

SOLUTION.   Let $t = 0.7121212\cdots$. Then $t = 0.7 + 0.012 + 0.00012 + 0.0000012 + \cdots = 0.7 + (0.012 + 0.00012 + 0.0000012 + \cdots) = 0.7 + 0.012/(1 - 0.01) = 0.7 + 0.012/0.99 = \frac{7}{10} + \frac{12}{990} = \frac{7}{10} + \frac{4}{330} = \frac{235}{330} = \frac{47}{66}$.

If we insert between two numbers x and y other numbers so that the combined set forms an ordered portion of a geometric sequence, the inserted numbers are called "geometric means" of x and y.

EXAMPLE 5.   Insert four geometric means between 2 and $-\frac{1}{16}$.

SOLUTION.   If four geometric means are inserted as desired, $-\frac{1}{16}$ is the sixth term of a geometric sequence whose first term is 2. Then $a_6 = r^5(2) = -\frac{1}{16} = -2^{-4}$, and so $r^5 = -2^{-5} = (-\frac{1}{2})^5$. Hence, $r = -\frac{1}{2}$, and the desired means are: $a_2 = -1$, $a_3 = \frac{1}{2}$, $a_4 = -\frac{1}{4}$, $a_5 = \frac{1}{8}$.

PROBLEMS

1. Derive the formula obtained in the theorem of this section, by expressing S_n and rS_n as sums of n terms, subtracting the latter from the former and solving the resulting expression for S_n.
2. Use mathematical induction to verify that the nth term of a geometric sequence (a_n), with common ratio r, is given by $a_n = a_1 r^{n-1}$.
3. With reference to a geometric sequence (a_n), find: (a) a_5 if $a_1 = 2$ and $r = 3$; (b) a_4 if $a_1 = 1$ and $r = -0.01$; (c) a_{10} if $a_3 = 8$ and $r = 0.2$.
4. With reference to a geometric sequence (a_n), find: (a) a_8 if $a_2 = 2$ and $a_5 = \frac{16}{81}$; (b) a_7 if $a_2 = \frac{3}{4}$ and $a_5 = \frac{81}{256}$.
5. Find the sum of 10 terms of the geometric sequence whose first term is 2 and common ratio is $\frac{2}{3}$.
6. Insert two geometric means between 56 and 875.

7. Insert three geometric means between 18 and $\frac{2}{9}$.

8. With the usual notation for sequences, find: (a) S_6 if $a_1 = \frac{1}{8}$ and $r = 2$; (b) S_8 if $a_1 = 6$ and $r = -2$.

9. If $a_1 = 3$ and $a_3 = 48$, for a geometric sequence (a_n), determine r.

10. Express each of the following repeating decimals as the quotient of two integers; (a) $0.314314\cdots$; (b) $0.237237\cdots$; (c) $1.56717171\cdots$.

11. Determine S_∞, for each of the indicated infinite geometric sequences: (a) $(2, \frac{4}{3}, \frac{8}{9}, \ldots)$; (b) $(1, \frac{1}{3}, \frac{1}{9}, \ldots)$; (c) $(\frac{2}{3}, \frac{1}{6}, \frac{1}{24}, \ldots)$.

12. If \$1,000 is invested for five years at 4 per cent interest compounded annually, determine the amount of the investment in five years.

13. How many years are necessary for \$20, invested at 8 per cent interest compounded annually, to exceed \$50?

14. Explain why the formula for S_∞ is meaningless if $|r| \geq 1$.

15. Evaluate each of the following sums: (a) $\sum\limits_{k=0}^{\infty} (\frac{1}{2})^k$; (b) $\sum\limits_{k=0}^{\infty} (-\frac{1}{3})^k$.

16. The bob of a pendulum travels 20 inches during its first swing. If each swing thereafter is $\frac{4}{5}$ as long as the preceding, determine the theoretical distance traveled by the bob before it comes to rest.

17. An elastic ball is dropped from a height of 50 feet, the ball rebounding $\frac{2}{3}$ of its height of fall for each subsequent descent. Determine the theoretical distance traveled by the ball before coming to rest.

18. A sequence of equilateral triangles is constructed, starting with a triangle with sides two feet in length and joining midpoints of these sides, and continuing this process indefinitely. Determine the theoretical sum of the perimeters of all the triangles of the infinite sequence constructed.

19. Find the theoretical sum of the areas of all triangles in Problem 18, ignoring the fact that the triangles overlap.

20. It is estimated that the enrollment of a certain university will increase 8 per cent per year. If the present enrollment is 2,000 students, in how many years will the enrollment have more than doubled?

21. A chemist has ten gallons of alcohol. If he drains off two gallons of alcohol and replaces it with water, stirs the resulting mixture thoroughly and then repeats the operation ten times, how much alcohol will remain?

22. The half life of a radioactive substance is the time required for the natural decomposition of half of any given amount of it. If the half life of a certain isotope is six years, how many of $3(10^{12})$ original isotopes will remain after 36 years?

23. Use mathematical induction to prove that: (a) $2^n < n!$ for every positive integer $n > 3$; (b) $n! < n^n$, for every positive integer $n > 1$. (Cf. Problem 12 of §10.7.)

24. A sequence (a_n) is called a "harmonic" sequence if (b_n) is an arithmetic sequence, where $b_n = 1/a_n$, for each positive integer n.
    (a) Find the first five terms of (a_n) if $b_1 = 5$ and $b_2 = 3$;
    (b) Find the first four terms of (a_n) if $b_1 = \frac{1}{3}$ and $b_2 = \frac{1}{2}$.
    (c) Make a reasonable definition for the harmonic mean of two numbers, and find a suitable formula.

APPENDIX A

Review of
High-School Algebra

In this very brief review, we shall merely recall the pertinent rules, give several examples of their use, and include a fairly large collection of problems. The letters a, b, c, d, wherever they are used in this Appendix, will designate integers.

1. Arithmetic of Fractions

(a) *Equality.* $a/b = c/d$ if and only if $ad = bc$. A consequence of this definition of equality is the following *basic principle*: If both numerator and denominator of a fraction are multiplied or divided by the same nonzero number, the fraction is unchanged except in form. In the case of division, we refer to the new form as a "reduction" of the original form.

EXAMPLE

$$\frac{2}{3} = \frac{2 \cdot 4}{3 \cdot 4} = \frac{8}{12}$$
$$= \frac{2 \cdot 5}{3 \cdot 5} = \frac{10}{15}.$$
$$\frac{8}{10} = \frac{8/2}{10/2} = \frac{4}{5}.$$

(b) *Addition and Subtraction.* $a/b \pm c/d = (ad \pm bc)/bd$. The gist of this rule is that the principle in (a) is used to express the fractions of an indicated sum or difference in a form which will exhibit the same denominator in each case. Then perform the indicated operations on the numerators, and reduce if possible.

EXAMPLE

$$\frac{1}{2} - \frac{3}{4} + \frac{2}{3} = \frac{6}{12} - \frac{9}{12} + \frac{8}{12} = \frac{6-9+8}{12} = \frac{5}{12}.$$

(c) *Multiplication.* $(a/b)(c/d) = ac/bd$. In this way the multiplication of fractions can be accomplished by the formal multiplication of the respective numerators and denominators, followed or accompanied by any possible reductions.

EXAMPLE

$$\left(\frac{2}{5}\right)\left(\frac{3}{4}\right)\left(\frac{5}{6}\right) = \frac{2\cdot3\cdot5}{5\cdot4\cdot6} = \frac{\overset{1}{2}\cdot\overset{1}{3}\cdot\overset{1}{5}}{\underset{1}{5}\cdot\underset{2}{4}\cdot\underset{2}{6}} = \frac{1\cdot1\cdot1}{1\cdot2\cdot2} = \frac{1}{4}.$$

(d) *Division.* $[a/b]/[c/d] = ad/bc$. Hence, to divide one fraction by another, we invert the divisor and multiply.

EXAMPLE

$$\frac{2/3}{5/6} = \left(\frac{2}{3}\right)\left(\frac{6}{5}\right) = \frac{2\cdot6}{3\cdot5} = \frac{2\cdot\overset{2}{6}}{\underset{1}{3}\cdot5} = \frac{2\cdot2}{1\cdot5} = \frac{4}{5}.$$

PROBLEMS*

1. Explain the process of "cancellation" in terms of the Basic Principle enunciated above.
2. Express each of the following numbers as a prime power product: (a) 64; (b) 36; (c) 72; (d) 160; (e) 42; (f) 18; (g) 125; (h) 60; (i) 80; (j) 90; (k) 102.
3. Determine the greatest common divisor of the integers in each of the following collections: (a) 8, 12, 15; (b) 21, 15, 42; (c) 2, 4, 8, 18; (d) 30, 45, 105, 120; (e) 3, 7, 13.
4. Reduce each of the following fractions by dividing numerator and denominator by the same number: (a) $\frac{4}{12}$; (b) $\frac{32}{48}$; (c) $\frac{7}{21}$; (d) $\frac{70}{21}$; (e) $\frac{90}{24}$; (f) $\frac{120}{260}$.
5. Replace each of the following fractions by an equivalent fraction, after multiplying numerator and denominator by 5: (a) $\frac{2}{3}$; (b) $\frac{3}{4}$; (c) $\frac{5}{3}$; (d) $\frac{4}{6}$; (e) $\frac{4}{9}$.
6. Replace each of the following fractions by an equivalent fraction, after multiplying numerator and denominator by 10: (a) $\frac{4}{3}$; (b) $\frac{2}{7}$; (c) $\frac{5}{8}$; (d) $\frac{5}{6}$; (e) $\frac{3}{4}$.

* The sets of problems in this Review have been taken, with the kind permission of the publisher, from *Fundamental Principles of Mathematics* by John T. Moore (New York: Holt, Rinehart and Winston, 1960).

7. Find the sum of the numbers in each of the following collections: (a) $\frac{2}{3}$, $\frac{3}{4}$, $\frac{5}{8}$, $\frac{1}{2}$; (b) $\frac{1}{2}$, $\frac{2}{3}$, $\frac{3}{4}$, $\frac{4}{5}$; (c) $\frac{1}{3}$, $\frac{3}{7}$, $\frac{1}{15}$, $\frac{3}{10}$.

8. In each of the following pairs of fractions, subtract the second member from the first: (a) 5, $\frac{2}{3}$; (b) $\frac{3}{4}$, $\frac{2}{3}$; (c) $\frac{5}{7}$, $\frac{2}{3}$; (d) 4, $\frac{3}{7}$; (e) $\frac{12}{5}$, 2.

9. Simplify each of the following expressions: (a) $\frac{3}{2} + \frac{3}{4} - \frac{1}{8} - \frac{1}{4}$; (b) $\frac{3}{5} - \frac{2}{3} + \frac{5}{8} - \frac{1}{3} + \frac{5}{8}$; (c) $\frac{3}{7} + \frac{8}{3} - \frac{3}{8} + \frac{2}{9}$.

10. Simplify each of the following expressions: (a) $(\frac{2}{3})(\frac{1}{4})(\frac{3}{8})(\frac{4}{3})$; (b) $(\frac{4}{5})(\frac{10}{3})(\frac{2}{5})(\frac{3}{10})$; (c) $(\frac{5}{8})(\frac{4}{3})(\frac{2}{3})(5)(\frac{1}{2})$.

11. Divide the first member of each of the following pairs of numbers by the second: (a) $\frac{3}{4}$, $\frac{2}{3}$; (b) $\frac{1}{2}$, $\frac{4}{5}$; (c) $\frac{3}{8}$, $\frac{4}{5}$; (d) $\frac{3}{7}$, 6; (e) 8, $\frac{1}{4}$; (f) $\frac{4}{3}$, 6.

12. Simplify each of the following expressions: (a) $\frac{3}{4} + (\frac{2}{3})(\frac{1}{4})$; (b) $(\frac{5}{6})(\frac{2}{3}) + (\frac{1}{4})(\frac{2}{3}) - (\frac{1}{3})(\frac{1}{8})$; (c) $(\frac{2}{3})(\frac{4}{5}) - (\frac{3}{8})(\frac{1}{2})$; (d) $(\frac{5}{6})(\frac{2}{3}) \div (\frac{3}{7})(\frac{2}{5})$; (e) $\frac{3}{4} \div [(\frac{2}{3})(\frac{1}{4}) - \frac{1}{8}]$.

13. From the sum of $7 + \frac{7}{8}$ and $3 + \frac{3}{4}$ subtract the sum of $2 + \frac{1}{3}$ and $4 + \frac{1}{2}$.

14. Subtract $5 + \frac{7}{8}$ from $16 + \frac{3}{4}$; subtract $15 + \frac{5}{12}$ from $27 + \frac{3}{4}$.

15. In building a fence, a man used steel posts $6\frac{1}{2}$ feet long. If he drove each post $2\frac{1}{4}$ feet into the ground, how much of each post was above ground?

16. What is the cost of $55\frac{1}{2}$ feet of sash cord at $\frac{3}{4}$¢ per foot?

17. A filling station advertised $6\frac{1}{4}$ gallons of gasoline for $1.00. What was the exact price per gallon?

18. Find the sum of $\frac{5}{2}$ and its reciprocal; find the sum of $3 + \frac{3}{4}$ and its reciprocal.

2. Arithmetic of Signed Numbers

(a) *Addition.* If the numbers to be added have the same signs, add their absolute values and attach the common sign.

EXAMPLE

$$(+\tfrac{2}{3}) + (+\tfrac{4}{5}) = +(\tfrac{2}{3} + \tfrac{4}{5}) = +(\tfrac{10}{15} + \tfrac{12}{15}) = +\tfrac{22}{15}.$$
$$(-\tfrac{1}{2}) + (-\tfrac{2}{3}) + (-\tfrac{1}{4}) = -(\tfrac{1}{2} + \tfrac{2}{3} + \tfrac{1}{4})$$
$$-(\tfrac{6}{12} + \tfrac{8}{12} + \tfrac{3}{12}) = -\tfrac{17}{12}.$$

If two numbers to be added have unlike signs, subtract the smaller absolute value from the larger and attach the sign of the larger.

EXAMPLE

$$(+\tfrac{1}{4}) + (-\tfrac{2}{3}) = -(\tfrac{2}{3} - \tfrac{1}{4}) = -(\tfrac{8}{12} - \tfrac{3}{12}) = -\tfrac{5}{12}$$

(b) *Subtraction.* To subtract a signed number, change its sign and add.

EXAMPLE

$$(-\tfrac{2}{5}) - (+\tfrac{1}{3}) = (-\tfrac{2}{5}) + (-\tfrac{1}{3}) = -(\tfrac{6}{15} + \tfrac{5}{15}) = -\tfrac{11}{15}.$$

(c) *Multiplication and Division.* For any compound product or quotient of signed numbers, perform the indicated operations on the absolute values and attach a positive sign if the number of negative signs is even, and a negative sign if the number of negative signs is odd.

EXAMPLE

$$\left(\frac{-1}{3}\right)\left(\frac{+2}{5}\right)\left(\frac{-6}{7}\right) = +\left[\left(\frac{1}{3}\right)\left(\frac{2}{5}\right)\left(\frac{6}{7}\right)\right] = +\frac{4}{35}$$

$$\left(\frac{-1}{2}\right)\left(\frac{+2}{3}\right)\left(\frac{+1}{5}\right) = -\left[\left(\frac{1 \cdot 2 \cdot 1}{2 \cdot 3 \cdot 5}\right)\right] = -\frac{1}{15}.$$

$$\frac{(2/3)\,(-1/2)}{(-1/4)\,(+5/2)} = +\frac{(2/3)\,(1/2)}{(1/4)\,(5/2)} = +\frac{(1/3)}{(5/8)} = +\frac{8}{15}.$$

NOTE: While we have included the $+$ sign in the above examples, this sign is usually omitted unless it is needed for emphasis.

PROBLEMS

1. Give the absolute value of each of the following: (a) 6; (b) -7; (c) -4; (d) $\tfrac{3}{5}$; (e) $-\tfrac{5}{7}$.
2. Find the sum of the numbers in each of the following collections: (a) 7, 4, 5, 1; (b) -3, -5, -2, -8, -3; (c) $-\tfrac{2}{3}$, $-\tfrac{3}{4}$, $-\tfrac{1}{6}$, $-\tfrac{5}{12}$, $-\tfrac{3}{8}$; (d) $\tfrac{3}{5}$, $\tfrac{2}{5}$, $\tfrac{3}{8}$.
3. Find the sum of the numbers in each of the following collections: (a) 6, 3, -8, -4; (b) 12, -7, 6, -33, 5; (c) -4, 12, -9, -3, 5; (d) -5, 8, 14, -3, -16.
4. Find the sum of the numbers in each of the following collections: (a) $\tfrac{2}{3}$, $-\tfrac{3}{4}$, $\tfrac{5}{8}$, $-\tfrac{1}{2}$; (b) $\tfrac{3}{2}$, $-\tfrac{5}{7}$, $\tfrac{7}{8}$, $-\tfrac{1}{2}$, $\tfrac{6}{7}$; (c) $\tfrac{3}{4}$, $-\tfrac{2}{5}$, $\tfrac{4}{7}$, $\tfrac{7}{8}$, $-\tfrac{1}{2}$, $\tfrac{3}{4}$.
5. Subtract the second number from the first in each of the following pairs: (a) $\tfrac{3}{4}$, $-\tfrac{2}{7}$; (b) $-\tfrac{5}{3}$, $\tfrac{2}{3}$; (c) 5, $-\tfrac{3}{4}$; (d) $-\tfrac{2}{7}$, 3; (e) $-\tfrac{4}{3}$, $-\tfrac{2}{5}$; (f) $\tfrac{3}{5}$, -4; (g) -1, $-\tfrac{5}{4}$.
6. Multiply together the numbers in each of the following collections, and reduce the result to lowest terms: (a) $\tfrac{2}{3}$, $-\tfrac{4}{5}$, $-\tfrac{3}{4}$; (b) -2, $-\tfrac{4}{5}$, -5; (c) $\tfrac{3}{5}$, $-\tfrac{6}{7}$, -3, $-\tfrac{5}{2}$.
7. Divide the first number by the second in each of the following pairs: (a) $\tfrac{3}{4}$, $-\tfrac{5}{4}$; (b) $-\tfrac{2}{3}$, $-\tfrac{6}{5}$; (c) 5, $-\tfrac{4}{5}$; (d) $\tfrac{6}{5}$, -4.
8. Simplify each of the following expressions: (a) $(\tfrac{2}{3})\,(-\tfrac{5}{2})\,(-\tfrac{3}{4})\,(-6)$; (b) $[(-4)\,(-\tfrac{2}{3})\,(-\tfrac{6}{7})] \div [(-\tfrac{5}{2})\,(\tfrac{7}{4})]$; (c) $(\tfrac{61}{12})\,(-\tfrac{15}{4}) + (-\tfrac{3}{2})\,(-\tfrac{2}{5})$.

NOTE: If a sign of aggregation is preceded by a negative sign, change all the signs within the sign of aggregation when it is removed; if the preceding sign is positive, the signs within remain the same.

9. Simplify each of the following: (a) $\tfrac{1}{2} - 2[3 + 5(1 - \tfrac{1}{2})]$; (b) $3 - 3[\tfrac{1}{2} - (2 + \tfrac{1}{4})] - 1$; (c) $2\{3[1 - \tfrac{2}{3}] + 1\} - 2$; (d) $3 - 2\{(1 - \tfrac{1}{2}) \times (2 + \tfrac{2}{3}) - 1\}$.
10. Simplify each of the following:

(a) $\dfrac{2\{3 + [5 - 2(1 - \frac{1}{2})]\}}{2 + 4[1 - (\frac{1}{4})(2 - \frac{1}{3})]}$;

(b) $1 - \dfrac{1}{2 - \dfrac{1}{3 - \frac{1}{2}}}$;

(c) $\dfrac{1}{2 + 3[2 - (\frac{1}{2})(3 - \frac{2}{3})]}$.

3. Algebraic Expressions

In elementary algebra the number symbols are merely unknown or unidentified real *numbers*. Hence, operations involving these symbols must obey the same rules as for the real numbers. In fact, an error in a manipulation of symbols may often be easily detected by noting an arithmetic error which appears when the symbols are replaced by specific real numbers. In particular, the rules of operation pertaining to signed numbers are applicable to these algebraic expressions.

EXAMPLE

$3x - 2\{3x - 2[1 - 4(x - 1)] + 2\} = 3x - 2\{3x - 2[1 - 4x + 4] + 2\}$
$= 3x - 2\{3x - 2[5 - 4x] + 2\} = 3x - 2\{11x - 8\} = 3x - 22x + 16$
$= 16 - 19x.$

There are a number of special products which should be familiar to the student of algebra, and which we now list.

(a) *The product of the sum and difference of two numbers.*
$(x + y)(x - y) = x^2 - y^2.$

EXAMPLE

$$(3x + 2y)(3x - 2y) = 9x^2 - 4y^2.$$

(b) *Powers of a Binomial*

$(x + y)^2 = x^2 + 2xy + y^2.$ $(x + y)^3 = x^3 + 3x^2y + 3xy^2 + y^3.$
$(x - y)^2 = x^2 - 2xy + y^2.$ $(x - y)^3 = x^3 - 3x^2y + 3xy^2 - y^3.$

EXAMPLE

$$(x - 2y)^2 = x^2 - 4xy + 4y^2;$$
$$(2x + y)^3 = 8x^3 + 3(2x)^2y + 3(2x)y^2 + y^3;$$
$$= 8x^3 + 12x^2y + 6xy^2 + y^3.$$

(c) *The Product of Two Binomials.*

$$(x + a)(x + b) = x^2 + (a + b)x + ab.$$
$$(ax + b)(cx + d) = acx^2 + (bc + ad)x + bd.$$

EXAMPLE

$$(x - 2)(x - 3) = x^2 + (-2 - 3)x + 6 = x^2 - 5x + 6$$
$$(2x - 3b)(x + 2b) = 2x^2 + (4b - 3b)x - 6b^2 = 2x^2 + bx - 6b^2.$$

PROBLEMS

1. Simplify each of the following: (a) $(-4x)(2x^2)$; (b) $3ab - 2ab + ab$; (c) $(2x)(-3x)(-4x)$; (d) $(-ay)(by)(-3)$; (e) $(-6xy)(2x) + 5x^2y$.

2. Find the sum of the quantities in each of the following collections: (a) $8a$, $-3a$, $9a$, $2a$; (b) $12ab$, $-5ab$, $-2ab$; (c) $2ab$, $-6ab$, $4ac$; (d) $2a^2$, $-3a$, $5b$, $5a$.

3. Subtract $12a - 7c$ from $6a - 7b - 10c$.

4. Subtract $12x^2 - 3x + 1$ from $-2x^2 + 9x - 7$.

5. (a) Subtract $18abc$ from $3abc$; (b) subtract $-5m$ from $-8m^2$; (c) subtract $-6x^2 + 4y$ from $2x^2 - 4y$.

6. (a) Subtract $2a + 3b + 5c$ from $5a - 8b + 11c$; (b) subtract $7x + 5y$ from $-6x + 4y$; (c) subtract $-6x^2 - 8$ from $3x^2 - 2y + 7$.

7. Simplify each of the following: (a) $3xy - 2xy + 9y - 2xy$; (b) $3x^2 - 2x^2 + (9y - 2x^2)$; (c) $7a - 4[(2a + 6b) - b^2 + c] - 4(2 - c)$.

8. Simplify each of the following: (a) $ab - 4b^2 - (2a^2 + b^2) - (-5a^2 - 3b^2)$; (b) $x - \{y - z - [x - (-x + y) - z]\} + (2x - y)$; (c) $-1\{-1 - [-1 - (-1)]\}$.

9. Expand each of the following products: (a) $(2x + 5y)(2x - 5y)$; (b) $(3x^2 + 2y^2)(3x^2 - 2y^2)$; (c) $(2x + y)^2$; (d) $(x - 2y)^3$.

10. Expand each of the following products: (a) $(5x - 2y)(5x + 2y)$; (b) $(x^2y - 3a)(x^2y + 3a)$; (c) $(2x - 6y)(2x + 6y)$; (d) $(3x - y)^3$.

11. Expand each of the following products: (a) $(2a - x)^2$; (b) $(1 + x)^3$; (c) $(2x - 1)^3$; (d) $(x + 2)(x + 3)$; (e) $(3xy - z)(3xy + 7z)$.

12. Expand each of the following products: (a) $(x - 2y)(2x - 2y)$; (b) $(a + 7b)(2a - 3b)$; (c) $(x^2 - 3)(x^2 + 4)$; (d) $[x/2 + 5y][x/2 - 5y]$; (e) $[x/2 - y/4]^2$.

13. Expand each of the following products: (a) $(6x - \frac{1}{2})^2$; (b) $(2 + 3x)^3$; (c) $(5m^3 - 6s^2)(5m^3 + s^2)$; (d) $(3xy - 7)^2$.

14. Simplify each of the following:

   (a) $\dfrac{3m^2 + 2m - 5m^3}{m}$;

   (b) $\dfrac{4x^3 - 2x^2}{2x}$;

   (c) $\dfrac{x^4 - 12x^3 + 6x^2}{x^2}$;

   (d) $\dfrac{a^2b^2 - a^3b^3 + ab^5}{ab^2}$;

   (e) $\dfrac{15xy^2z}{3xz}$.

15. Find the product of each of the following pairs of algebraic quantities: (a) $5mn^2$, $-4mn^2$; (b) $3b^2c$, $4bc^2$; (c) $5ty^3$, $-8y^2z$; (d) $2x^2y$, $-4x + 7y$, $-xy$; (e) a, $-a$, $-a$, $-a$.

16. Expand each of the following: (a) $(2x - y + 3z)^2$; (b) $(x - 2y)(1 - x)^2$; (c) $(x^2 - 6)^2(2x + 1)$; (d) $(x - 3y)(2x + y)(x + y)$; (e) $(2x + y - z)^3$.

4. Factoring

The ability to factor a given algebraic expression is largely a matter of identifying it as a member of a certain class of expressions. We list some of the more standard of these factoring types here.

(a) *Trinomials Which are Perfect Squares.*

$$x^2 \pm 2xy + y^2 = (x \pm y)^2.$$

EXAMPLE

$$4a^2 - 4ab + b^2 = (2a - b)^2.$$

(b) *Difference of Two Squares.* $x^2 - y^2 = (x + y)(x - y).$

EXAMPLE

$$4a^2 - 25b^2 = (2a + 5b)(2a - 5b).$$

(c) *Trinomials with Leading Coefficient of 1.* $x^2 + (a + b)x + ab = (x + a)(x + b).$

EXAMPLE

$$x^2 - 7x + 12 = (x - 4)(x - 3).$$

(d) *Sum or Difference of Two Cubes.*

$$x^3 \pm y^3 = (x \pm y)(x^2 \mp xy + y^2).$$

EXAMPLE

$$8a^3 - b^3 = (2a - b)(4a^2 + 2ab + b^2).$$

(e) *General Trinomials.* $ax^2 + bx + c = (px + r)(qx + s)$, by inspection.

EXAMPLE

$$8x^2 - 2x - 3 = (2x + 1)(4x - 3).$$

(f) *Grouping*

EXAMPLE

$$3ax - 3ay + acx - acy = a[3x - 3y + cx - cy] = a[x(3 + c) - y(3 + c)]$$
$$= a[(3 + c)(x - y)] = a(x - y)(3 + c).$$

PROBLEMS

Factor each of the following expressions completely, by first factoring out any common monomial, and then using one of the above typical forms.

1. $9x^8 - 4y^6$.
2. $225 - a^6$.
3. $r^4 - 11r^2 + 30$.
4. $16x^2 + 30x + 9$.
5. $3y^3 + 24$.
6. $6x^2 + 7x - 3$.
7. $c^3 + 27d^3$.
8. $x^2 - 16x + 48$.
9. $y^3 - 27z^3$.
10. $4x^2 - 3x - 7$.
11. $6 - t - 15t^2$.
12. $25t^4 - 1$.
13. $36a^2 - 132a + 121$.
14. $u^6 + u^3 - 110$.
15. $3x^4 - 12$.
16. $x^8 - y^8$.
17. $x^5 - xy^4 - x^4y + y^5$.
18. $x^4 - x^3y - xy^3 + y^4$.
19. $x^3 - 3x^2 + 3x - 1$.
20. $(x + y)^2 - a^2$.
21. $c^2 - (a + b)^2$.
22. $x^3y^3 + 1$.
23. $8 - 27x^3$.
24. $24m^2 + 22mn - 21n^2$.
25. $16x^2 - 6x - 27$.
26. $9 + 35x - 4x^2$.
27. $2x^4 + 11x^2y^2 - 21y^4$.
28. $(x - y)^2 - 4z^2$.
29. $(5x - 7)^2 - 1$.
30. $x^2 - (y - x)^2$.
31. $(3y + 5)^2 - (2y - 9)^2$.
32. $x^4y^4 - 9y^4$.
33. $x^2(2x + 1)^2 - (2y - 9)^2$.
34. $(x^2 - 4y^2) + x(x + 2y)$.
35. $a^2x + a^2y + abx + aby$.
36. $a^2x^3 - 64x^3y^2$.
37. $a^2x^2 - a^2y^2 + abx^2 - aby^2$.
38. $x^3 + x^2 + x + 1$.
39. $2 + 3x - 8x^2 - 12x^3$.
40. $56 - 32a + 21a^2 - 12a^3$.
41. $x^3 + (y - z)^3$.
42. $(m + n)^3 + 8t^3$.
43. $27a^3 - (a - b)^3$.
44. $(x + y)^2 - x^2y^2$.

5. Algebraic Fractions

Algebraic expressions arise because the results of designated operations must be merely formalized or expressed. For example, we can state that $2 + 3 = 5$, but $x + y$ must be left this way unless x and y are identified. With this understanding, the rules for the simplification of algebraic frac-' tions are precisely the rules associated with arithmetic fractions: Express all fractions with a common denominator for addition; factor and reduce for multiplication. We shall use two examples by way of illustration.

EXAMPLE

$$\frac{x^2 - 7x + 12}{x^2 + x} \cdot \frac{x^2 - 1}{x^2 - 4x + 3} = \frac{(x - 3)(x - 4)}{x(x + 1)} \cdot \frac{(x + 1)(x - 1)}{(x - 3)(x - 1)} = \frac{x - 4}{x}.$$

EXAMPLE

$$\frac{4x}{x^2 + x - 2} - \frac{3x + 1}{x^2 - 3x + 2} = \frac{4x}{(x - 1)(x + 2)} - \frac{3x + 1}{(x - 1)(x - 2)}$$

$$= \frac{4x(x - 2) - (3x + 1)(x + 2)}{(x - 1)(x - 2)(x + 2)}$$

$$= \frac{4x^2 - 8x - 3x^2 - 7x - 2}{(x - 1)(x - 2)(x + 2)}$$

$$= \frac{x^2 - 15x - 2}{(x - 1)(x - 2)(x + 2)}.$$

PROBLEMS

Simplify each of the following expressions as much as possible.

1. $\dfrac{x}{2} + \dfrac{y}{6} + \dfrac{x}{3}$.

2. $\dfrac{x}{2} - \dfrac{(x - 4)}{4}$.

3. $\dfrac{a - 1}{a} - \dfrac{b + 4}{b}$.

4. $\dfrac{5}{4x} + \dfrac{3}{5x^2} - \dfrac{7}{10x^3}$.

5. $\dfrac{x - y}{xy} + \dfrac{y - z}{yz} + \dfrac{z - x}{xz}$.

6. $\dfrac{2x + 1}{5} - \dfrac{2x - 1}{7} - \dfrac{x - 3}{10}$.

7. $\dfrac{x - 2}{x - 1} + \dfrac{x + 2}{x + 1}$.

8. $\dfrac{x}{x + 1} - \dfrac{2x}{x + 2} + \dfrac{x}{x + 3}$.

9. $\dfrac{2y - 3}{y - 2} + \dfrac{y + 3}{3y - 2}$.

10. $\dfrac{a}{x + a} - \dfrac{b}{x + b}$.

11. $\dfrac{3}{2 + a - 6a^2} - \dfrac{1}{1 + a - 2a^2}$.

12. $\dfrac{x + 2}{x - 2} - \dfrac{x^2 + 4}{x^2 - 4}$.

13. $\dfrac{4a^2 + 8a + 3}{2a^2 - 5a + 3} \cdot \dfrac{6a^2 - 9a}{4a^2 - 1}$.

14. $x + \dfrac{1}{x - 1/x}$.

15. $\dfrac{x + 2}{x} + \dfrac{x}{x - 3} - \dfrac{3}{x + 3}$.

16. $\dfrac{x - 1}{x^2 - 1} - \dfrac{x - 2}{x^2 - 4}$.

17. $\dfrac{1}{3 + x} + \dfrac{1}{3 - x} + \dfrac{6}{x^2 - 9}$.

18. $\dfrac{2x - 5}{x - 2} + x - 3$.

19. $\left(\dfrac{x}{y} - \dfrac{y}{x}\right) \div \left(x - \dfrac{x^2}{x + y}\right)$.

20. $\left(x - \dfrac{1}{x}\right) \div \left(x + \dfrac{1}{x} - 2\right)$.

21. $\dfrac{1 - 4/x + 3/x^2}{x - 9/x}$.

22. $\dfrac{x}{1 - \dfrac{1 - x}{1 + x}}$.

23. $[x^4 - 1/x^4] \div [(x - 1)/x]$.

24. $(x - 1/x) \div [(x + 1/x - 2)]$.

6.   Linear and Quadratic Equations

The basic principle underlying the solution of equations is that an equality remains true if both members are transformed in the same way. This usually means, adding the same quantity to both members, or multiplying or dividing both members by the same nonzero quantity. The principle of "transposition," whereby a term can be transferred from one member of an equation to the other if its sign is changed, is a natural consequence of this basic principle.

(a) *Linear.* Any linear equation in x can be transformed to one of the form $ax = b$. Hence, $x = b/a$ is the solution, if $a \neq 0$.

EXAMPLE

$$5x + 2 - 2x = x + 8;$$
$$5x - 2x - x = 8 - 2;$$
$$2x = 6;$$
$$x = 3.$$

(b) *Quadratic.* Any quadratic equation in x can be transformed to one of the form $ax^2 + bx + c = 0$. From this point, we may proceed in one of three ways.

(1) *Factoring.* The basis for this method is the fact that the product of two real or complex numbers is never 0 unless at least one of the numbers is 0.

EXAMPLE

$$2x^2 + 3x - 2 = (2x - 1)(x + 2) = 0;$$
$$2x - 1 = 0 \text{ or } x + 2 = 0;$$
$$x = \tfrac{1}{2} \text{ or } x = -2.$$

(2) *Completing the Square.* An expression $x^2 + ax$ can be transformed into the square of a binomial if the square of half the coefficient of x—i.e., $(a/2)^2$—is added.

EXAMPLE

$$2x^2 - 4x + 1 = 0;$$
$$x^2 - 2x = -\frac{1}{2};$$
$$x^2 - 2x + 1 = -\frac{1}{2} + 1 = \frac{1}{2};$$
$$(x - 1)^2 = \frac{1}{2};$$
$$x - 1 = \pm \sqrt{\frac{1}{2}} = \pm \frac{\sqrt{2}}{2};$$
$$x = 1 \pm \frac{\sqrt{2}}{2}.$$

(3) *The Quadratic Formula.* The Quadratic Formula is merely a condensation into a single formula of the operations involved in solving $ax^2 + bx + c = 0$ by completing the square. The result is the following formula:

$$x = \frac{-b \pm \sqrt{b^2 - 4ac}}{2a}$$

EXAMPLE. If $2x^2 - 4x + 1 = 0$, then $a = 2$, $b = -4$, $c = 1$. Hence,

$$x = \frac{4 \pm \sqrt{16 - 8}}{4} = \frac{4 \pm \sqrt{8}}{4} = \frac{4 \pm 2\sqrt{2}}{4} = 1 \pm \frac{\sqrt{2}}{2},$$

as above.

EXAMPLE. If $3x^2 - 2x + 1 = 0$, then $a = 3$, $b = -2$, $c = 1$. Hence,

$$x = \frac{2 \pm \sqrt{4 - 12}}{6} = \frac{2 \pm \sqrt{-8}}{6} = \frac{2 \pm 2\sqrt{2}i}{6} = \frac{1}{3} \pm \frac{\sqrt{2}i}{3},$$

where i is the complex number such that $i^2 = -1$.

PROBLEMS

Solve each of the following equations and check your result.

1. $2x + 2 = 7x - 18$.
2. $1 - x = 2 - 3x$.
3. $2 - 3x + 5 = -6x - 2$.
4. $5x + 6 = -7x$.
5. $(2x - 7) - (x - 5) = 0$.
6. $2(3x - 1) = 9(x - 2) - 7$.
7. $(x + 3)^2 - (x + 2)^2 = 1$.
8. $3 - (x - 1) = -1 - 2(5 - x)$.
9. $2x^2 + 5x - 3 = 0$.
10. $6x^2 = x + 35$.
11. $x^2 + 5x - 3 = 0$.
12. $x^2 - 5x = -4$.
13. $3x^2 + 4x = 7$.
14. $x^2 + 5x = 36$.
15. $8x^2 - 22x - 90 = 0$.
16. $x^2 - 105x + 2700 = 0$.
17. $(\frac{1}{4})x^2 - (\frac{3}{2})x + 2 = 0$.
18. $s^2 = 5s + 6$.
19. $3r^2 - 2r = 40$.
20. $u^4 - 29u^2 + 100 = 0$.
21. $2y + \frac{5}{2} = 5/(4y)$.
22. $t^2 - 6t = 6$.
23. $9y^2 - 12y - 8 = 0$.
24. $4x^2 + 4x - 5 = 0$.
25. $8y^2 - 8y - 3 = 0$.
26. $x^2 = 5 + (\frac{4}{3})x$.
27. $\dfrac{x}{x - 1} - \dfrac{x - 1}{x} = \dfrac{x^2 + 2x + 1}{x^2 - 1}$.
28. $x^2 + 100/(x^2) = 29$.
29. $\dfrac{1}{x - 1} - \dfrac{1}{x + 1} = \dfrac{1}{24}$.
30. $\dfrac{1}{x} + \dfrac{1}{x - 3} - \dfrac{7}{3x - 5} = 0$.
31. $(x + 1/x)^2 - (\frac{16}{3})(x + 1/x) + 7 = \frac{1}{3}$.
32. $x^6 - 12x^3 + 35 = 0$.

33. $(\frac{1}{3})x^2 - (\frac{1}{30})x - \frac{1}{2} = 0.$

34. $\dfrac{2x-7}{x^2-4} = \dfrac{10x-3}{5x(x+2)}.$

35. $6a^2 - 10a + 4 = 0.$

36. $1 + 2x - 15x^2 = 0.$

37. $18x^2 - 3x - 66 = 0.$

38. $1 - 20p - 10p^2 = 0.$

39. $t + 1/t = a + 1/a.$

40. $\dfrac{x-3}{x-2} - \dfrac{x+4}{x} = \dfrac{3}{2}.$

7.   Simultaneous Linear Equations

There are two elementary methods in common use for solving a system of n linear equations in n unknowns, provided $n = 2$ or $n = 3$. These are called "Elimination by addition or subtraction" and "Elimination by substitution." The idea of the first method is to multiply both members of one or more equations by a number, so that at least one unknown disappears when corresponding members of the two equations are added or subtracted. The idea of the second method is to solve one equation for one unknown in terms of the others, and then eliminate it from the remaining equations. We shall illustrate both of these methods with examples.

(a) *Elimination by Addition or Subtraction*

EXAMPLE

$$2x + 3y = -1. \qquad [1]$$
$$3x + 4y = -2. \qquad [2]$$

Multiply [1] by 3 and [2] by 2, and subtract:

$$6x + 9y = -3$$
$$\underline{6x + 8y = -4}$$
$$y = 1.$$

From [1],

$$2x + 3 = -1.$$
$$2x = -4.$$
$$x = -2.$$

The solution of the system is then: $x = -2,\ y = 1.$

EXAMPLE

$$x + y + z = 2. \qquad [1]$$
$$2x - 3y + 2z = 9. \qquad [2]$$
$$3x - 3y - 2z = 2. \qquad [3]$$

Subtract [2] from [3]:

$$x - 4z = -7. \qquad [4]$$

Multiply [1] by 3 and add to [2]:

$$3x + 3y + 3z = 6$$
$$2x - 3y + 2z = 9$$
$$\overline{5x \qquad + 5z = 15,}$$

or

$$x + z = 3. \qquad\qquad [5]$$

Subtract [4] from [5]:

$$5z = 10,$$
$$z = 2.$$

From [5],

$$x + 2 = 3, x = 1.$$

From [1],

$$1 + y + 2 = 2.$$
$$y = -1.$$

Hence, the complete solution is:

$$x = 1$$
$$y = -1$$
$$z = 2.$$

(b) *Elimination by Substitution.* We shall use the same two systems, as in (a), in order to illustrate this method.

EXAMPLE

$$2x + 3y = -1. \qquad\qquad [1]$$
$$3x + 4y = -2. \qquad\qquad [2]$$

From [1],

$$3y = -2x - 1.$$
$$y = (-\tfrac{2}{3})x - \tfrac{1}{3}.$$

Substituting this expression for y in [2], we obtain:

$$3x + 4[(-\tfrac{2}{3})x - \tfrac{1}{3}] = -2.$$
$$3x - \frac{8x}{3} - \frac{4}{3} = -2.$$
$$9x - 8x - 4 = -6.$$
$$x = -2.$$
$$y = \left(\frac{-2x}{3}\right) - \frac{1}{3} = \frac{4}{3} - \frac{1}{3} = 1, \text{ as before.}$$

EXAMPLE

$$x + y + z = 2. \qquad\qquad [1]$$
$$2x - 3y + 2z = 9. \qquad\qquad [2]$$
$$3x - 3y - 2z = 2. \qquad\qquad [3]$$

From [1],
$$z = 2 - x - y.$$
Hence, from [2] and [3],
$$2x - 3y + 4 - 2x - 2y = 9,$$
$$3x - 3y - 4 + 2x + 2y = 2,$$
or
$$-5y = 5.$$
$$5x - y = 6.$$
Hence,
$$y = -1, x = 1, z = 2 - x - y = 2 - 1 + 1 = 2,$$
as before.

PROBLEMS

Solve and check each of the following systems of linear equations.

1. $2x + 5y = 4;$
   $4x - 10y = 48.$

2. $x - y = 1;$
   $x + y = 9.$

3. $y = 2x + 3;$
   $x = 2y - 3.$

4. $2x - 7y = 5;$
   $5x + 2y = 5.$

5. $2(x + y) = 16;$
   $3(x - y) = 6.$

6. $x + y/5 = 17;$
   $x - y = 5.$

7. $3x + 4y = 24;$
   $5x - 3y = 11.$

8. $3x - 4y = -6;$
   $x + 5y = 17.$

9. $7x + 9y = 41;$
   $x + 4y = 14.$

10. $5x + 3y = 5;$
    $9x + 5y = 8.$

11. $x - y - z = -6;$
    $2x + y + z = 0;$
    $3x - 5y + 8z = 13.$

12. $x + 2y + z = 7;$
    $x + y - z = 2;$
    $3x - y + 2z = 12.$

13. $2x - y + 3z = 4;$
    $x + 3y + 3z = -2;$
    $3x + 2y - 6z = 6.$

14. $x + 2y + z = 0;$
    $2x + y + 2z = 3;$
    $4x - 6y + 3z = 14.$

15. $x/2 + y/3 = 9;$
    $x/3 + z/2 = 8;$
    $y/2 + z/3 = 13.$

16. $1/x + 1/y + 2/z = 1;$
    $2/x + 1/y - 2/z = 1;$
    $3/x + 4/y - 4/z = 2.$

17. A man can row downstream 3 miles in 20 minutes, but the return trip takes him 1 hour. What is his speed in still water, and what is the speed of the current?

18. Find two integers, the respective sum and difference of which are 95 and 15.

8. Exponents

For the purposes of this brief review, we shall regard a and b as positive integers.

Definition. $\sqrt[n]{a}$ is the positive n^{th} root of a, i.e., the positive real number such that $(\sqrt[n]{a})^n = a$.

Definition

If n is a positive integer: $a^n = a \cdot a \cdot a \cdot \ldots a$, with n factors.
If n is a positive integer: $a^{1/n} = \sqrt[n]{a}$.
If p and q are relatively prime positive integers:

$$a^{p/q} = \sqrt[q]{a^p} = (\sqrt[q]{a})^p.$$

If n and r are positive integers, such that $n/r = p/q$, with p and q relatively prime:

$$a^{n/r} = a^{p/q}.$$

Laws of Exponents

$$a^x \cdot a^y = a^{x+y}.$$

$$\frac{a^x}{a^y} = a^{x-y}, \text{ if } x > y; \frac{a^x}{a^y} = \frac{1}{a^{y-x}}, \text{ if } x < y; \frac{a^x}{a^y} = 1, \text{ if } x = y.$$

$$(a^x)^y = a^{xy}.$$
$$a^x \cdot b^x = (ab)^x.$$

EXAMPLE

$$5^{1/3} \cdot 5^{2/3} \cdot 5^{1/2} = 5^{1/3+2/3+1/2} = 5^{3/2} = \sqrt{125}.$$

EXAMPLE

$$\left[\frac{4a^{2/3}}{a^{1/2}}\right]^{1/2} = \frac{4^{1/2} \cdot a^{1/3}}{a^{1/4}} = 2a^{(1/3-1/4)} = 2a^{1/12} = 2\sqrt[12]{a}.$$

PROBLEMS

1. Write each of the following quantities in exponential form: (a) $\sqrt{a}$; (b) $\sqrt[4]{x^3}$; (c) $\sqrt[5]{a^7}$; (d) $\sqrt{a^3}$; (e) $\sqrt[5]{a+2}$.
2. Write each of the following quantities in exponential form: (a) $\sqrt{3}$; (b) $\sqrt[3]{2^5}$; (c) $\sqrt[5]{4^4}$; (d) $\sqrt{5}$; (e) $\sqrt[3]{2+x}$.
3. Find an integer equal to (a) $9^{1/2}$; (b) $81^{3/2}$; (c) $125^{5/3}$; (d) $64^{5/6}$; (e) $16^{1/4}$.
4. Write each of the following quantities in radical form: (a) $a^{1/3}$; (b) $x^{5/6}$; (c) $b^{n/3}$; (d) $n^{3/4}$; (e) $s^{7/6}$.
5. Write each of the following as a single exponential quantity: (a) $x^2 \cdot x^{n+1}$; (b) $a^{n-2} \cdot a^{3+n}$; (c) $u^{n+r} \cdot u^{n-r}$; (d) $(p^7)^3$; (e) $(a^4)^3$.
6. Write each of the following as a single exponential quantity: (a) $x^{3n} \div x^n$; (b) $10^{2r+1} \div 10^r$; (c) $u^{n+r} \div u^{n-r}$; (d) $(x^5/x^4)^4$; (e) $(p^3q^3)^r$; (f) $(r^2s^2)^5$; (g) $e^{n+5} \div e^3$.

7. Simplify each of the following expressions: (a) $x^{1/3}x^{7/3}$; (b) $a^{1/4}a^{1/5}$; (c) $a^{3/7}a^{2/3}$; (d) $x^{1/5}x^{3/10}$.

8. Simplify each of the following expressions: (a) $(a^{2/3})^{1/4}$; (b) $(x^{3/5})^{5/6}$; (c) $(a^{5/12})^4$; (d) $(a^2b^{1/2})^{1/2}$.

9. Simplify each of the following expressions: (a) $x^{1/2}/x^{1/2}$; (b) $[x^5/x^{2/3}]^{3/5}$; (c) $[9x^{3/4}/4x^{2/5}]^{3/2}$; (d) $(8a^{3/8}b^{9/4})^{4/9}$.

10. Find a rational number equal to (a) 2^{-1}; (b) $16^{-3/4}$; (c) 3^{-2}; (d) $7^{-1}/49^{-1/2}$; (e) 1^{-1}.

11. Find a rational number equal to (a) $2/3^{-2}$; (b) $1^{-8}/8^{-1}$; (c) $32^{-1/5}/2^{-1}$; (d) $512^{-1/3}$.

12. Write each of the following quantities in an equivalent form without negative exponents: (a) a^2b^{-2}; (b) $(a+b)^{-3}$; (c) $3x^{-2}y^{-1/2}$; (d) x^4/y^{-5}; (e) $1/x^{-2}$.

13. Write each of the following quantities as an equivalent expression with denominator 1: (a) $1/x^2$; (b) $(xy^2)/(c^3d^4)$; (c) $(2a^3b^{-3})/(4r^{-2}t^5)$; (d) $ab^{1/2}/(x^{-1/3}y^{s/t})$.

14. Simplify each of the following: (a) $(a^{-5}/a^{-4})^{-7}$; (b) $(x^{-4}/x^{-6})^{-2}$; (c) $\left[\dfrac{a^{-3}b}{x^3y^{-2}}\right]^{-3}$; (d) $(r^{-3/4})^{-2/3}$.

9.　Equations With Radicals

If the equation involves only one radical, this "radical" term should be isolated first on one side of the equation. Then both members should be raised to the same power as the index of the radical, so that this radical is eliminated. It is important to check "solutions" in the original equation, because extraneous "solutions" frequently arise for this type of equation. We must be careful to recall, in addition, that $\sqrt{a}$ is the *positive* square root of a, if $a > 0$. If more than one radical is involved, the most complicated one should be eliminated first, by the above process, followed by the successive elimination of any others that remain.

EXAMPLE

$$\sqrt{x-1} = x - 3;$$
$$x - 1 = x^2 - 6x + 9;$$
$$x^2 - 7x + 10 = 0;$$
$$(x-2)(x-5) = 0;$$
$$x = 5 \quad \text{or} \quad x = 2.$$

Check: If $x = 5$: $\sqrt{5-1} = \sqrt{4} = 2 = 5 - 3$, and so 5 is a solution. If $x = 2$: $\sqrt{2-1} = \sqrt{1} = 1 \neq 1 - 2 = -1$, and so 2 is extraneous and must be discarded. The only solution of the given equation is then 5.

EXAMPLE

$$\sqrt{5x-1} + \sqrt{x-1} - 2 = 0;$$
$$\sqrt{5x-1} = 2 - \sqrt{x-1};$$
$$5x - 1 = 4 - 4\sqrt{x-1} + x - 1;$$
$$4\sqrt{x-1} = 4 - 4x;$$
$$16(x-1) = 16 - 32x + 16x^2;$$
$$16x^2 - 48x + 32 = 0;$$
$$x^2 - 3x + 2 = 0;$$
$$(x-1)(x-2) = 0;$$
$$x = 1 \quad \text{or} \quad x = 2.$$

Check: If $x = 1$: $\sqrt{5-1} + \sqrt{1-1} - 2 = 2 + 0 - 2 = 0$, and so 1 is a solution.

If $x = 2$: $\sqrt{10-1} + \sqrt{2-1} - 2 = 3 + 1 - 2 \neq 0$, and so 2 is extraneous and must be discarded. The only solution to the given equation is then 1.

PROBLEMS

Solve and check each of the following equations.

1. $\sqrt{x+4} = 3$.

2. $\sqrt{3x-5} - 5 = 0$.

3. $\sqrt[3]{x-1} = 4$.

4. $\sqrt{11x-8} = 6$.

5. $\sqrt{x+11} = 1 - x$.

6. $\sqrt{3x-2} + 3 = 0$.

7. $\sqrt{x-5} + 2 = 0$.

8. $\sqrt{4x+1} - \sqrt{2x-3} = 2$.

9. $\sqrt{x-7} - \sqrt{5x-4} = \sqrt{3x+1}$.

10. $\sqrt{3x-11} = \sqrt{5-x}$.

11. $x - \sqrt{x} - 6 = 0$.

12. $\sqrt{10-x} - \sqrt{10+x} + 2 = 0$.

13. $\sqrt{6x+4} + \sqrt{2x} - 6 = 0$.

14. $\sqrt{2x+1} - \sqrt{5x-4} + 1 = 0$.

15. $1/\sqrt{x} + 1/\sqrt{4x} = 3$.

16. $1/(\sqrt{x} + \sqrt{4x}) = 3$.

17. $\sqrt{3x+4} + \sqrt{5-x} = 5$.

18. $(\sqrt{x} + \sqrt{3})/\sqrt{x+3} = 1$.

10. Ratio and Proportion

Definition. The *ratio* of a number m to a number n, written $m:n$, is a measure of *relative* size of the numbers. Two ratios $m:n$ and $r:s$ are *equal*, and we write $m:n = r:s$, if and only if $m/n = r/s$.

If we use a ratio to describe the relative size of two quantities, it is important that we use the same unit of measure in each case.

EXAMPLE. If the radii of two circles are $2''$ and $1'\ 2''$, the ratio of their respective areas is $4\pi:196\pi$ or, more simply, $1:49$.

Definition. A *proportion* is a statement of equality of two ratios. Thus, if *m*:*n* and *r*:*s* are equal ratios, we can express this fact in the form *m*:*n* = *r*:*s* or *m*:*n* :: *r*:*s*. For such a proportion, *n* and *r* are the *means*, while *m* and *s* are the *extremes*.

The following result follows immediately from the definition of equality of two ratios: In a proportion, the product of the means is equal to the product of the extremes.

EXAMPLE.   If $3:x = 5:4$, then $5x = 12$. Hence, $x = \frac{12}{5}$.

Definition. If *m*:*x* = *x*:*n*, *m*:*n* = *n*:*x*, or *m*:*n* = *r*:*x*, then *x* is known, respectively, as a *mean, third,* or *fourth proportional* to the indicated numbers.

EXAMPLE.   Suppose we wish to find a mean proportional to 3 and 8. Then, $3:x = x:8$, $x^2 = 24$, and $x = \pm 2\sqrt{6}$. If the third proportional is desired, we solve $3:8 = 8:y$ for *y*, and obtain $3y = 64$ or $y = \frac{64}{3}$.

EXAMPLE.   The solution of $3:5 = 7:x$ is the fourth proportional to the numbers 3, 5, 7. Hence, $3x = 35$ and $x = \frac{35}{3}$.

PROBLEMS

1. Simplify each of the following ratios: (a) 4:8; (b) $\frac{5}{2}:\frac{13}{4}$; (c) $\frac{13}{4}:\frac{9}{2}$; (d) $2:\frac{17}{8}$; (e) $(x^2 - y^2):(x + y)$.

2. Find the ratio of the first to the second of each of the following pairs of measurements of length: (a) 2 inches, 3 feet; (b) 8 inches, $2\frac{1}{4}$ feet; (c) 4 feet, 2 yards; (d) 5 centimeters, 45 millimeters.

3. Find the ratio of the first to the second of each of the following pairs of measurements of time: (a) 15 minutes, $1\frac{1}{2}$ hours; (b) 8 hours, 2 days; (c) 24 seconds, 10 minutes.

4. Express each of the following ratios in simplified form: (a) $(1 + 1/a):(1 - 1/a^2)$; (b) $[1/(x - 1)]:[2/(x^2 - 4x + 3)]$; (c) $(1/x):(3/x^2)$.

5. Separate 125 into two parts in the ratio 3:2.

6. Two numbers are in the ratio 2:5, while if 1 is added to each they are in the ratio 3:7. Find the numbers.

7. Solve each of the following proportions for the unknown member: (a) $2:5 = x:8$; (b) $3:x = 4:18$; (c) $4:7 = x:21$; (d) $x:12 = 3:4$.

8. Find the mean proportional to each of the following pairs of numbers: (a) 3, 12; (b) 8, 2; (c) 2, 32; (d) 3, 8; (e) 5, 12.

9. Find the third proportional to *a* and *b* if (a) $a = 4$, $b = 9$; (b) $a = 3$, $b = 10$; (c) $a = 8$, $b = 24$.

10. Find the fourth proportional to *a*, *b*, and *c* given that (a) $a = 2$, $b = 3$, $c = 4$; (b) $a = 7$, $b = 11$, $c = 21$; (c) $a = -3$, $b = 8$, $c = 10$.

11. Solve the following proportion for x: $(2 - x):(2 + x) = (1 - x):(1 + x)$.

12. Solve the following proportion for x: $x:(x - 2) = 3:4$.

TEST ON REVIEW MATERIAL

1. Add the numbers in each of the following collections: (a) $\frac{1}{2}, -\frac{2}{3}, \frac{3}{4}, -2$;
(b) $-\frac{5}{6}, \frac{3}{5}, \frac{2}{15}, -\frac{5'}{12}$.

2. Divide the first number by the second in each of the following pairs: (a) $-\frac{5}{4}, \frac{2}{3}$;
(b) $\frac{5}{6}, -\frac{3}{7}$; (c) $\frac{3}{5}, 5$; (d) $4, -\frac{2}{3}$.

3. Simplify each of the following expressions:

(a) $\dfrac{\dfrac{x}{x-1} - 1}{\dfrac{x}{1-x} + 1}$;

(b) $\dfrac{\dfrac{1}{x+3} + 1}{x - \dfrac{12}{x+1}}$.

4. (a) From the sum of $x^2/2$, $-5x^2/4$, and $2 - 3x + x^2$, subtract the sum of $2x^2/3$ and $-5x$. (b) Divide $a/b - b/a$ by $1/b - 1/a$, and simplify the result.

5. Factor completely each of the following expressions: (a) $m^2 - 4n^2$; (b) $t^2 + 6t - 55$; (c) $1 - y^6$.

6. Factor completely each of the following expressions: (a) $am + bm + b + a$;
(b) $(1 - x)^2 - (x - y)^2$; (c) $12x^2 + 25x - 7$.

7. Factor completely each of the following expressions: (a) $1 - x^2 - 2xy - y^2$;
(b) $(x + 1)^3 - 9(x + 1)^2 + 8(x + 1)$.

8. Use the quadratic formula to solve each of the following equations: (a) $2s^2 - 5s + 1 = 0$; (b) $2x^2 + 3x + 1 = 0$.

9. Solve each of the following quadratic equations, by first factoring the left member: (a) $2x^2 - x - 1 = 0$; (b) $6x^2 + 5x - 6 = 0$.

10. Solve each of the following quadratic equations by completing squares in the left members: (a) $4x^2 - x - 5 = 0$; (b) $2y^2 - 4y - 1 = 0$.

11. Solve each of the following systems of linear equations, and check:

(a) $x + y = 11$
$2x - 3y = 22$.

(b) $2y + 5z = 2$
$4y + z = 13$.

12. Solve each of the following systems of equations, and check:

(a) $x + y = 18$
$y + z = 13$
$x + z = 5$.

(b) $1/x + 1/y = 7$
$1/y + 1/z = \frac{11}{2}$
$1/z + 1/x = \frac{5}{2}$.

13. (a) Write each of the following in radical form: $2^{1/2}$, $3^{2/3}$, $4^{3/2}$, $6^{-1/2}$, $2^{-2/3}$.
(b) Write each of the following in exponential form: $\sqrt[5]{5}$, $\sqrt[3]{3^2}$, $1/\sqrt{3}$, $3/\sqrt[3]{5^2}$.

14. Simplify each of the following expressions: (a) $(x^{-2}y^3y^{-2})/(3x^2y^{-5}z)$; (b) $[(12x^3)(4x^{-2})^3(xy)^2]/[(3xy)^3(2x^{-3})^2]$.

15. (a) The heights of two posts are 18 inches and $3\frac{1}{2}$ feet, respectively. What is the ratio of their heights? (b) Solve the following proportion for x:
$3:11/2 = (x - 1):(x + 1)$.

16. Solve for x: $\sqrt{3x + 7} + \sqrt{x + 1} - 2 = 0$.

17. Solve for y: $\sqrt{3y - 2} - 2 = 8/\sqrt{3y - 2}$.

APPENDIX B

Matrix Inversion

If $A = [a_{ij}]$ and $B = [b_{ij}]$ are two n by n matrices, the *product* $AB = C$ is defined so that $C = [c_{ik}]$, where c_{ik} is the scalar product of the ith row of A by the kth column of B. That is, $c_{ik} = \sum_{j=1}^{n} a_{ij}b_{jk}$. The multiplication of a matrix by a "scalar" or real number is also defined so that $cA = [ca_{ij}]$, for any number c. This means that we accomplish this kind of multiplication by merely multiplying each element of the matrix by the scalar.

If $AB = I$, where I is the n by n identity matrix, it can be shown that also $BA = I$, and B is called the *inverse* of A (and likewise A is the inverse of B). The inverse of a matrix can be shown to be unique, and it is customary to designate the inverse of A, if it exists, by A^{-1}. The necessary and sufficient condition for the existence of the inverse of a square matrix A is that $|A| \neq 0$. In case $|A| \neq 0$, A is said to be "nonsingular," and there are two common methods for determining its inverse. The study of inverses of a matrix properly belongs in a more intensive course in matrix theory, but we shall present a brief outline of these two methods of "inverting" a nonsingular matrix.

(a) *The Adjoint Method.* If A_{ij} is the cofactor of the element a_{ij} of the nonsingular matrix $A = [a_{ij}]$, $A^{-1} = 1/|A| [A_{ij}^*]$, where $A_{ij}^* = A_{ji}$. The matrix $A^* = [A_{ij}^*]$ is called the *adjoint* of A. [Note that the element in the (i,j) position in A^* is the cofactor of the element in the (j,i) position in A.] The verification that A^{-1}, defined in this way, is in fact the inverse can be checked by actual multiplication, and we illustrate for the general case of $n = 3$.

$$A^*A = \begin{bmatrix} A_{11} & A_{21} & A_{31} \\ A_{12} & A_{22} & A_{32} \\ A_{13} & A_{23} & A_{33} \end{bmatrix} \begin{bmatrix} a_{11} & a_{12} & a_{13} \\ a_{21} & a_{22} & a_{23} \\ a_{31} & a_{32} & a_{33} \end{bmatrix}$$

$$= \begin{bmatrix} |A| & 0 & 0 \\ 0 & |A| & 0 \\ 0 & 0 & |A| \end{bmatrix} = |A| \begin{bmatrix} 1 & 0 & 0 \\ 0 & 1 & 0 \\ 0 & 0 & 1 \end{bmatrix} = |A|I,$$

and a similar computation shows that $AA^* = |A|I$. In the above multiplication, it should be observed that we have used Theorem 2.61, as well as the definition of $|A|$ in §2.5. It then follows that $A^{-1} = 1/|A|\,[A_{ij}^*]$, as asserted.

EXAMPLE 1.   As an illustration, let us determine A^{-1}, where

$$A = \begin{bmatrix} 1 & 0 & -1 \\ 0 & 2 & 2 \\ 1 & 1 & -1 \end{bmatrix}.$$

Here $|A| = -2$, and

$$A^* = \begin{bmatrix} -4 & -1 & 2 \\ 2 & 0 & -2 \\ -2 & -1 & 2 \end{bmatrix}.$$

Hence,

$$A^{-1} = \frac{-1}{2} \begin{bmatrix} -4 & -1 & 2 \\ 2 & 0 & -2 \\ -2 & -1 & 2 \end{bmatrix} = \begin{bmatrix} 2 & \frac{1}{2} & -1 \\ -1 & 0 & 1 \\ 1 & \frac{1}{2} & -1 \end{bmatrix},$$

and it is easy to verify that:

$$\begin{bmatrix} 1 & 0 & -1 \\ 0 & 2 & 2 \\ 1 & 1 & -1 \end{bmatrix} \begin{bmatrix} 2 & \frac{1}{2} & -1 \\ -1 & 0 & 1 \\ 1 & \frac{1}{2} & -1 \end{bmatrix} = \begin{bmatrix} 2 & \frac{1}{2} & -1 \\ -1 & 0 & 1 \\ 1 & \frac{1}{2} & -1 \end{bmatrix} \begin{bmatrix} 1 & 0 & -1 \\ 0 & 2 & 2 \\ 1 & 1 & -1 \end{bmatrix} = \begin{bmatrix} 1 & 0 & 0 \\ 0 & 1 & 0 \\ 0 & 0 & 1 \end{bmatrix} = I.$$

(b) *The L-array Method.* If $|A| \neq 0$, it is possible to use a sequence of elementary row operations, as discussed in §2.7, and reduce A to the identity matrix I. We may also define elementary *column* operations, as analogues of the elementary row operations, and it is usually simpler to reduce A to I by a sequence of elementary row or column operations, using operations of both types as convenient. It is shown in courses in matrix theory that any elementary row (column) operation can be effected on a matrix A by a premultiplication (postmultiplication) of A by the matrix which is the result of performing the same operation on the identity matrix I. Hence, the following practical procedure may be adopted.

Place one identity matrix I directly above the given nonsingular matrix

A, and another beside *A* on its right, so that we have the resulting array—in the shape of an *L*:

$$I$$
$$A \; I$$

Reduce *A* to *I*, by any sequence of row or column operations, including the identity matrix on the right as an extension of the rows of *A*, and the identity matrix above as an extension of the columns of *A*. When *A* has been reduced to *I*, the resulting array has the form:

$$C$$
$$I \; D$$

where *C* and *D* are the resulting transforms of the original identity matrices. Then, it can be shown that $A^{-1} = CD$. We shall not prove this result, but will illustrate the method by using the matrix of Example 1.

EXAMPLE 2.   If we form the *L*-array required by this method, for the matrix of Example 1, the result is:

$$\begin{bmatrix} 1 & 0 & 0 \\ 0 & 1 & 0 \\ 0 & 0 & 1 \end{bmatrix}$$

$$\begin{bmatrix} 1 & 0 & -1 \\ 0 & 2 & 2 \\ 1 & 1 & -1 \end{bmatrix} \begin{bmatrix} 1 & 0 & 1 \\ 0 & 1 & 0 \\ 0 & 0 & 1 \end{bmatrix}.$$

Let us now designate the rows and columns of the *extensions* of *A* by (1), (2), (3) and (1)′, (2)′, (3)′, respectively. Further we shall use the symbolism of §2.7 to indicate the row and column operations to be performed on the array. For example, (3) − (1) will mean that the first row is to be subtracted from the third row; (3)′ + (1)′ will mean that the first column is to be added to the third column (note order); $\frac{1}{2}$(2) will mean that the elements of the second row have been multiplied by $\frac{1}{2}$; etc. There is nothing unique about the sequence of operations to be used in the reduction of *A* to *I*, but if we use the sequence listed below in the order of listing, the result is the array at the right.

(3) − (1)
(3)′ + (1)′
(3)′ − (2)′

$$\begin{bmatrix} 1 & 0 & 1 \\ 0 & 1 & -1 \\ 0 & 0 & 1 \end{bmatrix}$$

$\frac{1}{2}$(2)
(3) − (2)
(−1) (3)

$$\begin{bmatrix} 1 & 0 & 0 \\ 0 & 1 & 0 \\ 0 & 0 & 1 \end{bmatrix} \begin{bmatrix} 1 & 0 & 0 \\ 0 & \frac{1}{2} & 0 \\ 1 & \frac{1}{2} & -1 \end{bmatrix}$$

It then follows, from the unproved assertion above, that

$$A^{-1} = \begin{bmatrix} 1 & 0 & 1 \\ 0 & 1 & -1 \\ 0 & 0 & 1 \end{bmatrix} \begin{bmatrix} 1 & 0 & 0 \\ 0 & \frac{1}{2} & 0 \\ 1 & \frac{1}{2} & -1 \end{bmatrix} = \begin{bmatrix} 2 & \frac{1}{2} & -1 \\ -1 & 0 & 1 \\ 1 & \frac{1}{2} & -1 \end{bmatrix}, \text{ as before.}$$

In Chapter 2, we used $F_1X = b_1$, $F_2X = b_2$, ..., $F_nX = b_n$ to designate a system of n linear equations in n unknowns. If we combine the row vectors $F_1, F_2, \ldots, F_n$ as the rows of a matrix A, and write $[b_1, b_2, \ldots, b_n]^T$ as B, the system of equations can be expressed in the compact form $AX = B$, with X, as usual, designating the vector variable $[x_1, x_2, \ldots, x_n]^T$. We have previously called A the "coefficient" matrix and, if $|A| \neq 0$, we are able to solve the system of equations immediately after we have obtained A^{-1}. Because, $A^{-1}(AX) = A^{-1}B$, on multiplying both members of the original system on the left by A^{-1}, and so

$$X = A^{-1}B.$$

In order to harmonize the vector and matrix notations, we are using square rather than round brackets here to designate vectors. The two are, of course, equivalent.

EXAMPLE 3.   Use a matrix inversion method to solve the system of equations:

$$\begin{aligned} x \quad\quad - z &= 1. \\ 2y + 2z &= 2. \\ x + y - z &= 1. \end{aligned}$$

SOLUTION.   In this case, the system of equations can be expressed in the form $AX = B$, where,

$$A = \begin{bmatrix} 1 & 0 & -1 \\ 0 & 2 & 2 \\ 1 & 1 & -1 \end{bmatrix}, X = \begin{bmatrix} x \\ y \\ z \end{bmatrix}, B = \begin{bmatrix} 1 \\ 2 \\ 1 \end{bmatrix}.$$

We have previously determined A^{-1} (in Example 1 and Example 2), and so,

$$X = A^{-1}B = \begin{bmatrix} 2 & \frac{1}{2} & -1 \\ -1 & 0 & 1 \\ 1 & \frac{1}{2} & -1 \end{bmatrix} \begin{bmatrix} 1 \\ 2 \\ 1 \end{bmatrix} = \begin{bmatrix} 2 \\ 0 \\ 1 \end{bmatrix}$$

Hence, $x = 2$, $y = 0$, $z = 1$.

It must be noted, however, that the methods of this Appendix are not available for solving a linear system *unless* the determinant of the coefficient matrix is nonzero. If this determinant is nonzero, and one of these methods is to be used, method (b) is to be preferred except for the case $n = 3$, in which case the two methods are of approximately equal merit. The development of skill in these two methods may be acquired by solving some of the linear systems given in the problem sets of Chapter 2.

Tables

Table 1 is taken with the permission of the publisher from *Fundamentals of College Algebra* by William H. Durfee (New York: The Macmillan Company, 1960).

Table 2 is taken with the permission of the publisher from *Fundamental Principles of Mathematics* by John T. Moore (New York: Holt, Rinehart and Winston, Inc., 1960).

TABLE 1

Four-Place Common Logarithms

N	0	1	2	3	4	5	6	7	8	9
10	0000	0043	0086	0128	0170	0212	0253	0294	0334	0374
11	0414	0453	0492	0531	0569	0607	0645	0682	0719	0755
12	0792	0828	0864	0899	0934	0969	1004	1038	1072	1106
13	1139	1173	1206	1239	1271	1303	1335	1367	1399	1430
14	1461	1492	1523	1553	1584	1614	1644	1673	1703	1732
15	1761	1790	1818	1847	1875	1903	1931	1959	1987	2014
16	2041	2068	2095	2122	2148	2175	2201	2227	2253	2279
17	2304	2330	2355	2380	2405	2430	2455	2480	2504	2529
18	2553	2577	2601	2625	2648	2672	2695	2718	2742	2765
19	2788	2810	2833	2856	2878	2900	2923	2945	2967	2989
20	3010	3032	3054	3075	3096	3118	3139	3160	3181	3201
21	3222	3243	3263	3284	3304	3324	3345	3365	3385	3404
22	3424	3444	3464	3483	3502	3522	3541	3560	3579	3598
23	3617	3636	3655	3674	3692	3711	3729	3747	3766	3784
24	3802	3820	3838	3856	3874	3892	3909	3927	3945	3962
25	3979	3997	4014	4031	4048	4065	4082	4099	4116	4133
26	4150	4166	4183	4200	4216	4232	4249	4265	4281	4298
27	4314	4330	4346	4362	4378	4393	4409	4425	4440	4456
28	4472	4487	4502	4518	4533	4548	4564	4579	4594	4609
29	4624	4639	4654	4669	4683	4698	4713	4728	4742	4757
30	4771	4786	4800	4814	4829	4843	4857	4871	4886	4900
31	4914	4928	4942	4955	4969	4983	4997	5011	5024	5038
32	5051	5065	5079	5092	5105	5119	5132	5145	5159	5172
33	5185	5198	5211	5224	5237	5250	5263	5276	5289	5302
34	5315	5328	5340	5353	5366	5378	5391	5403	5416	5428
35	5441	5453	5465	5478	5490	5502	5514	5527	5539	5551
36	5563	5575	5587	5599	5611	5623	5635	5647	5658	5670
37	5682	5694	5705	5717	5729	5740	5752	5763	5775	5786
38	5798	5809	5821	5832	5843	5855	5866	5877	5888	5899
39	5911	5922	5933	5944	5955	5966	5977	5988	5999	6010
40	6021	6031	6042	6053	6064	6075	6085	6096	6107	6117
41	6128	6138	6149	6160	6170	6180	6191	6201	6212	6222
42	6232	6243	6253	6263	6274	6284	6294	6304	6314	6325
43	6335	6345	6355	6365	6375	6385	6395	6405	6415	6425
44	6435	6444	6454	6464	6474	6484	6493	6503	6513	6522
45	6532	6542	6551	6561	6571	6580	6590	6599	6609	6618
46	6628	6637	6646	6656	6665	6675	6684	6693	6702	6712
47	6721	6730	6739	6749	6758	6767	6776	6785	6794	6803
48	6812	6821	6830	6839	6848	6857	6866	6875	6884	6893
49	6902	6911	6920	6928	6937	6946	6955	6964	6972	6981
50	6990	6998	7007	7016	7024	7033	7042	7050	7059	7067
51	7076	7084	7093	7101	7110	7118	7126	7135	7143	7152
52	7160	7168	7177	7185	7193	7202	7210	7218	7226	7235
53	7243	7251	7259	7267	7275	7284	7292	7300	7308	7316
54	7324	7332	7340	7348	7356	7364	7372	7380	7388	7396
N	0	1	2	3	4	5	6	7	8	9

TABLE 1

Four-Place Common Logarithms

N	0	1	2	3	4	5	6	7	8	9
55	7404	7412	7419	7427	7435	7443	7451	7459	7466	7474
56	7482	7490	7497	7505	7513	7520	7528	7536	7543	7551
57	7559	7566	7574	7582	7589	7597	7604	7612	7619	7627
58	7634	7642	7649	7657	7664	7672	7679	7686	7694	7701
59	7709	7716	7723	7731	7738	7745	7752	7760	7767	7774
60	7782	7789	7796	7803	7810	7818	7825	7832	7839	7846
61	7853	7860	7868	7875	7882	7889	7896	7903	7910	7917
62	7924	7931	7938	7945	7952	7959	7966	7973	7980	7987
63	7993	8000	8007	8014	8021	8028	8035	8041	8048	8055
64	8062	8069	8075	8082	8089	8096	8102	8109	8116	8122
65	8129	8136	8142	8149	8156	8162	8169	8176	8182	8189
66	8195	8202	8209	8215	8222	8228	8235	8241	8248	8254
67	8261	8267	8274	8280	8287	8293	8299	8306	8312	8319
68	8325	8331	8338	8344	8351	8357	8363	8370	8376	8382
69	8388	8395	8401	8407	8414	8420	8426	8432	8439	8445
70	8451	8457	8463	8470	8476	8482	8488	8494	8500	8506
71	8513	8519	8525	8531	8537	8543	8549	8555	8561	8567
72	8573	8579	8585	8591	8597	8603	8609	8615	8621	8627
73	8633	8639	8645	8651	8657	8663	8669	8675	8681	8686
74	8692	8698	8704	8710	8716	8722	8727	8733	8739	8745
75	8751	8756	8762	8768	8774	8779	8785	8791	8797	8802
76	8808	8814	8820	8825	8831	8837	8842	8848	8854	8859
77	8865	8871	8876	8882	8887	8893	8899	8904	8910	8915
78	8921	8927	8932	8938	8943	8949	8954	8960	8965	8971
79	8976	8982	8987	8993	8998	9004	9009	9015	9020	9025
80	9031	9036	9042	9047	9053	9058	9063	9069	9074	9079
81	9085	9090	9096	9101	9106	9112	9117	9122	9128	9133
82	9138	9143	9149	9154	9159	9165	9170	9175	9180	9186
83	9191	9196	9201	9206	9212	9217	9222	9227	9232	9238
84	9243	9248	9253	9258	9263	9269	9274	9279	9284	9289
85	9294	9299	9304	9309	9315	9320	9325	9330	9335	9340
86	9345	9350	9355	9360	9365	9370	9375	9380	9385	9390
87	9395	9400	9405	9410	9415	9420	9425	9430	9435	9440
88	9445	9450	9455	9460	9465	9469	9474	9479	9484	9489
89	9494	9499	9504	9509	9513	9518	9523	9528	9533	9538
90	9542	9547	9552	9557	9562	9566	9571	9576	9581	9586
91	9590	9595	9600	9605	9609	9614	9619	9624	9628	9633
92	9638	9643	9647	9652	9657	9661	9666	9671	9675	9680
93	9685	9689	9694	9699	9703	9708	9713	9717	9722	9727
94	9731	9736	9741	9745	9750	9754	9759	9763	9768	9773
95	9777	9782	9786	9791	9795	9800	9805	9809	9814	9818
96	9823	9827	9832	9836	9841	9845	9850	9854	9859	9863
97	9868	9872	9877	9881	9886	9890	9894	9899	9903	9908
98	9912	9917	9921	9926	9930	9934	9939	9943	9948	9952
99	9956	9961	9965	9969	9974	9978	9983	9987	9991	9996
N	0	1	2	3	4	5	6	7	8	9

TABLE 2

Four-Place Values of the Circular Functions

x (degrees)	θ (radians)	sin θ(x°)	csc θ(x°)	cos θ(x°)	sec θ(x°)	tan θ(x°)	cot θ(x°)		
0.0	0.0000	0.00000	—	1.0000	1.0000	0.00000	—	1.5708	**90.0**
0.1	0.0017	0.00175	572.96	1.0000	1.0000	0.00175	573.0	1.5691	89.9
0.2	0.0035	0.00349	286.48	1.0000	1.0000	0.00349	286.5	1.5673	89.8
0.3	0.0052	0.00524	190.99	1.0000	1.0000	0.00524	191.0	1.5656	89.7
0.4	0.0070	0.00698	143.24	1.0000	1.0000	0.00698	143.24	1.5638	89.6
0.5	0.0087	0.00873	114.59	1.0000	1.0000	0.00873	114.59	1.5621	**89.5**
0.6	0.0105	0.01047	95.495	0.9999	1.0001	0.01047	95.49	1.5603	89.4
0.7	0.0122	0.01222	81.853	0.9999	1.0001	0.01222	81.85	1.5586	89.3
0.8	0.0140	0.01396	71.622	0.9999	1.0001	0.01396	71.62	1.5568	89.2
0.9	0.0157	0.01571	63.665	0.9999	1.0001	0.01571	63.66	1.5551	89.1
1.0	0.0175	0.01745	57.299	0.9998	1.0002	0.01746	57.29	1.5533	**89.0**
1.1	0.0192	0.01920	52.090	0.9998	1.0002	0.01920	52.08	1.5516	88.9
1.2	0.0209	0.02094	47.750	0.9998	1.0002	0.02095	47.74	1.5499	88.8
1.3	0.0227	0.02269	44.077	0.9997	1.0003	0.02269	44.07	1.5481	88.7
1.4	0.0244	0.02443	40.930	0.9997	1.0003	0.02444	40.92	1.5464	88.6
1.5	0.0262	0.02618	38.202	0.9997	1.0003	0.02619	38.19	1.5446	**88.5**
1.6	0.0279	0.02792	35.815	0.9996	1.0004	0.02793	35.80	1.5429	88.4
1.7	0.0297	0.02967	33.708	0.9996	1.0004	0.02968	33.69	1.5411	88.3
1.8	0.0314	0.03141	31.836	0.9995	1.0005	0.03143	31.82	1.5394	88.2
1.9	0.0332	0.03316	30.161	0.9995	1.0006	0.03317	30.14	1.5376	88.1
2.0	0.0349	0.03490	28.654	0.9994	1.0006	0.03492	28.64	1.5359	**88.0**
2.1	0.0367	0.03664	27.290	0.9993	1.0007	0.03667	27.27	1.5341	87.9
2.2	0.0384	0.03839	26.050	0.9993	1.0007	0.03842	26.03	1.5324	87.8
2.3	0.0401	0.04013	24.918	0.9992	1.0008	0.04016	24.90	1.5307	87.7
2.4	0.0419	0.04188	23.880	0.9991	1.0009	0.04191	23.86	1.5289	87.6
2.5	0.0436	0.04362	22.926	0.9990	1.0010	0.04366	22.90	1.5272	**87.5**
2.6	0.0454	0.04536	22.044	0.9990	1.0010	0.04541	22.02	1.5254	87.4
2.7	0.0471	0.04711	21.229	0.9989	1.0011	0.04716	21.20	1.5237	87.3
2.8	0.0489	0.04885	20.471	0.9988	1.0012	0.04891	20.45	1.5219	87.2
2.9	0.0506	0.05059	19.766	0.9987	1.0013	0.05066	19.74	1.5202	87.1
3.0	0.0524	0.05234	19.107	0.9986	1.0014	0.05241	19.081	1.5184	**87.0**
3.1	0.0541	0.05408	18.492	0.9985	1.0015	0.05416	18.464	1.5167	86.9
3.2	0.0559	0.05582	17.914	0.9984	1.0016	0.05591	17.886	1.5149	86.8
3.3	0.0576	0.05756	17.372	0.9983	1.0017	0.05766	17.343	1.5132	86.7
3.4	0.0593	0.05931	16.862	0.9982	1.0018	0.05941	16.832	1.5115	86.6
3.5	0.0611	0.06105	16.380	0.9981	1.0019	0.06116	16.350	1.5097	**86.5**
3.6	0.0628	0.06279	15.926	0.9980	1.0020	0.06291	15.895	1.5080	86.4
3.7	0.0646	0.06453	15.496	0.9979	1.0021	0.06467	15.464	1.5062	86.3
3.8	0.0663	0.06627	15.089	0.9978	1.0022	0.06642	15.056	1.5045	86.2
3.9	0.0681	0.06802	14.703	0.9977	1.0023	0.06817	14.669	1.5027	86.1
4.0	0.0698	0.06976	14.336	0.9976	1.0024	0.06993	14.301	1.5010	**86.0**
4.1	0.0716	0.07150	13.987	0.9974	1.0026	0.07168	13.951	1.4992	85.9
4.2	0.0733	0.07324	13.654	0.9973	1.0027	0.07344	13.617	1.4975	85.8
4.3	0.0750	0.07498	13.337	0.9972	1.0028	0.07519	13.300	1.4957	85.7
4.4	0.0768	0.07672	13.035	0.9971	1.0030	0.07695	12.996	1.4940	85.6
	cos θ(x°)	sec θ(x°)	sin θ(x°)	csc θ(x°)	cot θ(x°)	tan θ(x°)	θ (radians)	x (degrees)	

293

TABLE 2

Four-Place Values of the Circular Functions

x (de-grees)	θ (radians)	sin θ(x°)	csc θ(x°)	cos θ(x°)	sec θ(x°)	tan θ(x°)	cot θ(x°)		
4.5	0.0785	0.07846	12.745	0.9969	1.0031	0.07870	12.706	1.4923	**85.5**
4.6	0.0803	0.08020	12.469	0.9968	1.0032	0.08046	12.429	1.4905	85.4
4.7	0.0820	0.08194	12.204	0.9966	1.0034	0.08221	12.163	1.4888	85.3
4.8	0.0838	0.08368	11.951	0.9965	1.0035	0.08397	11.909	1.4870	85.2
4.9	0.0855	0.08542	11.707	0.9963	1.0037	0.08573	11.664	1.4853	85.1
5.0	0.0873	0.08716	11.474	0.9962	1.0038	0.08749	11.430	1.4835	**85.0**
5.1	0.0890	0.08889	11.249	0.9960	1.0040	0.08925	11.205	1.4818	84.9
5.2	0.0908	0.09063	11.034	0.9959	1.0041	0.09101	10.988	1.4800	84.8
5.3	0.0925	0.09237	10.826	0.9957	1.0043	0.09277	10.780	1.4783	84.7
5.4	0.0942	0.09411	10.626	0.9956	1.0045	0.09453	10.579	1.4765	84.6
5.5	0.0960	0.09585	10.433	0.9954	1.0046	0.09629	10.385	1.4748	**84.5**
5.6	0.0977	0.09758	10.248	0.9952	1.0048	0.09805	10.199	1.4731	84.4
5.7	0.0995	0.09932	10.068	0.9951	1.0050	0.09981	10.019	1.4713	84.3
5.8	0.1012	0.10106	9.8955	0.9949	1.0051	0.10158	9.845	1.4696	84.2
5.9	0.1030	0.10279	9.7283	0.9947	1.0053	0.10334	9.677	1.4678	84.1
6.0	0.1047	0.10453	9.5668	0.9945	1.0055	0.10510	9.514	1.4661	**84.0**
6.1	0.1065	0.10626	9.4105	0.9943	1.0057	0.10687	9.357	1.4643	83.9
6.2	0.1082	0.10800	9.2593	0.9942	1.0059	0.10863	9.205	1.4626	83.8
6.3	0.1100	0.10973	9.1129	0.9940	1.0061	0.11040	9.058	1.4608	83.7
6.4	0.1117	0.11147	8.9711	0.9938	1.0063	0.11217	8.915	1.4591	83.6
6.5	0.1134	0.11320	8.8337	0.9936	1.0065	0.11394	8.777	1.4573	**83.5**
6.6	0.1152	0.11494	8.7004	0.9934	1.0067	0.11570	8.643	1.4556	83.4
6.7	0.1169	0.11667	8.5711	0.9932	1.0069	0.11747	8.513	1.4539	83.3
6.8	0.1187	0.11840	8.4457	0.9930	1.0071	0.11924	8.386	1.4521	83.2
6.9	0.1204	0.12014	8.3238	0.9928	1.0073	0.12101	8.264	1.4504	83.1
7.0	0.1222	0.12187	8.2055	0.9925	1.0075	0.12278	8.144	1.4486	**83.0**
7.1	0.1239	0.12360	8.0905	0.9923	1.0077	0.12456	8.028	1.4469	82.9
7.2	0.1257	0.12533	7.9787	0.9921	1.0079	0.12633	7.916	1.4451	82.8
7.3	0.1274	0.12706	7.8700	0.9919	1.0082	0.12810	7.806	1.4434	82.7
7.4	0.1292	0.12880	7.7642	0.9917	1.0084	0.12988	7.700	1.4416	82.6
7.5	0.1309	0.13053	7.6613	0.9914	1.0086	0.13165	7.596	1.4399	**82.5**
7.6	0.1326	0.13226	7.5611	0.9912	1.0089	0.13343	7.495	1.4382	82.4
7.7	0.1344	0.13399	7.4635	0.9910	1.0091	0.13521	7.396	1.4364	82.3
7.8	0.1361	0.13572	7.3684	0.9907	1.0093	0.13698	7.300	1.4347	82.2
7.9	0.1379	0.13744	7.2757	0.9905	1.0096	0.13876	7.207	1.4329	82.1
8.0	0.1396	0.13917	7.1853	0.9903	1.0098	0.14054	7.115	1.4312	**82.0**
8.1	0.1414	0.14090	7.0972	0.9900	1.0101	0.14232	7.026	1.4294	81.9
8.2	0.1431	0.14263	7.0112	0.9898	1.0103	0.14410	6.940	1.4277	81.8
8.3	0.1449	0.14436	6.9273	0.9895	1.0106	0.14588	6.855	1.4259	81.7
8.4	0.1466	0.14608	6.8454	0.9893	1.0108	0.14767	6.772	1.4242	81.6
8.5	0.1484	0.14781	6.7655	0.9890	1.0111	0.14945	6.691	1.4224	**81.5**
8.6	0.1501	0.14954	6.6874	0.9888	1.0114	0.15124	6.612	1.4207	81.4
8.7	0.1518	0.15126	6.6111	0.9885	1.0116	0.15302	6.535	1.4190	81.3
8.8	0.1536	0.15299	6.5366	0.9882	1.0119	0.15481	6.460	1.4172	81.2
8.9	0.1553	0.15471	6.4637	0.9880	1.0122	0.15660	6.386	1.4155	81.1
		cos θ(x°)	sec θ(x°)	sin θ(x°)	csc θ(x°)	cot θ(x°)	tan θ(x°)	θ (radians)	x (de-grees)

TABLE 2

Four-Place Values of the Circular Functions

x (de-grees)	θ (radians)	sin θ(x°)	csc θ(x°)	cos θ(x°)	sec θ(x°)	tan θ(x°)	cot θ(x°)		
9.0	0.1571	0.15643	6.3925	0.9887	1.0125	0.15838	6.314	1.4137	**81.0**
9.1	0.1588	0.15816	6.3228	0.9874	1.0127	0.16017	6.243	1.4120	80.9
9.2	0.1606	0.15988	6.2546	0.9871	1.0130	0.16196	6.174	1.4102	80.8
9.3	0.1623	0.16160	6.1880	0.9869	1.0133	0.16376	6.107	1.4085	80.7
9.4	0.1641	0.16333	6.1227	0.9866	1.0136	0.16555	6.041	1.4067	80.6
9.5	0.1658	0.16505	6.0589	0.9863	1.0139	0.16734	5.976	1.4050	**80.5**
9.6	0.1676	0.16677	5.9963	0.9860	1.0142	0.16914	5.912	1.4032	80.4
9.7	0.1693	0.16849	5.9351	0.9857	1.0145	0.17093	5.850	1.4015	80.3
9.8	0.1710	0.17021	5.8751	0.9854	1.0148	0.17273	5.789	1.3998	80.2
9.9	0.1728	0.17193	5.8164	0.9851	1.0151	0.17453	5.730	1.3980	80.1
10.0	0.1745	0.1736	5.7588	0.9848	1.0154	0.1763	5.671	1.3963	**80.0**
10.1	0.1763	0.1754	5.7023	0.9845	1.0157	0.1781	5.614	1.3945	79.9
10.2	0.1780	0.1771	5.6470	0.9842	1.0161	0.1799	5.558	1.3928	79.8
10.3	0.1798	0.1788	5.5928	0.9839	1.0164	0.1817	5.503	1.3910	79.7
10.4	0.1815	0.1805	5.5396	0.9836	1.0167	0.1835	5.449	1.3893	79.6
10.5	0.1833	0.1822	5.4874	0.9833	1.0170	0.1853	5.396	1.3875	**79.5**
10.6	0.1850	0.1840	5.4362	0.9829	1.0174	0.1871	5.343	1.3858	79.4
10.7	0.1868	0.1857	5.3860	0.9826	1.0177	0.1890	5.292	1.3840	79.3
10.8	0.1885	0.1874	5.3367	0.9823	1.0180	0.1908	5.242	1.3823	79.2
10.9	0.1902	0.1891	5.2883	0.9820	1.0184	0.1926	5.193	1.3806	79.1
11.0	0.1920	0.1908	5.2408	0.9816	1.0187	0.1944	5.145	1.3788	**79.0**
11.1	0.1937	0.1925	5.1942	0.9813	1.0191	0.1962	5.097	1.3771	78.9
11.2	0.1955	0.1942	5.1484	0.9810	1.0194	0.1980	5.050	1.3753	78.8
11.3	0.1972	0.1959	5.1034	0.9806	1.0198	0.1998	5.005	1.3736	78.7
11.4	0.1990	0.1977	5.0593	0.9803	1.0201	0.2016	4.959	1.3718	78.6
11.5	0.2007	0.1994	5.0159	0.9799	1.0205	0.2035	4.915	1.3701	**78.5**
11.6	0.2025	0.2011	4.9732	0.9796	1.0209	0.2053	4.872	1.3683	78.4
11.7	0.2042	0.2028	4.9313	0.9792	1.0212	0.2071	4.829	1.3666	78.3
11.8	0.2059	0.2045	4.8901	0.9789	1.0216	0.2089	4.787	1.3648	78.2
11.9	0.2077	0.2062	4.8496	0.9785	1.0220	0.2107	4.745	1.3631	78.1
12.0	0.2094	0.2079	4.8097	0.9781	1.0223	0.2126	4.705	1.3614	**78.0**
12.1	0.2112	0.2096	4.7706	0.9778	1.0227	0.2144	4.665	1.3596	77.9
12.2	0.2129	0.2113	4.7321	0.9774	1.0231	0.2162	4.625	1.3579	77.8
12.3	0.2147	0.2130	4.6942	0.9770	1.0235	0.2180	4.586	1.3561	77.7
12.4	0.2164	0.2147	4.6569	0.9767	1.0239	0.2199	4.548	1.3544	77.6
12.5	0.2182	0.2164	4.6202	0.9763	1.0243	0.2217	4.511	1.3526	**77.5**
12.6	0.2199	0.2181	4.5841	0.9759	1.0247	0.2235	4.474	1.3509	77.4
12.7	0.2217	0.2198	4.5486	0.9755	1.0251	0.2254	4.437	1.3491	77.3
12.8	0.2234	0.2215	4.5137	0.9751	1.0255	0.2272	4.402	1.3474	77.2
12.9	0.2251	0.2233	4.4793	0.9748	1.0259	0.2290	4.366	1.3456	77.1
13.0	0.2269	0.2250	4.4454	0.9744	1.0263	0.2309	4.331	1.3439	**77.0**
13.1	0.2286	0.2267	4.4121	0.9740	1.0267	0.2327	4.297	1.3422	76.9
13.2	0.2304	0.2284	4.3792	0.9736	1.0271	0.2345	4.264	1.3404	76.8
13.3	0.2321	0.2300	4.3469	0.9732	1.0276	0.2364	4.230	1.3387	76.7
13.4	0.2339	0.2317	4.3150	0.9728	1.0280	0.2382	4.198	1.3369	76.6
		cos θ(x°)	sec θ(x°)	sin θ(x°)	csc θ(x°)	cot θ(x°)	tan θ(x°)	θ (radians)	x (de-grees)

TABLE 2

Four-Place Values of the Circular Functions

x (de-grees)	θ (radians)	sin θ(x°)	csc θ(x°)	cos θ(x°)	sec θ(x°)	tan θ(x°)	cot θ(x°)		
13.5	0.2356	0.2334	4.2837	0.9724	1.0284	0.2401	4.165	1.3352	**76.5**
13.6	0.2374	0.2351	4.2527	0.9720	1.0288	0.2419	4.134	1.3334	76.4
13.7	0.2391	0.2368	4.2223	0.9715	1.0293	0.2438	4.102	1.3317	76.3
13.8	0.2409	0.2385	4.1923	0.9711	1.0297	0.2456	4.071	1.3299	76.2
13.9	0.2426	0.2402	4.1627	0.9707	1.0302	0.2475	4.041	1.3282	76.1
14.0	0.2443	0.2419	4.1336	0.9703	1.0306	0.2493	4.011	1.3265	**76.0**
14.1	0.2461	0.2436	4.1048	0.9699	1.0311	0.2512	3.981	1.3247	75.9
14.2	0.2478	0.2453	4.0765	0.9694	1.0315	0.2530	3.952	1.3230	75.8
14.3	0.2496	0.2470	4.0486	0.9690	1.0320	0.2549	3.923	1.3212	75.7
14.4	0.2513	0.2487	4.0211	0.9686	1.0324	0.2568	3.895	1.3195	75.6
14.5	0.2531	0.2504	3.9939	0.9681	1.0329	0.2586	3.867	1.3177	**75.5**
14.6	0.2548	0.2521	3.9672	0.9677	1.0334	0.2605	3.839	1.3160	75.4
14.7	0.2566	0.2538	3.9408	0.9673	1.0338	0.2623	3.812	1.3142	75.3
14.8	0.2583	0.2554	3.9147	0.9668	1.0343	0.2642	3.785	1.3125	75.2
14.9	0.2601	0.2571	3.8890	0.9664	1.0348	0.2661	3.758	1.3107	75.1
15.0	0.2618	0.2588	3.8637	0.9659	1.0353	0.2679	3.732	1.3090	**75.0**
15.1	0.2635	0.2605	3.8387	0.9655	1.0358	0.2698	3.706	1.3073	74.9
15.2	0.2653	0.2622	3.8140	0.9650	1.0363	0.2717	3.681	1.3055	74.8
15.3	0.2670	0.2639	3.7897	0.9646	1.0367	0.2736	3.655	1.3038	74.7
15.4	0.2688	0.2656	3.7657	0.9641	1.0372	0.2754	3.630	1.3020	74.6
15.5	0.2705	0.2672	3.7420	0.9636	1.0377	0.2773	3.606	1.3003	**74.5**
15.6	0.2723	0.2689	3.7186	0.9632	1.0382	0.2792	3.582	1.2985	74.4
15.7	0.2740	0.2706	3.6955	0.9627	1.0388	0.2811	3.558	1.2968	74.3
15.8	0.2758	0.2723	3.6727	0.9622	1.0393	0.2830	3.534	1.2950	74.2
15.9	0.2775	0.2740	3.6502	0.9617	1.0398	0.2849	3.511	1.2933	74.1
16.0	0.2793	0.2756	3.6280	0.9613	1.0403	0.2867	3.487	1.2915	**74.0**
16.1	0.2810	0.2773	3.6060	0.9608	1.0408	0.2886	3.465	1.2898	73.9
16.2	0.2827	0.2790	3.5843	0.9603	1.0413	0.2905	3.442	1.2881	73.8
16.3	0.2845	0.2807	3.5629	0.9598	1.0419	0.2924	3.420	1.2863	73.7
16.4	0.2862	0.2823	3.5418	0.9593	1.0424	0.2943	3.398	1.2846	73.6
16.5	0.2880	0.2840	3.5209	0.9588	1.0429	0.2962	3.376	1.2828	**73.5**
16.6	0.2897	0.2857	3.5003	0.9583	1.0435	0.2981	3.354	1.2811	73.4
16.7	0.2915	0.2874	3.4799	0.9578	1.0440	0.3000	3.333	1.2793	73.3
16.8	0.2932	0.2890	3.4598	0.9573	1.0446	0.3019	3.312	1.2776	73.2
16.9	0.2950	0.2907	3.4399	0.9568	1.0451	0.3038	3.291	1.2758	73.1
17.0	0.2967	0.2924	3.4203	0.9563	1.0457	0.3057	3.271	1.2741	**73.0**
17.1	0.2985	0.2940	3.4009	0.9558	1.0463	0.3076	3.251	1.2723	72.9
17.2	0.3002	0.2957	3.3817	0.9553	1.0468	0.3096	3.230	1.2706	72.8
17.3	0.3019	0.2974	3.3628	0.9548	1.0474	0.3115	3.211	1.2689	72.7
17.4	0.3037	0.2990	3.3440	0.9542	1.0480	0.3134	3.191	1.2671	72.6
17.5	0.3054	0.3007	3.3255	0.9537	1.0485	0.3153	3.172	1.2654	**72.5**
17.6	0.3072	0.3024	3.3072	0.9532	1.0491	0.3172	3.152	1.2636	72.4
17.7	0.3089	0.3040	3.2891	0.9527	1.0497	0.3191	3.133	1.2619	72.3
17.8	0.3107	0.3057	3.2712	0.9521	1.0503	0.3211	3.115	1.2601	72.2
17.9	0.3124	0.3074	3.2535	0.9516	1.0509	0.3230	3.096	1.2584	72.1
		cos θ(x°)	sec θ(x°)	sin θ(x°)	csc θ(x°)	cot θ(x°)	tan θ(x°)	θ (radians)	x (de-grees)

TABLE 2

Four-Place Values of the Circular Functions

x (degrees)	θ (radians)	sin θ(x°)	csc θ(x°)	cos θ(x°)	sec θ(x°)	tan θ(x°)	cot θ(x°)		
18.0	0.3142	0.3090	3.2361	0.9511	1.0515	0.3249	3.078	1.2566	**72.0**
18.1	0.3159	0.3107	3.2188	0.9505	1.0521	0.3269	3.060	1.2549	71.9
18.2	0.3176	0.3123	3.2017	0.9500	1.0527	0.3288	3.042	1.2531	71.8
18.3	0.3194	0.3140	3.1848	0.9494	1.0533	0.3307	3.024	1.2514	71.7
18.4	0.3211	0.3156	3.1681	0.9489	1.0539	0.3327	3.006	1.2497	71.6
18.5	0.3229	0.3173	3.1515	0.9483	1.0545	0.3346	2.989	1.2479	**71.5**
18.6	0.3246	0.3190	3.1352	0.9478	1.0551	0.3365	2.971	1.2462	71.4
18.7	0.3264	0.3206	3.1190	0.9472	1.0557	0.3385	2.954	1.2444	71.3
18.8	0.3281	0.3223	3.1030	0.9466	1.0564	0.3404	2.937	1.2427	71.2
18.9	0.3299	0.3239	3.0872	0.9461	1.0570	0.3424	2.921	1.2409	71.1
19.0	0.3316	0.3256	3.0716	0.9455	1.0576	0.3443	2.904	1.2392	**71.0**
19.1	0.3334	0.3272	3.0561	0.9449	1.0583	0.3463	2.888	1.2374	70.9
19.2	0.3351	0.3289	3.0407	0.9444	1.0589	0.3482	2.872	1.2357	70.8
19.3	0.3368	0.3305	3.0256	0.9438	1.0595	0.3502	2.856	1.2339	70.7
19.4	0.3386	0.3322	3.0106	0.9432	1.0602	0.3522	2.840	1.2322	70.6
19.5	0.3403	0.3338	2.9957	0.9426	1.0608	0.3541	2.824	1.2305	**70.5**
19.6	0.3421	0.3355	2.9811	0.9421	1.0615	0.3561	2.808	1.2287	70.4
19.7	0.3438	0.3371	2.9665	0.9415	1.0622	0.3581	2.793	1.2270	70.3
19.8	0.3456	0.3387	2.9521	0.9409	1.0628	0.3600	2.778	1.2252	70.2
19.9	0.3473	0.3404	2.9379	0.9403	1.0635	0.3620	2.762	1.2235	70.1
20.0	0.3491	0.3420	2.9238	0.9397	1.0642	0.3640	2.747	1.2217	**70.0**
20.1	0.3508	0.3437	2.9099	0.9391	1.0649	0.3659	2.733	1.2200	69.9
20.2	0.3526	0.3453	2.8960	0.9385	1.0655	0.3679	2.718	1.2182	69.8
20.3	0.3543	0.3469	2.8824	0.9379	1.0662	0.3699	2.703	1.2165	69.7
20.4	0.3560	0.3486	2.8688	0.9373	1.0669	0.3719	2.689	1.2147	69.6
20.5	0.3578	0.3502	2.8555	0.9367	1.0676	0.3739	2.675	1.2130	**69.5**
20.6	0.3595	0.3518	2.8422	0.9361	1.0683	0.3759	2.660	1.2113	69.4
20.7	0.3613	0.3535	2.8291	0.9354	1.0690	0.3779	2.646	1.2095	69.3
20.8	0.3630	0.3551	2.8161	0.9348	1.0697	0.3799	2.633	1.2078	69.2
20.9	0.3648	0.3567	2.8032	0.9342	1.0704	0.3819	2.619	1.2060	69.1
21.0	0.3665	0.3584	2.7904	0.9336	1.0711	0.3839	2.605	1.2043	**69.0**
21.1	0.3683	0.3600	2.7778	0.9330	1.0719	0.3859	2.592	1.2025	68.9
21.2	0.3700	0.3616	2.7653	0.9323	1.0726	0.3879	2.578	1.2008	68.8
21.3	0.3718	0.3633	2.7529	0.9317	1.0733	0.3899	2.565	1.1990	68.7
21.4	0.3735	0.3649	2.7407	0.9311	1.0740	0.3919	2.552	1.1973	68.6
21.5	0.3752	0.3665	2.7285	0.9304	1.0748	0.3939	2.539	1.1956	**68.5**
21.6	0.3770	0.3681	2.7165	0.9298	1.0755	0.3959	2.526	1.1938	68.4
21.7	0.3787	0.3697	2.7046	0.9291	1.0763	0.3979	2.513	1.1921	68.3
21.8	0.3805	0.3714	2.6927	0.9285	1.0770	0.4000	2.500	1.1903	68.2
21.9	0.3822	0.3730	2.6811	0.9278	1.0778	0.4020	2.488	1.1886	68.1
22.0	0.3840	0.3746	2.6695	0.9272	1.0785	0.4040	2.475	1.1868	**68.0**
22.1	0.3857	0.3762	2.6580	0.9265	1.0793	0.4061	2.463	1.1851	67.9
22.2	0.3875	0.3778	2.6466	0.9259	1.0801	0.4081	2.450	1.1833	67.8
22.3	0.3892	0.3795	2.6354	0.9252	1.0808	0.4101	2.438	1.1816	67.7
22.4	0.3910	0.3811	2.6242	0.9245	1.0816	0.4122	2.426	1.1798	67.6
		cos θ(x°)	sec θ(x°)	sin θ(x°)	csc θ(x°)	cot θ(x°)	tan θ(x°)	θ (radians)	x (degrees)

TABLE 2

Four-Place Values of the Circular Functions

x (degrees)	θ (radians)	sin θ(x°)	csc θ(x°)	cos θ(x°)	sec θ(x°)	tan θ(x°)	cot θ(x°)		
22.5	0.3927	0.3827	2.6131	0.9239	1.0824	0.4142	2.414	1.1781	**67.5**
22.6	0.3944	0.3843	2.6022	0.9232	1.0832	0.4163	2.402	1.1764	67.4
22.7	0.3962	0.3859	2.5913	0.9225	1.0840	0.4183	2.391	1.1746	67.3
22.8	0.3979	0.3875	2.5805	0.9219	1.0848	0.4204	2.379	1.1729	67.2
22.9	0.3997	0.3891	2.5699	0.9212	1.0856	0.4224	2.367	1.1711	67.1
23.0	0.4014	0.3907	2.5593	0.9205	1.0864	0.4245	2.356	1.1694	**67.0**
23.1	0.4032	0.3923	2.5488	0.9198	1.0872	0.4265	2.344	1.1676	66.9
23.2	0.4049	0.3939	2.5384	0.9191	1.0880	0.4286	2.333	1.1659	66.8
23.3	0.4067	0.3955	2.5282	0.9184	1.0888	0.4307	2.322	1.1641	66.7
23.4	0.4084	0.3971	2.5180	0.9178	1.0896	0.4327	2.311	1.1624	66.6
23.5	0.4102	0.3987	2.5078	0.9171	1.0904	0.4348	2.300	1.1606	**66.5**
23.6	0.4119	0.4003	2.4978	0.9164	1.0913	0.4369	2.289	1.1589	66.4
23.7	0.4136	0.4019	2.4879	0.9157	1.0921	0.4390	2.278	1.1572	66.3
23.8	0.4154	0.4035	2.4780	0.9150	1.0929	0.4411	2.267	1.1554	66.2
23.9	0.4171	0.4051	2.4683	0.9143	1.0938	0.4431	2.257	1.1537	66.1
24.0	0.4189	0.4067	2.4586	0.9135	1.0946	0.4452	2.246	1.1519	**66.0**
24.1	0.4206	0.4083	2.4490	0.9128	1.0955	0.4473	2.236	1.1502	65.9
24.2	0.4224	0.4099	2.4395	0.9121	1.0963	0.4494	2.225	1.1484	65.8
24.3	0.4241	0.4115	2.4300	0.9114	1.0972	0.4515	2.215	1.1467	65.7
24.4	0.4259	0.4131	2.4207	0.9107	1.0981	0.4536	2.204	1.1449	65.6
24.5	0.4276	0.4147	2.4114	0.9100	1.0989	0.4557	2.194	1.1432	**65.5**
24.6	0.4294	0.4163	2.4022	0.9092	1.0998	0.4578	2.184	1.1414	65.4
24.7	0.4311	0.4179	2.3931	0.9085	1.1007	0.4599	2.174	1.1397	65.3
24.8	0.4328	0.4195	2.3841	0.9078	1.1016	0.4621	2.164	1.1380	65.2
24.9	0.4346	0.4210	2.3751	0.9070	1.1025	0.4642	2.154	1.1362	65.1
25.0	0.4363	0.4226	2.3662	0.9063	1.1034	0.4663	2.145	1.1345	**65.0**
25.1	0.4381	0.4242	2.3574	0.9056	1.1043	0.4684	2.135	1.1327	64.9
25.2	0.4398	0.4258	2.3486	0.9048	1.1052	0.4706	2.125	1.1310	64.8
25.3	0.4416	0.4274	2.3400	0.9041	1.1061	0.4727	2.116	1.1292	64.7
25.4	0.4433	0.4289	2.3314	0.9033	1.1070	0.4748	2.106	1.1275	64.6
25.5	0.4451	0.4305	2.3228	0.9026	1.1079	0.4770	2.097	1.1257	**64.5**
25.6	0.4468	0.4321	2.3144	0.9018	1.1089	0.4791	2.087	1.1240	64.4
25.7	0.4485	0.4337	2.3060	0.9011	1.1098	0.4813	2.078	1.1222	64.3
25.8	0.4503	0.4352	2.2976	0.9003	1.1107	0.4834	2.069	1.1205	64.2
25.9	0.4520	0.4368	2.2894	0.8996	1.1117	0.4856	2.059	1.1188	64.1
26.0	0.4538	0.4384	2.2812	0.8988	1.1126	0.4877	2.050	1.1170	64.0
26.1	0.4555	0.4399	2.2730	0.8980	1.1136	0.4899	2.041	1.1153	63.9
26.2	0.4573	0.4415	2.2650	0.8973	1.1145	0.4921	2.032	1.1135	63.8
26.3	0.4590	0.4431	2.2570	0.8965	1.1155	0.4942	2.023	1.1118	63.7
26.4	0.4608	0.4446	2.2490	0.8957	1.1164	0.4964	2.014	1.1100	63.6
26.5	0.4625	0.4462	2.2412	0.8949	1.1174	0.4986	2.006	1.1083	**63.5**
26.6	0.4643	0.4478	2.2333	0.8942	1.1184	0.5008	1.997	1.1065	63.4
26.7	0.4660	0.4493	2.2256	0.8934	1.1194	0.5029	1.988	1.1048	63.3
26.8	0.4677	0.4509	2.2179	0.8926	1.1203	0.5051	1.980	1.1030	63.2
26.9	0.4695	0.4524	2.2103	0.8918	1.1213	0.5073	1.971	1.1013	63.1
		cos θ(x°)	sec θ(x°)	sin θ(x°)	csc θ(x°)	cot θ(x°)	tan θ(x°)	θ (radians)	x (degrees)

TABLE 2

Four-Place Values of the Circular Functions

x (degrees)	θ (radians)	sin θ(x°)	csc θ(x°)	cos θ(x°)	sec θ(x°)	tan θ(x°)	cot θ(x°)		
27.0	0.4712	0.4540	2.2027	0.8910	1.1223	0.5095	1.963	1.0996	**63.0**
27.1	0.4730	0.4555	2.1952	0.8902	1.1233	0.5117	1.954	1.0978	62.9
27.2	0.4747	0.4571	2.1877	0.8894	1.1243	0.5139	1.946	1.0961	62.8
27.3	0.4765	0.4586	2.1803	0.8886	1.1253	0.5161	1.937	1.0943	62.7
27.4	0.4782	0.4602	2.1730	0.8878	1.1264	0.5184	1.929	1.0926	62.6
27.5	0.4800	0.4617	2.1657	0.8870	1.1274	0.5206	1.921	1.0908	**62.5**
27.6	0.4817	0.4633	2.1584	0.8862	1.1284	0.5228	1.913	1.0891	62.4
27.7	0.4835	0.4648	2.1513	0.8854	1.1294	0.5250	1.905	1.0873	62.3
27.8	0.4852	0.4664	2.1441	0.8846	1.1305	0.5272	1.897	1.0856	62.2
27.9	0.4869	0.4679	2.1371	0.8838	1.1315	0.5295	1.889	1.0838	62.1
28.0	0.4887	0.4695	2.1301	0.8829	1.1326	0.5317	1.881	1.0821	**62.0**
28.1	0.4904	0.4710	2.1231	0.8821	1.1336	0.5340	1.873	1.0804	61.9
28.2	0.4922	0.4726	2.1162	0.8813	1.1347	0.5362	1.865	1.0786	61.8
28.3	0.4939	0.4741	2.1093	0.8805	1.1357	0.5384	1.857	1.0769	61.7
28.4	0.4957	0.4756	2.1025	0.8796	1.1368	0.5407	1.849	1.0751	61.6
28.5	0.4974	0.4772	2.0957	0.8788	1.1379	0.5430	1.842	1.0734	**61.5**
28.6	0.4992	0.4787	2.0890	0.8780	1.1390	0.5452	1.834	1.0716	61.4
28.7	0.5009	0.4802	2.0824	0.8771	1.1401	0.5475	1.827	1.0699	61.3
28.8	0.5027	0.4818	2.0757	0.8763	1.1412	0.5498	1.819	1.0681	61.2
28.9	0.5044	0.4833	2.0692	0.8755	1.1423	0.5520	1.811	1.0664	61.1
29.0	0.5061	0.4848	2.0627	0.8746	1.1434	0.5543	1.804	1.0647	**61.0**
29.1	0.5079	0.4863	2.0562	0.8738	1.1445	0.5566	1.797	1.0629	60.9
29.2	0.5096	0.4879	2.0498	0.8729	1.1456	0.5589	1.789	1.0612	60.8
29.3	0.5114	0.4894	2.0434	0.8721	1.1467	0.5612	1.782	1.0594	60.7
29.4	0.5131	0.4909	2.0371	0.8712	1.1478	0.5635	1.775	1.0577	60.6
29.5	0.5149	0.4924	2.0308	0.8704	1.1490	0.5658	1.767	1.0559	**60.5**
29.6	0.5166	0.4939	2.0245	0.8695	1.1501	0.5681	1.760	1.0542	60.4
29.7	0.5184	0.4955	2.0183	0.8686	1.1512	0.5704	1.753	1.0524	60.3
29.8	0.5201	0.4970	2.0122	0.8678	1.1524	0.5727	1.746	1.0507	60.2
29.9	0.5219	0.4985	2.0061	0.8669	1.1535	0.5750	1.739	1.0489	60.1
30.0	0.5236	0.5000	2.0000	0.8660	1.1547	0.5774	1.7321	1.0472	**60.0**
30.1	0.5253	0.5015	1.9940	0.8652	1.1559	0.5797	1.7251	1.0455	59.9
30.2	0.5271	0.5030	1.9880	0.8643	1.1570	0.5820	1.7182	1.0437	59.8
30.3	0.5288	0.5045	1.9821	0.8634	1.1582	0.5844	1.7113	1.0420	59.7
30.4	0.5306	0.5060	1.9762	0.8625	1.1594	0.5867	1.7045	1.0402	59.6
30.5	0.5323	0.5075	1.9703	0.8616	1.1606	0.5890	1.6977	1.0385	**59.5**
30.6	0.5341	0.5090	1.9645	0.8607	1.1618	0.5914	1.6909	1.0367	59.4
30.7	0.5358	0.5105	1.9587	0.8599	1.1630	0.5938	1.6842	1.0350	59.3
30.8	0.5376	0.5120	1.9530	0.8590	1.1642	0.5961	1.6775	1.0332	59.2
30.9	0.5393	0.5135	1.9473	0.8581	1.1654	0.5985	1.6709	1.0315	59.1
31.0	0.5411	0.5150	1.9416	0.8572	1.1666	0.6009	1.6643	1.0297	**59.0**
31.1	0.5428	0.5165	1.9360	0.8563	1.1679	0.6032	1.6577	1.0280	58.9
31.2	0.5445	0.5180	1.9304	0.8554	1.1691	0.6056	1.6512	1.0263	58.8
31.3	0.5463	0.5195	1.9249	0.8545	1.1703	0.6080	1.6447	1.0245	58.7
31.4	0.5480	0.5210	1.9194	0.8536	1.1716	0.6104	1.6383	1.0228	58.6
		cos θ(x°)	sec θ(x°)	sin θ(x°)	csc θ(x°)	cot θ(x°)	tan θ(x°)	θ (radians)	x (degrees)

TABLE 2

Four-Place Values of the Circular Functions

x (de-grees)	θ (radians)	sin θ(x°)	csc θ(x°)	cos θ(x°)	sec θ(x°)	tan θ(x°)	cot θ(x°)	
31.5	0.5498	0.5225	1.9139	0.8526	1.1728	0.6128	1.6319	1.0210	**58.5**
31.6	0.5515	0.5240	1.9084	0.8517	1.1741	0.6152	1.6255	1.0193	58.4
31.7	0.5533	0.5255	1.9031	0.8508	1.1753	0.6176	1.6191	1.0175	58.3
31.8	0.5550	0.5270	1.8977	0.8499	1.1766	0.6200	1.6128	1.0158	58.2
31.9	0.5568	0.5284	1.8924	0.8490	1.1779	0.6224	1.6066	1.0140	58.1
32.0	0.5585	0.5299	1.8871	0.8480	1.1792	0.6249	1.6003	1.0123	**58.0**
32.1	0.5603	0.5314	1.8818	0.8471	1.1805	0.6273	1.5941	1.0105	57.9
32.2	0.5620	0.5329	1.8766	0.8462	1.1818	0.6297	1.5880	1.0088	57.8
32.3	0.5637	0.5344	1.8714	0.8453	1.1831	0.6322	1.5818	1.0071	57.7
32.4	0.5655	0.5358	1.8663	0.8443	1.1844	0.6346	1.5757	1.0053	57.6
32.5	0.5672	0.5373	1.8612	0.8434	1.1857	0.6371	1.5697	1.0036	**57.5**
32.6	0.5690	0.5388	1.8561	0.8425	1.1870	0.6395	1.5637	1.0018	57.4
32.7	0.5707	0.5402	1.8510	0.8415	1.1883	0.6420	1.5577	1.0001	57.3
32.8	0.5725	0.5417	1.8460	0.8406	1.1897	0.6445	1.5517	0.9983	57.2
32.9	0.5742	0.5432	1.8410	0.8396	1.1910	0.6469	1.5458	0.9966	57.1
33.0	0.5760	0.5446	1.8361	0.8387	1.1924	0.6494	1.5399	0.9948	**57.0**
33.1	0.5777	0.5461	1.8312	0.8377	1.1937	0.6519	1.5340	0.9931	56.9
33.2	0.5794	0.5476	1.8263	0.8368	1.1951	0.6544	1.5282	0.9913	56.8
33.3	0.5812	0.5490	1.8214	0.8358	1.1964	0.6569	1.5224	0.9896	56.7
33.4	0.5829	0.5505	1.8166	0.8348	1.1978	0.6594	1.5166	0.9879	56.6
33.5	0.5847	0.5519	1.8118	0.8339	1.1992	0.6619	1.5108	0.9861	**56.5**
33.6	0.5864	0.5534	1.8070	0.8329	1.2006	0.6644	1.5051	0.9844	56.4
33.7	0.5882	0.5548	1.8023	0.8320	1.2020	0.6669	1.4994	0.9826	56.3
33.8	0.5899	0.5563	1.7976	0.8310	1.2034	0.6694	1.4938	0.9809	56.2
33.9	0.5917	0.5577	1.7929	0.8300	1.2048	0.6720	1.4882	0.9791	56.1
34.0	0.5934	0.5592	1.7883	0.8290	1.2062	0.6745	1.4826	0.9774	**56.0**
34.1	0.5952	0.5606	1.7837	0.8281	1.2076	0.6771	1.4770	0.9756	55.9
34.2	0.5969	0.5621	1.7791	0.8271	1.2091	0.6796	1.4715	0.9739	55.8
34.3	0.5986	0.5635	1.7745	0.8261	1.2105	0.6822	1.4659	0.9721	55.7
34.4	0.6004	0.5650	1.7700	0.8251	1.2120	0.6847	1.4605	0.9704	55.6
34.5	0.6021	0.5664	1.7655	0.8241	1.2134	0.6873	1.4550	0.9687	**55.5**
34.6	0.6039	0.5678	1.7610	0.8231	1.2149	0.6899	1.4496	0.9669	55.4
34.7	0.6056	0.5693	1.7566	0.8221	1.2163	0.6924	1.4442	0.9652	55.3
34.8	0.6074	0.5707	1.7522	0.8211	1.2178	0.6950	1.4388	0.9634	55.2
34.9	0.6091	0.5721	1.7478	0.8202	1.2193	0.6976	1.4335	0.9617	55.1
35.0	0.6109	0.5736	1.7434	0.8192	1.2208	0.7002	1.4281	0.9599	**55.0**
35.1	0.6126	0.5750	1.7391	0.8181	1.2223	0.7028	1.4229	0.9582	54.9
35.2	0.6144	0.5764	1.7348	0.8171	1.2238	0.7054	1.4176	0.9564	54.8
35.3	0.6161	0.5779	1.7305	0.8161	1.2253	0.7080	1.4124	0.9547	54.7
35.4	0.6178	0.5793	1.7263	0.8151	1.2268	0.7107	1.4071	0.9529	54.6
35.5	0.6196	0.5807	1.7221	0.8141	1.2283	0.7133	1.4019	0.9512	**54.5**
35.6	0.6213	0.5821	1.7179	0.8131	1.2299	0.7159	1.3968	0.9495	54.4
35.7	0.6231	0.5835	1.7137	0.8121	1.2314	0.7186	1.3916	0.9477	54.3
35.8	0.6248	0.5850	1.7095	0.8111	1.2329	0.7212	1.3865	0.9460	54.2
35.9	0.6266	0.5864	1.7054	0.8100	1.2345	0.7239	1.3814	0.9442	54.1
		cos θ(x°)	sec θ(x°)	sin θ(x°)	csc θ(x°)	cot θ(x°)	tan θ(x°)	θ (radians)	x (de-grees)

TABLE 2

Four-Place Values of the Circular Functions

x (de-grees)	θ (radians)	sin θ(x°)	csc θ(x°)	cos θ(x°)	sec θ(x°)	tan θ(x°)	cot θ(x°)		
36.0	0.6283	0.5878	1.7013	0.8090	1.2361	0.7265	1.3764	0.9425	**54.0**
36.1	0.6301	0.5892	1.6972	0.8080	1.2376	0.7292	1.3713	0.9407	53.9
36.2	0.6318	0.5906	1.6932	0.8070	1.2392	0.7319	1.3663	0.9390	53.8
36.3	0.6336	0.5920	1.6892	0.8059	1.2408	0.7346	1.3613	0.9372	53.7
36.4	0.6353	0.5934	1.6852	0.8049	1.2424	0.7373	1.3564	0.9355	53.6
36.5	0.6370	0.5948	1.6812	0.8039	1.2440	0.7400	1.3514	0.9338	**53.5**
36.6	0.6388	0.5962	1.6772	0.8028	1.2456	0.7427	1.3465	0.9320	53.4
36.7	0.6405	0.5976	1.6733	0.8018	1.2472	0.7454	1.3416	0.9303	53.3
36.8	0.6423	0.5990	1.6694	0.8007	1.2489	0.7481	1.3367	0.9285	53.2
36.9	0.6440	0.6004	1.6655	0.7997	1.2505	0.7508	1.3319	0.9268	53.1
37.0	0.6458	0.6018	1.6616	0.7986	1.2521	0.7536	1.3270	0.9250	**53.0**
37.1	0.6475	0.6032	1.6578	0.7976	1.2538	0.7563	1.3222	0.9233	52.9
37.2	0.6493	0.6046	1.6540	0.7965	1.2554	0.7590	1.3175	0.9215	52.8
37.3	0.6510	0.6060	1.6502	0.7955	1.2571	0.7618	1.3127	0.9198	52.7
37.4	0.6528	0.6074	1.6464	0.7944	1.2588	0.7646	1.3079	0.9180	52.6
37.5	0.6545	0.6088	1.6427	0.7934	1.2605	0.7673	1.3032	0.9163	**52.5**
37.6	0.6562	0.6101	1.6390	0.7923	1.2622	0.7701	1.2985	0.9146	52.4
37.7	0.6580	0.6115	1.6353	0.7912	1.2639	0.7729	1.2938	0.9128	52.3
37.8	0.6597	0.6129	1.6316	0.7902	1.2656	0.7757	1.2892	0.9111	52.2
37.9	0.6615	0.6143	1.6279	0.7891	1.2673	0.7785	1.2846	0.9093	52.1
38.0	0.6632	0.6157	1.6243	0.7880	1.2690	0.7813	1.2799	0.9076	**52.0**
38.1	0.6650	0.6170	1.6207	0.7869	1.2708	0.7841	1.2753	0.9058	51.9
38.2	0.6667	0.6184	1.6171	0.7859	1.2725	0.7869	1.2708	0.9041	51.8
38.3	0.6685	0.6198	1.6135	0.7848	1.2742	0.7898	1.2662	0.9023	51.7
38.4	0.6702	0.6211	1.6099	0.7837	1.2760	0.7926	1.2617	0.9006	51.6
38.5	0.6720	0.6225	1.6064	0.7826	1.2778	0.7954	1.2572	0.8988	**51.5**
38.6	0.6737	0.6239	1.6029	0.7815	1.2796	0.7983	1.2527	0.8971	51.4
38.7	0.6754	0.6252	1.5994	0.7804	1.2813	0.8012	1.2482	0.8954	51.3
38.8	0.6772	0.6266	1.5959	0.7793	1.2831	0.8040	1.2437	0.8936	51.2
38.9	0.6789	0.6280	1.5925	0.7782	1.2849	0.8069	1.2393	0.8919	51.1
39.0	0.6807	0.6293	1.5890	0.7771	1.2868	0.8098	1.2349	0.8901	**51.0**
39.1	0.6824	0.6307	1.5856	0.7760	1.2886	0.8127	1.2305	0.8884	50.9
39.2	0.6842	0.6320	1.5822	0.7749	1.2904	0.8156	1.2261	0.8866	50.8
39.3	0.6859	0.6334	1.5788	0.7738	1.2923	0.8185	1.2218	0.8849	50.7
39.4	0.6877	0.6347	1.5755	0.7727	1.2941	0.8214	1.2174	0.8831	50.6
39.5	0.6894	0.6361	1.5721	0.7716	1.2960	0.8243	1.2131	0.8814	**50.5**
39.6	0.6912	0.6374	1.5688	0.7705	1.2978	0.8273	1.2088	0.8796	50.4
39.7	0.6929	0.6388	1.5655	0.7694	1.2997	0.8302	1.2045	0.8779	50.3
39.8	0.6946	0.6401	1.5622	0.7683	1.3016	0.8332	1.2002	0.8762	50.2
39.9	0.6964	0.6414	1.5590	0.7672	1.3035	0.8361	1.1960	0.8744	50.1
40.0	0.6981	0.6428	1.5557	0.7660	1.3054	0.8391	1.1918	0.8727	**50.0**
40.1	0.6999	0.6441	1.5525	0.7649	1.3073	0.8421	1.1875	0.8709	49.9
40.2	0.7016	0.6455	1.5493	0.7638	1.3093	0.8451	1.1833	0.8692	49.8
40.3	0.7034	0.6468	1.5461	0.7627	1.3112	0.8481	1.1792	0.8674	49.7
40.4	0.7051	0.6481	1.5429	0.7615	1.3131	0.8511	1.1750	0.8657	49.6
	cos θ(x°)	sec θ(x°)	sin θ(x°)	csc θ(x°)	cot θ(x°)	tan θ(x°)	θ (radians)	x (de-grees)	

301

TABLE 2

Four-Place Values of the Circular Functions

x (de-grees)	θ (radians)	sin θ(x°)	csc θ(x°)	cos θ(x°)	sec θ(x°)	tan θ(x°)	cot θ(x°)		
40.5	0.7069	0.6494	1.5398	0.7604	1.3151	0.8541	1.1708	0.8639	**49.5**
40.6	0.7086	0.6508	1.5366	0.7593	1.3171	0.8571	1.1667	0.8622	49.4
40.7	0.7103	0.6521	1.5335	0.7581	1.3190	0.8601	1.1626	0.8604	49.3
40.8	0.7121	0.6534	1.5304	0.7570	1.3210	0.8632	1.1585	0.8587	49.2
40.9	0.7138	0.6547	1.5273	0.7559	1.3230	0.8662	1.1544	0.8570	49.1
41.0	0.7156	0.6561	1.5243	0.7547	1.3250	0.8693	1.1504	0.8552	**49.0**
41.1	0.7173	0.6574	1.5212	0.7536	1.3270	0.8724	1.1463	0.8535	48.9
41.2	0.7191	0.6587	1.5182	0.7524	1.3291	0.8754	1.1423	0.8517	48.8
41.3	0.7208	0.6600	1.5151	0.7513	1.3311	0.8785	1.1383	0.8500	48.7
41.4	0.7226	0.6613	1.5121	0.7501	1.3331	0.8816	1.1343	0.8482	48.6
41.5	0.7243	0.6626	1.5092	0.7490	1.3352	0.8847	1.1303	0.8465	**48.5**
41.6	0.7261	0.6639	1.5062	0.7478	1.3373	0.8878	1.1263	0.8447	48.4
41.7	0.7278	0.6652	1.5032	0.7466	1.3393	0.8910	1.1224	0.8430	48.3
41.8	0.7295	0.6665	1.5003	0.7455	1.3414	0.8941	1.1184	0.8412	48.2
41.9	0.7313	0.6678	1.4974	0.7443	1.3435	0.8972	1.1145	0.8395	48.1
42.0	0.7330	0.6691	1.4945	0.7431	1.3456	0.9004	1.1106	0.8378	**48.0**
42.1	0.7348	0.6704	1.4916	0.7420	1.3478	0.9036	1.1067	0.8360	47.9
42.2	0.7365	0.6717	1.4887	0.7408	1.3499	0.9067	1.1028	0.8343	47.8
42.3	0.7383	0.6730	1.4859	0.7396	1.3520	0.9099	1.0990	0.8325	47.7
42.4	0.7400	0.6743	1.4830	0.7385	1.3542	0.9131	1.0951	0.8308	47.6
42.5	0.7418	0.6756	1.4802	0.7373	1.3563	0.9163	1.0913	0.8290	**47.5**
42.6	0.7435	0.6769	1.4774	0.7361	1.3585	0.9195	1.0875	0.8273	47.4
42.7	0.7453	0.6782	1.4746	0.7349	1.3607	0.9228	1.0837	0.8255	47.3
42.8	0.7470	0.6794	1.4718	0.7337	1.3629	0.9260	1.0799	0.8238	47.2
42.9	0.7487	0.6807	1.4690	0.7325	1.3651	0.9293	1.0761	0.8221	47.1
43.0	0.7505	0.6820	1.4663	0.7314	1.3673	0.9325	1.0724	0.8203	**47.0**
43.1	0.7522	0.6833	1.4635	0.7302	1.3696	0.9358	1.0686	0.8186	46.9
43.2	0.7540	0.6845	1.4608	0.7290	1.3718	0.9391	1.0649	0.8168	46.8
43.3	0.7557	0.6858	1.4581	0.7278	1.3741	0.9424	1.0612	0.8151	46.7
43.4	0.7575	0.6871	1.4554	0.7266	1.3763	0.9457	1.0575	0.8133	46.6
43.5	0.7592	0.6884	1.4527	0.7254	1.3786	0.9490	1.0538	0.8116	**46.5**
43.6	0.7610	0.6896	1.4501	0.7242	1.3809	0.9523	1.0501	0.8098	46.4
43.7	0.7627	0.6909	1.4474	0.7230	1.3832	0.9556	1.0464	0.8081	46.3
43.8	0.7645	0.6921	1.4448	0.7218	1.3855	0.9590	1.0428	0.8063	46.2
43.9	0.7662	0.6934	1.4422	0.7206	1.3878	0.9623	1.0392	0.8046	46.1
44.0	0.7679	0.6947	1.4396	0.7193	1.3902	0.9657	1.0355	0.8029	**46.0**
44.1	0.7697	0.6959	1.4370	0.7181	1.3925	0.9691	1.0319	0.8011	45.9
44.2	0.7714	0.6972	1.4344	0.7169	1.3949	0.9725	1.0283	0.7994	45.8
44.3	0.7732	0.6984	1.4318	0.7157	1.3972	0.9759	1.0247	0.7976	45.7
44.4	0.7749	0.6997	1.4293	0.7145	1.3996	0.9793	1.0212	0.7959	45.6
44.5	0.7767	0.7009	1.4267	0.7133	1.4020	0.9827	1.0176	0.7941	**45.5**
44.6	0.7784	0.7022	1.4242	0.7120	1.4044	0.9861	1.0141	0.7924	45.4
44.7	0.7802	0.7034	1.4217	0.7108	1.4069	0.9896	1.0105	0.7906	45.3
44.8	0.7819	0.7046	1.4192	0.7096	1.4093	0.9930	1.0070	0.7889	45.2
44.9	0.7837	0.7059	1.4167	0.7083	1.4118	0.9965	1.0035	0.7871	45.1
45.0	0.7854	0.7071	1.4142	0.7071	1.4142	1.0000	1.0000	0.7854	**45.0**
		cos θ(x°)	sec θ(x°)	sin θ(x°)	csc θ(x°)	cot θ(x°)	tan θ(x°)	θ (radians)	x (de-grees)

ANSWERS TO ODD-NUMBERED PROBLEMS

CHAPTER 1

Section 1.1

1. Natural Numbers: (a) 2; (b) none; (c) 3, $\sqrt{2}/\sqrt{2}$.
   Integers: (a) 2; (b) $-6, 0$; (c) $-2, 3, \sqrt{2}/\sqrt{2}$.
   Rational Numbers: (a) 2, $-\frac{1}{2}, \frac{1}{3}, 0.272727\cdots$; (b) $\frac{1}{2}, 1.571571\cdots, -6, 0$;
   (c) $-2, 3, \frac{5}{6}, \sqrt{2}/\sqrt{2}$.
   Irrational Numbers: (a) $\sqrt{3}$; (b) $-\sqrt{2}/2, \sqrt[3]{5}$; (c) $2/\sqrt{5}, \sqrt[7]{2}$.
3. (a) $\frac{11}{13} = 0.846153846153\cdots$; (b) $\frac{27}{37} = 0.729729\cdots$.
5. Direct everyone to take a dancing partner of the opposite sex.
7. Remove the fruit in pairs, with one orange and one grapefruit in each pair.
9. 2 and II are merely different names or "numerals" for the same number. This is the same for 4 and IV.

Section 1.2

1. $a + (b - a) = a + [b + (-a)]$ [Def. of subtraction]
              $= [a + (-a)] + b$ $[A_2, A_5]$
              $= 0 + b$ $[A_4]$
              $= b$ $[A_3]$
   Hence, $a + (b - a) = b$. $[E_3^*]$
3. $(a + 1) + (1 + b) = a + [1 + (1 + b)]$ $[A_2]$
              $= a + [(1 + 1) + b]$ $[A_2]$
              $= a + (2 + b)$
              $= a + b + 2$ $[A_2, A_5]$
5. $(b + a + 1) + [(-a) + (-b) + 2]$
           $= (b + a) + [1 + 2 + (-a) + (-b)]$ $[A_2, A_5]$
           $= (b + a) + [(-a) + (-b)] + 3$ $[A_2, A_5]$
           $= [b + (-b)] + [a + (-a)] + 3$ $[A_2, A_5]$
           $= 0 + 0 + 3$ $[A_4]$
           $= 3.$ $[A_3]$
   Hence, $(b + a + 1) + [(-a) + (-b) + 2] = 3$ $[E_3^*]$
7. $(a - b) + b = [a + (-b)] + b$
              $= a + [(-b) + b]$
              $= a + 0$
              $= a.$
9. 6 is divisible by 2 but 2 is *not* divisible by 6 in the set of integers.
11. A_3, A_4, A_5, Definition of subtraction.
13. No. This argument would require the *existence* of b such that $a = b$, while the existence of such an element is not postulated. (Do not confuse the special properties of this "equals" relation with the generalized concept.)

303

Section 1.3

1. $(a + b)c + ab = (ac + bc) + ab$ [D]
   $= (bc + ba) + ac$ [A$_2$, A$_5$, M$_5$]
   $= b(c + a) + ac.$ [D]
   Hence, $(a + b)c + ab = b(c + a) + ac.$ [E$_3^*$]

3. $b(a + 1) + [(-b) + a] = (ba + b) + [(-b) + a]$ [D, M$_3$]
   $= ba + [b + (-b)] + a$ [A$_2$]
   $= ab + 0 + a$ [M$_5$, A$_4$]
   $= ab + a$ [A$_3$]
   $= a(b + 1).$ [D, M$_3$]
   Hence, $b(a + 1) + [(-b) + a] = a(b + 1).$ [E$_3^*$]

5. $(ab)(cd) = (cd)(ab)$ [M$_5$]
   $= c[d(ab)]$ [M$_2$]
   $= c[(ab)d]$ [M$_5$]
   $= c[b(ad)]$ [M$_5$]
   $= (cb)(ad).$ [M$_2$]
   Hence, $(ab)(cd) = (cb)(ad)$ [E$_3^*$]

7. (a) Yes; (b) yes; (c) no; (d) yes; (e) no.

9. $\frac{3}{2} \neq \frac{2}{3}$; $3/[\frac{4}{5}] = 3(\frac{5}{4}) = \frac{15}{4}$, $[\frac{3}{4}]/5 = \frac{3}{20}.$

11. $ab = b$, $(ab)b^{-1} = bb^{-1}$, $a(bb^{-1}) = bb^{-1}$, $a(1) = 1$, $a = 1.$

Section 1.4

1. $ab + (-a)b = [a + (-a)]b = 0b = 0.$ Hence, $(-a)b = -ab$ by Theorem 1.43.

3. $(a + b) + [(-a) + (-b)] = [a + (-a)] + [b + (-b)] = 0 + 0 = 0.$ Hence, $(-a) + (-b) = -(a + b).$

5. $a + (-a) = 0 = b + (-a).$ Hence, by Theorem 1.43, $-a = -b.$

7. By Theorem 1.410, either $x + 1 = 0$, $x - 2 = 0$, or $x - 1 = 0.$ Hence, $x = -1$, $x = 2$, or $x = 1.$

9. $a(b + c) = (b + c)a$ [M$_5$]
   $= ba + ca$ [Right distributive law]
   $= ab + ac.$ [M$_5$]
   Hence, $a(b + c) = ab + ac.$ [E$_3^*$]

11. $(a + b)/c = (a + b)c^{-1}$ [Def. of division]
    $= ac^{-1} + bc^{-1}$ [D]
    $= a/c + b/c.$ [Def. of division]

13. $a(b/a) = a(ba^{-1})$ [Def. of division]
    $= a(a^{-1}b)$ [M$_5$]
    $= (aa^{-1}b)$ [M$_2$]
    $= (1)b = b.$ [M$_4$, M$_3$]

Section 1.5

1. By O$_3$, $a + c < b + c$ and $b + c < b + d.$ By O$_2$, $a + c < b + d.$

3. By Example 2, $(-1)a > (-1)0 = 0.$ Since $(-1)a = -a$ [Problem 2, §1.4], $-a > 0.$

5. By Example 2, $(-1)a > (-1)b$. Hence, [Problem 2, §1.4] $-a > -b$.

7. By O_1 and supposition, $a < 0$ or $a > 0$. If $a < 0$, $aa = a^2 > 0$, by Example 2. If $a > 0$, $0 < a$ and $0 < a^2$ by O_4. Hence, in every case, $a^2 > 0$.

9. $1/a < 1/b$ is equivalent to $a^{-1} < b^{-1}$. If $b^{-1} < a^{-1}$, $ab > 0$ would require (by O_4) that $b^{-1}(ab) < a^{-1}(ab)$, i.e., $a < b$, a contradiction. Hence, $a^{-1} < b^{-1}$.

11. By Problem 7, $(a - b)^2 = a^2 - 2ab + b^2 \geq 0$, i.e., $a^2 + b^2 \geq 2ab$.

13. (a) 2; (b) 3; (c) 4; (d) 0; (e) $\sqrt{2}$.

15. Four cases:
   (1) If $a > 0$, $b > 0$, then $ab > 0$ and so $|ab| = ab = |a| \, |b|$.
   (2) If $a < 0$, $b < 0$, then $ab > 0$, by Example 1, and so $|ab| = ab = (-1)^2 ab = (-a)(-b) = |a| \, |b|$.
   (3) If $a > 0$, $b < 0$, then $ab < 0$, by O_4. Hence, $|ab| = -ab = a[(-1)b] = a(-b) = |a| \, |b|$.
   (4) If $a < 0$, $b > 0$, proof similar to (3).

17. $x = |(4 - 9)/12| = |(-5)/12| = \frac{5}{12}$.

19. If $x \geq 0$, $|x| = x$. Since $x \leq m$, $|x| \leq m$. If $x < 0$, $|x| = -x$. But $-m \leq x$, so that, $-x \leq m$, whence, $|x| \leq m$.

Section 1.6

1. (a) 5, -3; (b) 10, -2; (c) 1, $-\frac{2}{3}$.

3. Suppose both u and v are least upper bounds of a set. Then $u \leq v$ and also $v \leq u$, whence, $u = v$. Similarly for greatest lower bounds.

5. The set of negative integers contains its least upper bound -1; the set of positive rational numbers x such that $x^2 < 3$ does not contain its least real upper bound $\sqrt{3}$.

7. Suppose kc is a least upper bound for some integer $k > 0$. But $(k + 1)c = kc + c > kc$, since $c > 0$, and we have a contradiction.

9. Suppose $0 < c < 1$, and $n/(n + 1) \leq c$ for all n. Then $1 - c \leq 1 - n/(n + 1) = 1/(n + 1)$. But $1 - c > 0$, and so $(n + 1)(1 - c) \leq 1$ for all n, in contradiction to Problem 8. Hence, no such c exists.

11. Let $a < b$ for real a, b. By Problem 8, there exists an integer n such that $na > 1$ and $n(b - a) > 1$. Likewise, there exists an integer m such that $m = m(1) > na$ and $m - 1 \leq na$. Then $m/n = m(1/n) > a$, since $1/n > 0$. Also $m/n = [(m - 1) + 1]/n \leq (na + 1)/n = a + 1/n < a + (b - a) = b$. Hence, $a < m/n < b$.

CHAPTER 2

Section 2.1

1. (c), (d), (e).

3. (a), (d).

5. Each element of A is in B, while each element of B is in C, and so each element of A is in C. But each element of C is in D, so that each element of A is in D. Similarly, each element of D is in A, and so A-D.

7. $(A \cap B) \cap C = A \cap (B \cap C)$, so that parentheses are unnecessary.

9. $\emptyset$, $\{a\}$, $\{b\}$, $\{c\}$, $\{a, b\}$, $\{a, c\}$, $\{b, c\}$, $\{a, b, c\}$.

11. (a) For example, the subset of men and the subset of women; (b) for example, the subset of men and the subset of State employees.

13. (a) 2, 3; (b) 1, 2, 3, 4, 5; (c) 2, 3, 4, 5; (d) 2, 3.

15.

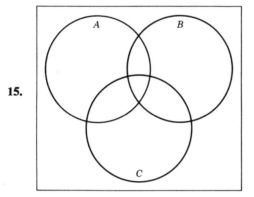

Section 2.2

1. (a) There exists an integer which is divisible by 5; (b) every orange is a fruit; (c) every student who studies hard will pass his examinations; (d) there exists a dog which is dangerous.

3. (a) open; (b) open; (c) a (false) statement; (d) a (true) statement; (e) open; (f) a (true) statement.

5. (a) (1, 1), (1, 2), (2, 1), (2, 2), (3, 1), (3, 2); (b) $(a, 2)$, $(b, 2)$, $(a, 4)$, $(b, 4)$, $(a, 6)$, $(b, 6)$; (c) (1, 3), $(1, x)$, $(1, a)$, $(a, 3)$, (a, x), (a, a), $(c, 3)$, (c, x), (c, a); (d) (1, 2), (1, 3).

7. (a) 50; (b) 25; (c) 100.

9. 16.

11.

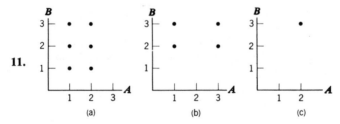

13. The statement is false for any replacement of the variable from the given universe.

15. (a) $\{3, -3\}$; (b) $\emptyset$; (c) $\{2\}$; (d) $\{0, 2, 3\}$; (e) $\{x | x \in R, x < 5\}$; (f) $\{x | x \in R, -2 < x < 2\}$.

Section 2.3

1. (a) Today is warm and it is cloudy; (b) It is cloudy and the air is humid;

(c) Today is warm, it is cloudy, and the air is humid; (d) Today is warm, it is cloudy, and a breeze is blowing.

3. (a) x is an even integer and y is an even integer; (b) The problem can be solved by algebra and the problem can be solved by arithmetic; (c) t is an odd number and t is larger than 10; (d) Mary and I had a date, and Mary and I went to a movie; (e) The room was hot and the room was crowded and no one opened a window; (f) The sum of two integers is 15, and the difference of the two integers is 1.

5. (a) $(2 \; -5 \quad 4)(1 \; 0 \; -2)^{\text{T}} = 2 + 0 - 8 = -6$;
   (b) $(1 \quad 2 \; -3)(1 \; 0 \; -2)^{\text{T}} = 1 + 0 + 6 = 7$;
   (c) $(4 \quad 0 \; -2)(1 \; 0 \; -2)^{\text{T}} = 4 + 0 + 4 = 8$;
   (d) $(0 \quad 0 \; -1)(1 \; 0 \; -2)^{\text{T}} = 0 + 0 + 2 = 2$.

7. For $2x - 3y + z = 10$, we may choose $(1 \; 1 \; 11)^{\text{T}}$ and $(2 \; 1 \; 9)^{\text{T}}$, for example. For $3x + y - 2z = 5$, we may choose $(1 \; 2 \; 0)^{\text{T}}$ and $(2 \; 1 \; 1)^{\text{T}}$. The solution $(1 \; 1 \; 11)$ will also be a solution of the second equation if we replace its right member 5 by -18.

Section 2.4

1. We illustrate with an equation $ax + by = c$, with (x_0, y_0) as a solution. Then $ax_0 + by_0 = c$ and also $kax_0 + kby_0 = kc$, for any real k. Hence, (x_0, y_0) is a solution of $kax + kay = kc$. Moreover, if $k \neq 0$, $kax_0 + kby_0 = kc$ implies that $ax_0 + by_0 = c$, so that any solution of $kax + kby = c$ is also a solution of $ax + by = c$. In like fashion for the other elementary operations.

3. $(x, y) = (-1, 4)$.   5. $(x, y) = (4, 1)$.
7. $(x, y) = (1, 3)$.   9. $(x, y) = (2, -3)$.
11. $(x, y) = (1, 0.1)$.   13. $\frac{4}{3}$ gallons of 20 per cent solution; $\frac{2}{3}$ gallons of 5 per cent solution.

Section 2.5

1. (a) $m = 3$, $n = 4$; (b) 2, 1, 2, 2.   3. (a) 4; (b) -1; (c) -4.
5. By every expansion, $|A| = -22$.   7. -873.
9. (a) $3x^2 - 4xy + 3x + 2y$; (b) $xy^2 - x^2y + yz^2 - y^2z + zx^2 - xz^2$.
11. There are actually six cases to consider, each similar to the following:

$$\begin{vmatrix} ca & b & c \\ cd & e & f \\ cg & h & i \end{vmatrix} = ca(ei - hf) - cd(bi - ch) + cg(bf - ec) =$$

$$c[a(ei - hf) - d(bi - ch) + g(bf - ec)] = c\begin{vmatrix} a & b & c \\ d & e & f \\ g & h & i \end{vmatrix}$$

Section 2.6

1. $(1, -\frac{1}{3}, \frac{4}{3})$.   3. $(-1, 3, 1)$.
5. $(-1, -1, 2)$.   7. $(\frac{1}{2}, -\frac{1}{2}, -1)$.

9. Let us use $\begin{vmatrix} 1 & 5 & 3 \\ 9 & 2 & 6 \\ 4 & 7 & 8 \end{vmatrix}$. (a) $1 \begin{vmatrix} 9 & 2 \\ 4 & 7 \end{vmatrix} - 9 \begin{vmatrix} 1 & 5 \\ 4 & 7 \end{vmatrix} + 4 \begin{vmatrix} 1 & 5 \\ 9 & 2 \end{vmatrix} = 55 + 117 - 172 = 0.$

(b) $9 \begin{vmatrix} 2 & 6 \\ 7 & 8 \end{vmatrix} - 2 \begin{vmatrix} 9 & 6 \\ 4 & 8 \end{vmatrix} + 6 \begin{vmatrix} 9 & 2 \\ 4 & 7 \end{vmatrix} = 0.$

11. For y: Multiply equations by A_{12}, A_{22}, A_{32}, respectively. For z: Multiply equations by A_{13}, A_{23}, A_{33}, respectively.

13. $\begin{vmatrix} a & 0 & 3 \\ 0 & b & -2 \\ 1 & 0 & c \end{vmatrix} \neq 0$, i.e., $abc \neq 3b.$

Section 2.7

1. $\begin{bmatrix} 1 & 0 & 0 \\ 0 & 1 & 0 \\ 0 & 0 & 1 \end{bmatrix}$ **3.** $\begin{bmatrix} 17 & 0 & 0 & 43 \\ 0 & 1 & 0 & -2 \\ 0 & 0 & 17 & -6 \end{bmatrix}$ **5.** $\begin{bmatrix} 1 & 0 & 0 & 0 \\ 0 & 1 & 0 & 0 \\ 0 & 0 & 1 & 0 \\ 0 & 0 & 0 & 1 \end{bmatrix}$

7. $\begin{bmatrix} 1 & 0 & 0 & 17 & -39 \\ 0 & 5 & 0 & -36 & 83 \\ 0 & 0 & 1 & -2 & 5 \end{bmatrix}$ **9.** $\begin{bmatrix} 1 & 0 & 0 & 0 \\ 0 & 1 & 0 & 0 \\ 0 & 0 & 1 & 0 \\ 0 & 0 & 0 & 1 \end{bmatrix}$

Section 2.8

1. (a) $(x\ y\ z) = (\frac{5}{2}\ -\frac{6}{5}\ \frac{1}{4})$; (b) $(x\ y\ z) = (-\ \frac{3}{4}\ \frac{5}{2}\ -1).$

3. (a) $(x\ y\ z) = (-9\ 0\ 13)$; (b) $(x\ y\ z) = (-1\ -4\ 0) - k(2\ 1\ -1)$; (c) $(x\ y\ z\ w) = (-\frac{5}{2}\ 0\ -8\ \frac{7}{4}) + k(0\ 1\ 5\ 0).$

5. $(x\ y\ z) = (-29\ 1\ 24).$ **7.** $(x\ y\ z) = (-1\ 1\ 0).$

9. $(x\ y\ z) = (\frac{39}{32}\ -\frac{15}{16}\ -\frac{19}{32}).$

11. The system $\begin{matrix} 2x + 3y + z = 5 \\ 2x + 3y + z = 7 \end{matrix}$ has no solution.

13. No.

Section 2.9

1. $(3, 3), (-3, -3), (3, -3), (-3, 3).$ **3.** $(-2, 6), (4, -3).$

5. $(-3, 2), (3, -2), (\sqrt{2}, 1/\sqrt{2}), (-\sqrt{2}, -1/\sqrt{2}).$ **7.** $(0, 0).$ **9.** 6 in. by 9 in.

11. $a = 1, b = \frac{25}{3} = 8\frac{1}{3}, c = \frac{47}{3} = 15\frac{2}{3}.$

CHAPTER 3

Section 3.1

1. $x < \frac{7}{2}.$ **3.** $x \geq \frac{7}{4}.$ **5.** (a) $\{-8, -7, -6, -5, -4, -3, -2, -1, 0\}$; (b) $[-8, 0].$

7. No real solutions.   **9.** $-1 \leq x < 43.$

11. (a) 1; (b) $1 - \sqrt{2}/2 \le x \le 1 + \sqrt{2}/2$.   **13.** No real solutions.
15. $x > 1$; $x < \frac{1}{3}$.   **17.** No real solutions.   **19.** $-\frac{1}{3} < x < \frac{5}{9}$.
21. $x < 0$ or $x > 1/(1 + k)$.

Section 3.2

1. $-\frac{3}{2} < x < \frac{1}{2}$.   **3.** $x < \frac{2}{3}$ or $x > 2$.
5. $x \ge -1$ or $x < -3$.   **7.** $2 < x < 3$.
9. $x < -5$ or $-1 < x < 2$.   **11.** $x < 0$.
13. $x < -1$ or $1 < x < 2$.   **15.** $x < -1$ or $0 < x < 1$.
17. If $ab > 0$ and $bc > 0$, then $1/c < 1/b < 1/a$; if $ab < 0$ and $bc < 0$, then $1/a < 1/b < 1/c$.
19. $x = 0$ or $x \le -\frac{1}{2}$.

Section 3.3

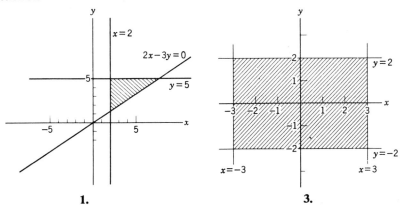

1.   **3.**

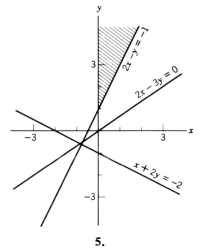

5.

7. Any two points in an intersection of sets also lie within each of the sets.

9. Since a half plane is a convex set (Problem 8), and any intersection of convex sets is convex (Problem 7), the intersection of any number of half planes is a convex set.

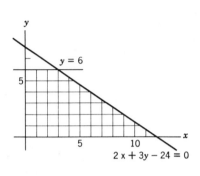

11.

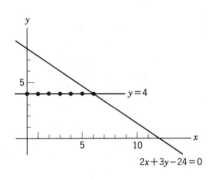

13.

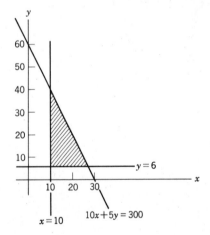

15.

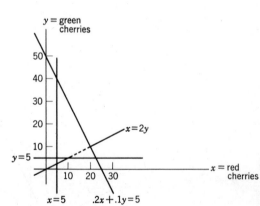

17.

19. (a) The half plane lying above the graph of $2x - 3y + 2 = 0$.
    (b) The half plane lying below the graph of $3x - 2y = 7$.
    (c) The half plane lying below the graph of $x + 3y = -3$.
    (d) The half plane lying above the graph of $2x + 5y = 8$.

Section 3.4

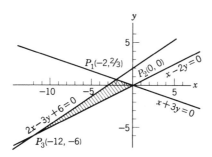

1. (a) 0, -6; (b) 0, -24; (c) 0, -30; (d) 0, -30. [See accompanying figure.]
3. (a) $\frac{93}{2}$, 8; (b) 15, -27; (c) -6, -16.
5. 600 gals gasoline; 200 gals fuel oil.
7. $x = 4$, $y = 2$.
9. 12 tables and 36 chairs per five-day week.
11. 1 of item A and 2 of item B.

CHAPTER 4

Section 4.1

1. A function is defined where the store articles comprise the domain and the prices the range, because each article has a well-defined price at any given time. No function is defined in the case of the telephone numbers and subscribers, for neither is uniquely determined by the other in every case.
3. (a) $F(2) = 0$; $F(3) = 1$;   (b) Domain is $\{1, 2, 3, 4, 5\}$ and range is $(-1, 0, 1, 2, 3\}$.
5. (a) $f(2) = 5$; $f(3) = 10$; $f(6) = 37$; (b) -15; (c) 19.
7. (a) All real $x \neq 1$, -1; (b) $F(0) = 0$; $F(-2) = -\frac{4}{3}$.
9. The set of all nonnegative integers.

Section 4.2

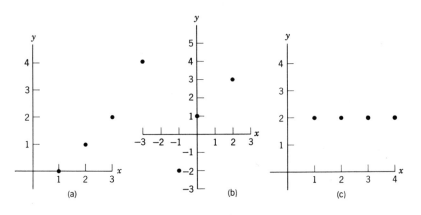

1.

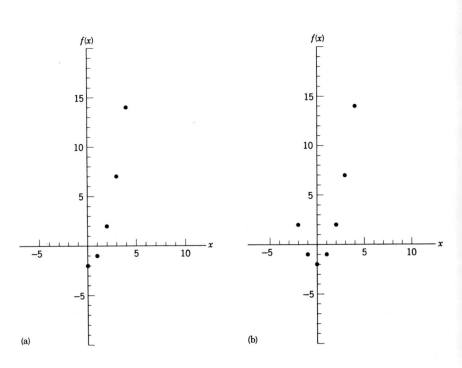

3.

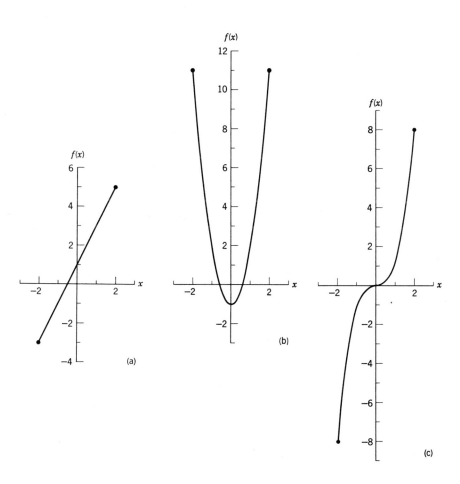

5.

7. $f(x) = 1$, if x is rational;
$= 0$, if x is irrational.
No satisfactory graph of this function could be constructed.

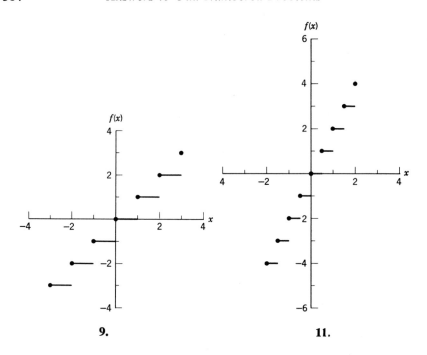

9.   11.

Section 4.3

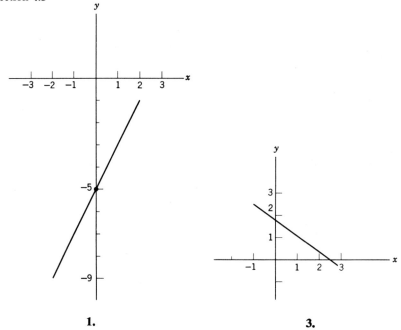

1.   3.

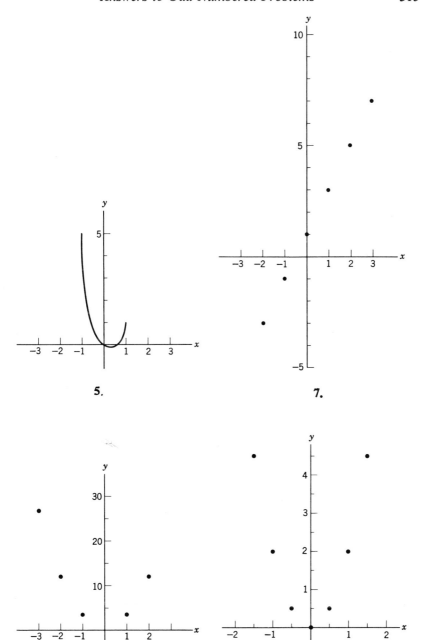

5.

7.

9.

11.

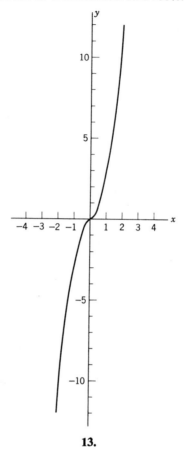

13.

Section 4.4

1. No. Two zero functions with different domains are not the same, because the two sets of ordered pairs characterizing the functions are not identical.

3. *Addition.*   Let $x \in D$.   Then $(f + g)(x) = f(x) + g(x) = g(x) + f(x) = (g + f)(x)$, so that, $f + g = g + f$. *Multiplication.*   Same proof as for addition, with multiplication replacing addition.

5. $(f + g)(x) = 3x^2 + 2x + 8.$ **7.** $(f/g)(x) = (3x^2 + 1)/(2x + 7).$

9. $(1/g)(x) = 1/(2x + 7).$ **11.** $(f + g)(x) = \dfrac{(3x^3 - 6x^2 + 3x - 2)}{x(x - 2)}, \quad x \neq 0, 2.$

13. $(f + g)(x) = 2/x + 2/[(x - 1)(x + 1)], \qquad x \neq 1, -1, 0$
$\qquad\qquad\qquad\qquad\qquad\qquad\qquad\quad = 25, x = 1.$

15. $(f - g)(x) = (x^2 - 5x + 5)/[(x - 1)(x - 2)^2], \qquad x \neq 1, 2;$
$\quad (f/g)(x) = (x - 2)^2/(x - 1), \quad x \neq 1, 2.$

17. $(f \cdot g)(x) = 2[x], \qquad x \in [0, 5]; \; (f - g)(x) = 2 - [x], \qquad x \in [0, 5].$

19. $(f/g)(x) = |x|/x, x \in [-3, 0) \cup (0, 3].$

21. $(g - f)(x) = 1 - 1 = 0, \qquad x \in A$
$\qquad\qquad\quad = 1 - 0 = 1, \qquad x \in A'.$
Hence, $g - f$ is the characteristic function of A'.

23.

x	$2f(x)$	$(3f + 2g)(x)$	$4f^2(x)$	$(2f + 3g - 1)(x)$	$(4g^2 + 3f - 2)(x)$
-1	4	12	16	12	40
0	-2	-9	4	-12	31
1	10	27	100	27	157

Section 4.5

1. Assume $f(x) = y$, so that $f^{-1}(y) = x$. Then, $(ff^{-1})(y) = f[f^{-1}(y)] = f(x) = y$; and also $(f^{-1}f)(x) = f^{-1}[f(x)] = f^{-1}(y) = x$. Hence, $ff^{-1} = I$ and $f^{-1}f = I$. The equality is not strictly accurate, because the domains of ff^{-1} and $f^{-1}f$ are, in general, different.

3. $(fg)(x) = 9x^3 - 2$; $(gf)(x) = 3(3x - 2)^3$.

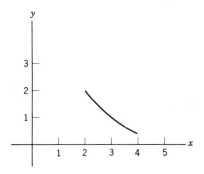

5. $(gf)(x) = 6/x - 1, x \in [2, 4]$; No. [See accompanying figure.]

7. (a) Yes; (b) No; (c) No; (d) Yes.

9. For example, the function f defined on $[-3, -2] \cup [2, 3]$ such that $f(x) = 2x$, for $x \in [-3, -2]$, and $f(x) = -2x$, for $x \in [2, 3]$.

11. $(f\ f)(x) = x^4 + 2x^2 + 1$; $(ff)(x) = x^4 + 2x^2 + 2$.

13. $(fg)\ (x) = |[x]| = (gf)\ (x)$, for $x \geq 0$ or x a negative integer; otherwise $(fg)\ (x) = (gf)\ (x) + 1$.

15. The single-point intersection guarantees that there is a one-to-one correspondence between the domain and the range, and so the inverse exists. It would not be appropriate to use the word "precisely," because the domain of the function is not required to be R.

17. $f^{-1}(x) = (x + 2)/3$, for each $x \in [-8, 7]$.

19. Define f so that $f(x) = x^2$, for each $x \geq 0$. There are many such functions.

21. Let $f(x) = b$ and $g(x) = c$. Then, if $b - c$, the common solution set is D; if $b \neq c$, the common solution set is $\emptyset$.

CHAPTER 5

Section 5.1

1. (a) 16; (b) $-2\sqrt[3]{2}$; (c) 3; (d) 64; (e) 4.   **3.** (a) $\sqrt[5]{2^{16}}$; (b) $\sqrt[25]{3^{38}}$; (c) $\sqrt[50]{5^{107}}$;
(d) $\sqrt[2500]{1000}$.   **5.** (a) $(2x)^{1/2}\,3^{1/3}x$; (b) $(-2x)^{1/2}$, $3^{1/3}x$.   **7.** (a) a^5b^8; (b) a^3; (c) 2^53^7;
(d) xy^4; (e) $xy/(x + y)$.   **9.** (a) $a^{-1}bc^{-1}/1$; (b) $2^{-1}3x^{-3}/1$; (c) $(x^{-1} + 2y^{-1})/1$.
11. (a) $1/\sqrt[30]{x^{41}}$; (b) $\sqrt[6]{108a^{11}b^7}$; (c) $\sqrt[12]{\tfrac{512}{3}x^{11}y^6}$; (d) $\sqrt[8]{3^7}$.   **13.** $6, -4$.

Section 5.2

1. The graph of the function defined on R by $y = b^x$ is intersected at some point
by the horizontal line $y = a$. The abscissa of this point is the desired solution $x = k$.
3. (a) 1.73, 3 14; (b) 1.732, 3.141; (c) 1.7320, 3.1416.
5. (a) 4.7; (b) 31.6; (c) 1.4. [See accompanying figure.]

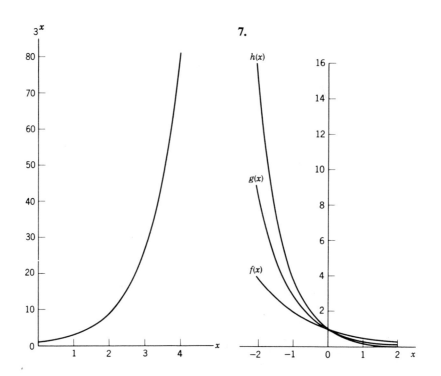

9. $a = 3$, $c = 2$.   **11.** 3 years.   **13.** No. $f(x_1 + x_2) = ca^{x_1 + x_2} \neq f(x_1) \cdot f(x_2)$.
15. $3^{2-x} = 3^2 \cdot 3^{-x} = 9(\tfrac{1}{3})^x$; i.e., $c = 9$, $a = \tfrac{1}{3}$, $k = 1$. [Or, if preferred, $3^{2-x}) =$
$9(3^{-x})$; i.e., $c = 9$, $a = 3$, $k = -1$.]

Section 5.3

1. (a) $\log_2 16 = 4$; (b) $\log_{10} 1000 = 3$; (c) $\log_{10} 1 = 0$; (d) $\log_3 27 = 3$; (e) $\log_{25} 5$ = $\frac{1}{2}$. **3.** (a) $\log_x 12 = 5$; (b) $\log_5 7 = x$; (c) $\log_6 x = 7$; (d) $\log_{10} 55 = x$. **5.** (a) 9; (b) $\sqrt[3]{16}$; (c) $\sqrt[4]{32}$; (d) $\frac{3}{2}$; (e) $\frac{1}{2}$. **7.** (a) 1.3; (b) 1.6; (c) 1.8. **9.** (a) 7; (b) 3; (c) -2; (d) Any $x > 0$ (since logs were not defined for $x \leq 0$); (e) Any $x > 0$. **11.** (a) 0.6; (b) 1.4; (c) 1.9. [See accompanying figure.] **13.** (a) 3; (b) 2.

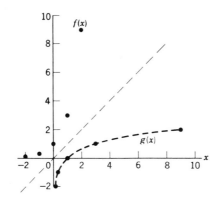

[The above graph also provides the answers to Problem 10.]

Section 5.4

1. Let $MN = Q$, so that $\log_a MNP = \log_a QP = \log_a Q + \log_a P = \log_a MN + \log_a P = \log_a M + \log_a N + \log_a P$. **3.** (a) 1.792; (b) 2.995; (c) 3.584; (d) 5.010; (e) 1.700; (f) 2.389; (g) 3.250. **5.** (a) 3; (b) 0.307; (c) $\frac{1}{2}$; (d) $\sqrt{a}$. **7.** (a) 4.27; (b) When $b = c$ or $bc = 1$. **9.** $y = cb^{-kt}$. **11.** (a) 0; (b) 0.01; (c) $\frac{1}{7}$; (d) $\frac{1}{4}$. **13.** $t = \log_e (M_0/M)^{1/\alpha}$. **15.** $x = 2, y = 4$.

Section 5.5

1. (a) 2; (b) -4; (c) 4; (d) -3. **3.** (a) 2.5465; (b) 0.5465 $- 2$; (c) 0.5465; (d) 5.5465; (e) 0.5465 $- 4$. **5.** (a) 401; (b) 0.0455; (c) 5.21; (d) 0.00701; (e) 591. **7.** (a) 0.00592; (b) 0.000732; (c) 0.0696; (d) 0.0000353; (e) 0.348. **9.** (a) 352; (b) 29.6; (c) 0.00546; (d) 0.000208. **11.** (a) 44.8; (b) 0.00249; (c) 646; (d) 0.0554. **13.** $10^{0.8068}$.

Section 5.6

1. $10^{0.5490} = 3.54$; (b) $10^{0.7143} = 5.18$; (c) $10^{0.9253} = 8.42$. **3.** (a) $10^{-2.9101}$ = 0.00123; (b) $10^{-1.2351} = 0.0582$; (c) $10^{-3.6383} = 0.00023$. **5.** (a) 803; (b) 35170; (c) 0.00568. **7.** (a) 351.6; (b) 0.2828; (c) 4.790. **9.** 9.60. **11.** 0.479. **13.** -26.0. **15.** 1.78 in.

Section 5.7

1. (a) 0.683; (b) -0.281; (c) -0.292; (d) -0.693. **3.** (a) -0.369; (b) -0.0693; (c) -0.843; (d) 1.61. **5.** (a) $e^{1.238} = 3.45$; (b) $e^{-0.844} = 0.43$; (c) $e^{2.595} = 13.4$; (d) $e^{-6.46} = 0.00156$. **7.** (a) 0.450; (b) 10002. **9.** The equation would require $(5x - 1)/(2x - 1) = 2$, and so $5x - 1 = 4x - 2$, whence $x = -1$. But $\log(-6)$ and $\log(-3)$ are not defined! **11.** 12.6, i.e., 13. **13.** (a) $(1 \pm 3\sqrt{89})/4$; (b) $(5 \pm 5\sqrt{5})/2$. **15.** \$35,500. **17.** (a) $-2, -1, 0, 1, 2, 3, 4$; (b) 4; (c) 1, 2, 3, 4. **19.** $x > \frac{1}{9}$. **21.** No. (Equation leads to $\log^2 \alpha = -1$, which is impossible.)

CHAPTER 6

Section 6.1

1. (a) 0.58; (b) 2.3; (c) 1.2; (d) 10.4. **3.** (a) $\sin 25°46'$; (b) $\csc 3°30'$; (c) $\sec 15°7'$; (d) $\tan 6°5'$; (e) $\cot 1°5'$. **5.** (a) $\cos 24°$; (b) $\sin 35°10'$; (c) $\cot 52°15'$; (d) $\tan 50°$. **7.** 67 ft. **9.** 3700 ft. **11.** 1.02 in. **13.** 164 ft. **15.** No.

Section 6.2

1. For example, consider $\triangle OPN$ and $\triangle ONS$: $\overline{OP} = \overline{OS}$, ON is common, and $\angle PON = \angle SON$. The triangles then have two sides and the included angle respectively equal, and are congruent by a well-known theorem of geometry. **3.** (a) $+$; (b) $-$. **5.** (a) $-12°, 168°, -168°$; (b) $-63°, 117°, -117°$; (c) $47°, 133°, -133°$; (d) $-125°, 55°, -55°$; (e) $56°, -56°, 124°$; (f) $-48°, 132°, -132°$. **7.** (a) -0.8018; (b) -0.1262; (c) 0.7590. **9.** (a) 146.76°; (b) 33.24°. **11.** (a) 220.18°; (b) 285.35°; (c) $-111.45°$; (d) $-232.81°$. **13.** Draw figure similar to Figure 36, the "equal" angles being formed with the vertical axis, and prove triangles congruent. **15.** (a) $-\cos 15°40'$; (b) $-\sin 15°15'$; (c) $\cot 30°45'$; (d) $-\tan 10°$. **17.** (a) $\cos A$; (b) $-\sin A$; (c) $-\csc A$; (d) $-\tan A$; (e) $-\cos A$; (f) $-\sec A$. **19.** (a) odd multiples of 90°; (b) odd multiples of 90°; (c) even multiples of 90°.

Section 6.3

1. *Cosecant*: All angles except even multiples of 90°; *secant*: All angles except odd multiples of 90°; *cotangent*: All angles except even multiples of 90°. **3.** (a) $\sqrt{3}/2$, $-\sqrt{3}/2$; (b) $1/\sqrt{3}$, $2\sqrt{3}/3$; (c) $\sqrt{3}/2$, $\sqrt{3}$; (d) $\sqrt{3}/2$, $\frac{1}{4}$. **5.** (a) $(-1, 0)$; (b) $(0, 1)$; (c) $(0, 1)$; (d) $(0, 1)$; (e) $(0, -1)$; (f) $(-1, 0)$. **7.** 1.732. **9.** $2/(1 + 2\sqrt{3})$. **11.** 45°, 315°. **13.** 135°, 315°. **15.** 60°, 240°. **17.** 45°, 135°, 225°, 315°. **19.** $-90°$. **21.** $-150°$. **23.** (a) $\sqrt{3}/2 = 2(\frac{1}{2})(\sqrt{3}/2)$; (b) $-\sqrt{3} = 2(\sqrt{3})/[1 - 3]$; (c) $1 = (\sqrt{3}/2)$ $(\sqrt{3}/2) - (-\frac{1}{2})(\frac{1}{2})$; (d) $0 = (\sqrt{3}/2)(\frac{1}{2}) - (\frac{1}{2})(\sqrt{3}/2)$; (e) $-\frac{1}{2} = \frac{1}{4} - \frac{3}{4}$. **25.** 0.8495 -1, 0.30103. **27.** 270°.

Section 6.4

1. $-2\sqrt{13}/13,\ -\sqrt{13}/3.$ **3.** $\sqrt{7}/3,\ -4\sqrt{7}/7.$ **5.** $-7\sqrt{58}/58,\ 3\sqrt{58}/58,$ $-3/7.$ **7.** (1): Even multiples of $90°$; (2): Odd multiples of $90°$; (3): Even multiples of $90°$; (4): Odd multiples of $90°$. **9.** $\frac{145}{48},\ -\frac{55}{48}.$ **11.** $\sqrt{13}(2\sqrt{5}-6)/39.$

Section 6.5

3. (a) $\sqrt{13}$; (b) $\sqrt{37}$; (c) $4\sqrt{2}.$ **5.** (a) $c = 21,\ A = 27°,\ B = 113°$; (b) $a = 3.6,$ $B = 30.8°,\ C = 120.4°$; (c) $b = 37.2,\ A = 24.5°,\ B = 69.6°.$ **7.** 20.5 miles. **9.** 8.7 miles. **13.** $48.2°, 58.4°, 73.4°.$ **15.** $a^2 = b^2 + c^2 - 2bc\cos A = b^2 + b^2 - 2b^2$ $\cos A = 2b^2(1 - \cos A).$ **17.** Either $b\sin C$ or $a\sin C$ may be taken as an altitude of the triangle, and use Area = Base X Altitude. **19.** 3,600 ft.

Section 6.6

1. $|BP_1| < |C_3D| + |BD_3|,\ |P_1P_2| < |C_2C_3| + |D_2D_3|,\ |P_2P_3| < |C_1C_2| + |D_1D_2|,$ $|P_3C| < |CC_1| + |D_1D|.$ Hence, $|S| < |BD| + |CD|.$ **3.** (a) $25.7°$; (b) $120°$; (c) $240°$; (d) $-150°$; (e) $154.3°.$ **5.** (a) 0.59^r; (b) 2.83^r; (c) 0.46^r; (d) 0.62^r; (e) -1.26^r; (f) $2.32^r.$ **7.** 2.2 in. **9.** (a) 0.2412; (b) 0.13521; (c) -1.886; (d) 0.03674; (e) -0.5610; (f) $1.5574.$ **11.** (a) 5.24 in.; (b) 7.51 in.; (c) 12.85 in. **13.** 11,700 miles. **15.** (a) $1 + \sqrt{3}$; (b) $2\sqrt{3} + 3\sqrt{2}$; (c) $-\dfrac{2\sqrt{3}+3}{3}$; (d) $(1 + \sqrt{3})/2.$

CHAPTER 7

Section 7.1

1. (a) $(-\frac{1}{2}, -\sqrt{3}/2)$; (b) $(-\sqrt{2}/2), \sqrt{2}/2)$; (c) $(-\sqrt{3}/2, \frac{1}{2})$; (d) $(-\sqrt{3}/2, -\frac{1}{2}).$ **3.** (a) $(-0.4162, 0.9093)$; (b) $(-0.9900, -0.1410)$; (c) $(0.9602, -0.2795)$; (d) $(0.9602, 0.2795)$; (e) $(0.5403, 0.8415).$ **5.** (a) 0.91; (b) -0.41; (c) 0.16; (d) -0.97; (e) -0.94; (f) $0.28.$ **7.** $0.84, 0.54, 1.56.$ **9.** (a) IV; (b) II; (c) I; (d) I. **11.** All real numbers; All real numbers; All real numbers except odd multiples of $\pi/2$. **13.** (a) 0.5985; (b) -0.8968; (c) -1.5013; (d) 0.8547; (e) $0.5261.$ **15.** $144\pi\sin 24\pi t.$ (Consider the diameter as the x-axis.) **17.** $\sqrt{36 - \sin^2 2\pi T} + \cos 2\pi T.$ **19.** (a) $180/\pi$; (b) $(\pi - 2)(180)/\pi$; (c) $(\pi - 2.5)(180)/\pi$; (d) $-270/\pi$; (e) $(\pi - 4)(180)/\pi.$ **21.** $\sin \pi/5 = \sqrt{2\sqrt{5} - 2}/2,\ \cos \pi/5 = (\sqrt{5} - 1)/2,\ \tan \pi/5 =$ $[\sqrt{2\sqrt{5} - 2}(\sqrt{5} + 1)]/4,\ \cot \pi/5 = \sqrt{2\sqrt{5} - 2}/2,\ \sec \pi/5 = (\sqrt{5} + 1)/2,\ \csc$ $\pi/5 = [\sqrt{2\sqrt{5} - 2}(\sqrt{5} + 1)]/4 = \sqrt{2\sqrt{5} + 2}/2.$

Section 7.2

1. (a) 0.66; (b) -0.80; (c) 1.57; (d) $0.43.$ **3.** Consider the positions of points on the graphs corresponding to $-\theta$, as compared with θ. **5.** (a) increasing; (b) neither; (c) neither; (d) increasing; (e) neither. **7.** None. **9.** sine, cosecant, tangent, cotangent. **11.** $\theta = PM$ and $\tan\theta = AM$, and it is intuitively evident that $AM > PM.$

Section 7.3

1. Sin 2, Tan $2\pi/3$, Cos (-1.3). **3.** (a) $-\pi/3$; (b) $-\pi/4$; (c) π; (d) $\pi/4$. **5.** Arcsin $(\sin \pi) = 0 \neq \pi$; however, sin (Arcsin x) $= x$ by definition of sine and Arcsine. **7.** (a) $\sqrt{5}/3$; (b) $3\sqrt{10}/10$; (c) -0.5708; (d) $4\sqrt{7}/7$. **9.** $\pi/6 + (-\pi/2) + \pi/3 = 0$. **11.** Let $y =$ Arccos x. Then, Arcsin $x = \pi/2 - y$, and sin (Arccos x) $= \sin y = \cos (\pi/2 - y) = \cos$ (Arcsin x). (Consider both $x > 0$ and $x < 0$ for complete argument.) **13.** (a) 0.9600; (b) -0.7383. **15.** 1.

Section 7.4

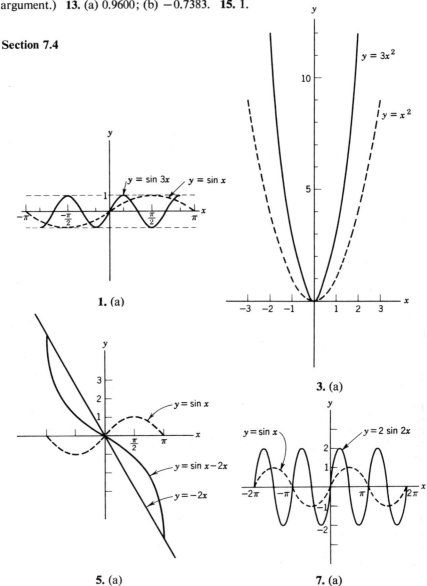

1. (a)

3. (a)

5. (a)

7. (a)

9. (a) 3, π, $.3/2$; (b) $\frac{1}{2}$, 2π, -2; (c) 3, 4π, $-\frac{3}{4}$; (d) 2, 2, $-2/\pi$. **11.** (a) No; (b) Yes (c) No; (d) Yes, π; (e) No.

13. $(e^2 + 1)/2e$, 2π. [See accompanying figure.]

15. $\alpha = \alpha' = \frac{1}{3}$, $\beta = 3\beta' = -5$.

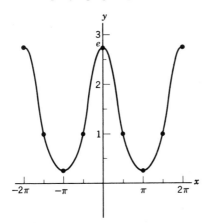

Section 7.5

1. $\cos(-\theta) = \cos(0 - \theta) = \cos 0 \cos \theta + \sin 0 \sin \theta = \cos \theta$. **3.** $\tan(\theta_1 + \theta_2) = \sin(\theta_1 + \theta_2)/\cos(\theta_1 + \theta_2) = [\sin \theta_1 \cos \theta_2 + \cos \theta_1 \sin \theta_2]/[\cos \theta_1 \cos \theta_2 - \sin \theta_1 \sin \theta_2] = [\tan \theta_1 + \tan \theta_2]/[1 - \tan \theta_1 \tan \theta_2]$. Similarly, for $\tan(\theta_1 - \theta_2)$. **5.** (a) $\tan(\theta + \pi/4) - \tan(\theta - 3\pi/4) = \dfrac{\tan \theta + \tan \pi/4}{1 - \tan \theta \tan \pi/4} - \dfrac{\tan \theta - \tan 3\pi/4}{1 + \tan \theta \tan 3\pi/4} = \dfrac{\tan \theta + 1}{1 - \tan \theta}$

$- \dfrac{\tan \theta + 1}{1 - \tan \theta} = 0$; (b) $\tan(\pi/4 + \theta) = \dfrac{\tan \pi/4 + \tan \theta}{1 - \tan \pi/4 \tan \theta} = \dfrac{1 + \tan \theta}{1 - \tan \theta}$. **7.** (a) $\sin(\pi + \theta) = \sin \pi \cos \theta + \cos \pi \sin \theta = -\sin \theta$; (b) $\cos(\pi - \theta) = \cos \pi \cos \theta + \sin \pi \cos \theta = -\cos \theta$; (c) $\tan(\theta - \pi) = \dfrac{\tan \theta + \tan \pi}{1 - \tan \theta \tan \pi} = \tan \theta$; (d) $\tan(\theta + \pi)$

$= \dfrac{\tan \theta + \tan \pi}{1 - \tan \theta \tan \pi} = \tan \theta$. **9.** (a) $\sec(\pi/2 + \theta) = 1/\cos(\pi/2 + \theta) = 1/(-\sin \theta)$

$= -\csc \theta$; (b) $\csc(\pi/2 + \theta) = 1/\sin(\pi/2 + \theta) = 1/(-\cos \theta) = -\sec \theta$; (c) $\cot(\theta - 3\pi/2) = \dfrac{\cos(\theta - 3\pi/2)}{\sin(\theta - 3\pi/2)} = \dfrac{\cos \theta \cos 3\pi/2 + \sin \theta \sin 3\pi/2}{\sin \theta \cos 3\pi/2 - \cos \theta \sin 3\pi/2} = \dfrac{-\sin \theta}{\cos \theta} = -\tan \theta$.

11. $\sin(\theta_1 + \theta_2) = \sin \theta_1 \cos \theta_2 + \cos \theta_1 \sin \theta_2$, $\sin(\theta_1 - \theta_2) = \sin \theta_1 \cos \theta_2 - \cos \theta_1 \sin \theta_2$. On addition, $\sin(\theta_1 + \theta_2) + \sin(\theta_1 - \theta_2) = 2 \sin \theta_1 \cos \theta_2$, so that $\sin \theta_1 \cos \theta_2 = [\sin(\theta_1 + \theta_2) + \sin(\theta_1 - \theta_2)]/2$.

13. (a) $\theta_1 = (\alpha + \beta)/2$ and $\theta_2 = (\alpha - \beta)/2$. Hence, by Problem 11, $\sin \alpha + \sin \beta = 2 \sin(\alpha + \beta)/2 \cos(\alpha + \beta)/2$; (b) By Problem 11, $\sin \theta_2 \cos \theta_1 = [\sin(\theta_1 + \theta_2) + \sin(\theta_2 - \theta_1)]/2 = [\sin(\theta_1 + \theta_2) - \sin(\theta_1 - \theta_2)]/2$. Hence, as in (a), $\sin \alpha - \sin \beta = 2 \cos(\alpha + \beta)/2 \sin(\alpha - \beta)/2$. **15.** (a) $(\sqrt{3} \cos \theta + \sin \theta)/2$; (b) $(\sqrt{3} \cos \theta + \sin \theta)/2$; (c) $(\tan \theta - \sqrt{3})/1 + \sqrt{3} \tan \theta$; (d) $\sqrt{2}/(\sin \theta - \cos \theta)$; (e) $2/(\sqrt{3} \cos \theta$

$- \sin \theta$).   **17.** (a) $-2(1 + \sqrt{10})/9$, $(\sqrt{5} - \sqrt{10})/9$; (b) $-(4\sqrt{3} + 3)/10$, $(4 - 3\sqrt{3})/10$. **19.** (a) $2 \sin \pi/2 \cos \pi/6$; (b) $- 2 \sin \pi/4 \sin \pi/12$; (c) $2 \cos 13\pi/4$ $\sin 5\pi/24$; (d) $2 \cos \pi/2 \cos \pi/6$. **21.** For example, if $s = t = \frac{1}{2}$, Arcsin s + Arccos $t =$ $\pi/6 + \pi/6 = \pi/3$, while Arcsin $1 = \pi/2$. **23.** Arctan $\frac{1}{2}$ + Arctan $\frac{1}{3} = 0.4636 + 0.3217$ $= 0.7854 = \pi/4$.   Or, better, tan [Arctan $\frac{1}{2}$ + Arctan $\frac{1}{3}$] $= (\frac{1}{2} + \frac{1}{3})/(1 - \frac{1}{6}) =$ $(\frac{5}{6})/(\frac{5}{6}) = 1 = \tan \pi/4$.   **25.** Apply (17), noting that tan (Arctan a) $= a$ and tan (Arctan b) $= b$.   **27.** (a) $y = 2 \sin x$; (b) $y = 3 \sin (2x + \pi - 3)$; (c) $y = 3 \sin$ $(\pi - 3x)$; (d) $y = 4 \sin (\pi/2 - 2x)$.   **29.** $A \sin ax + B \cos ax = A/[\sqrt{A^2 + B^2}]$ $\sin ax + B/[\sqrt{A^2 + B^2}] \cos ax = C(\sin ax \cos b + \cos ax \sin b)$, where $C =$ $\sqrt{A^2 + B^2}$, $\cos b = A/\sqrt{A^2 + B^2}$, $\sin b = B/\sqrt{A^2 + B^2}$.

Section 7.6

1. $\sin \pi/8 = (\sqrt{2 - \sqrt{2}})/2$, $\cos \pi/8 = (\sqrt{2 + \sqrt{2}})/2$, $\tan \pi/8 = \sqrt{2} - 1$, $\csc \pi/8$ $= (2 + \sqrt{2})\sqrt{2 - \sqrt{2}}$, $\sec \pi/8 = (2 - \sqrt{2})\sqrt{2 + \sqrt{2}}$, $\cot \pi/8 = \sqrt{2} + 1$. **3.** Use "Half Angle" formulas. For example, $\sin \pi/2 = (\sqrt{1 - \cos \pi})/2 = 1$, etc. **5.** (a) 0.5154; (b) -0.9900; (c) -2.438.   **7.** (a) $\cos \theta$; (b) $1 - \cos \theta$; (c) (sin $2\theta)/2$; (d) $\tan \theta$; (e) $\sec 2\theta$; (f) $\cos \theta$.   **9.** $|\sin t + \cos t| = \sqrt{(\sin t + \cos t)^2} =$ $\sqrt{\sin^2 t + 2 \sin t \cos t + \cos^2 t} = \sqrt{1 + \sin 2t}$.   **11.** $(\cos \theta + \sin \theta)/(\cos \theta - \sin \theta)$. **13.** Not an identity. For example, if $\theta = \pi/8$, $\tan 2\theta = 1$ while $(1 + \cos 2\theta)/\sin 2\theta =$ $1 + \sqrt{2}$. **15.** Not an identity. For example, if $t = \pi/6$, $\cos 3t = 0$ while $3 \sin t -$ $4 \sin^3 t = 3(\frac{1}{2}) - 4(\frac{1}{8}) = \frac{3}{2} - \frac{1}{2} = 1$. **17.** Identity. **19.** Identity. **21.** Identity. **23.** Identity. **25.** $\cos (\theta - \theta/2) = \cos \theta \cos \theta/2 + \sin \theta \sin \theta/2 = \cos \theta \cos \theta/2 + 2 \sin \theta/2$ $\cos \theta/2 \sin \theta/2 = \cos \theta \cos \theta/2 + 2 \sin^2 \theta/2 \cos \theta$. If $\cos \theta = 0$, (23) is clearly true, hence assume $\cos \theta \neq 0$ and divide by it. Then $\cos \theta + 2(1 - \cos^2\theta/2) = 1$, and solve for $\cos \theta/2$. **27.** $A \sin x + B \cos x = \sqrt{A^2 + B^2} [(A \sin x)/\sqrt{A^2 + B^2} +$ $(B \cos x)/\sqrt{A^2 + B^2}] = \sqrt{A^2 + B^2} \sin (x + \alpha)$, where $\sin \alpha = B/\sqrt{A^2 + B^2}$ and $\cos \alpha = A/\sqrt{A^2 + B^2}$. **29.** $\sqrt{17} \cos (2\theta + 0.24)$.

Section 7.7

1. $\pi/2, \pi, 3\pi/2$.   **3.** $0°, 60°, 180°, 300°, 360°$.   **5.** No solution.   **7.** $\pi/8, 5\pi/8, 9\pi/8$, $13\pi/8$.   **9.** $-$ Arccos $\frac{2}{3}$ (i.e., -0.84), Arccos $\frac{2}{3}$ (i.e., 0.84).   **11.** $\pi/6, \pi/4, 3\pi/4, 5\pi/6$. **13.** $315°$.   **15.** $r = \frac{1}{2}, \theta = \pi/3; r = \frac{1}{2}, \theta = 5\pi/3$.   **17.** (a) $\pi/3, 5\pi/3$; (b) π.   **19.** 0.0523, 0.999.   **21.** 0.052336, 0.998630.   **23.** From (1) obtain $\cos \theta < (\sin \theta)/\theta < 1$, and then use (2) to get $\theta - \theta^3/2 < \sin \theta < \theta$.   **25.** (a) 0; (b) $\sqrt{3} - 1$; (c) $(2 \pm \sqrt{2})/2$.

CHAPTER 8

Section 8.1

1. $[(a, b) + (c, d)] + (e, f) = (a + c, b + d) + (e, f) = ((a + c) + e, (b + d) + f)$ $= (a + (c + e), b + (d + f)) = (a, b) + (c + e, d + f) = (a, b) + [(c, d) + (e, f)]$. **3.** $(a, b) (c, d) = (ac - bd, bc + ad) = (ca - db, cb + da) = (c, d) (a, b)$.   **5.** (a, b)

$(1, 0) = (a, b) = (1, 0) (a, b)$. **7.** (a) $(6, -8)$; (b) $(23, 2)$; (c) $(-7, -4)$; (d) $(22, 3)$.
9. (a) $(-\frac{1}{2}, 0)$; (b) $(\frac{7}{13}, \frac{22}{13})$; (c) $(\frac{1}{13}, -\frac{8}{13})$; (d) $(-\frac{18}{17}, -\frac{13}{17})$. **11.** $(ac + bd)/(c^2 + d^2)$,
$(bc - ad)/(c^2 + d^2)$. **13.** $(0, 1)^2 = (0, 1) (0, 1) = (0, -1)$. Since $(0, -1)$ may be
identified with -1, $(0, 1)$ is a solution of the equation $x^2 = -1$. **15.** $(\frac{1}{2}, \frac{1}{2})$.
17. $(4, -7)$.

Section 8.2

1. (a) $-3 + 5i$; (b) $3 - 2i$; (c) $2 + 6i$; (d) i; (e) 0; (f) $-1 - i$. **3.** (a) $11 - 16i$;
(b) $20 - 20i$; (c) $-23 + 9i$; (d) $-10 + 5i$; (e) -24; (f) $12i$. **5.** (a) $-26 - 13i$;
(b) $-\frac{64}{5} + 83i/5$; (c) $\frac{3}{5} - 2i/5$; (d) $1 - i$. **7.** $(-\frac{1}{2} - \sqrt{3}i/2)^2 (-\frac{1}{2} - \sqrt{3}i/2) =$
$(-\frac{1}{2} + \sqrt{3}i/2) (-\frac{1}{2} - \sqrt{3}i/2) = \frac{1}{4} + \frac{3}{4} = 1$. **9.** (a) $x = -5, y = -3$; (b) $x = \frac{3}{2}$,
$y = -\frac{5}{3}$; (c) $x = 3, y = -\frac{3}{4}$; (d) $x = 1, y = -2$. **11.** $(a + bi) + (a - bi) = 2a$,
which is real: $(a + bi) (a - bi) = a^2 + b^2$, which is real. **13.** $i \neq 0$, by definition
of i; if $i > 0$, then $i^2 > 0$, which contradicts $i^2 = -1 < 0$; if $i < 0$, then $i^2 > 0$,
again in contradiction to $i^2 = -1 < 0$. Hence, this type of ordering is not possible.
15. (a) $(x - 2i) (x + i) = 0, x = 2i, -i$; (b) $(x - 2) (x + 3i) = 0, x = 2, -3i$;
(c) $(x - 1) (x + 1) (x + i) (x - i) = 0, x = 1, -1, i, -i$; (d) $x(x - 3i) (x - 2i)$
$= 0, x = 0, 3i\, 2i$. **17.** $x = \frac{4}{3}, y = \frac{4}{3}; x = -4, y = 4$. **19.** Let $a + bi$ be a solution,
i.e., $2(a + bi)^2 + 5(a + bi) + 11 = 0 = (2a^2 - 2b^2 + 5a + 11) + (4ab + 5b)i$.
On substituting $a - bi$ for x, we obtain $(2a^2 - 2b^2 + 5a + 11) - (4ab + 5b)i = 0$,
since $2a^2 - 2b^2 + 5a + 11 = 0 = 4ab + 5b$. **21.** (a) $2i/3$; (b) $1 + i$; (c) 0;
(d) $\frac{3}{2} + i/2$.

Section 8.3

1. (a) $\sqrt{2}[\cos (-\pi/4) + i \sin (-\pi/4)]$; (b) $2\sqrt{2}(\cos \pi/4 + i \sin \pi/4)$; (c) $\cos 2\pi/3 +$
$i \sin 2\pi/3$; (d) $\cos \pi/6 + i \sin \pi/6$; (e) $2[\cos (-\pi/2) + i \sin (-\pi/2)]$. **3.** (a) $\sqrt{13}$
$(\cos 0.9828 + i \sin 0.9828)$; (b) $\sqrt{13}(\cos 4.1244 + i \sin 4.1244)$; (c) $\sqrt{10}(\cos$
$1.2490 + i \sin 1.2490)$; (d) $\sqrt{10}(\cos 4.3906 + i \sin 4.3906)$; (e) $5(\cos 0.9273 +$
$i \sin 0.9273)$; (f) $5(\cos 4.0689 + i \sin 4.0689)$. **5.** (a) $27(\cos 6 + i \sin 6)$ or $27[\cos$
$(-0.2832) + i \sin (-0.2832)]$; (b) $16(\cos 12 + i \sin 12)$ or $16[\cos (-0.5664) + i \sin$
$(-0.5664)]$; (c) $16(\cos 2.4 + i \sin 2.4)$; (d) $10^5(\cos 2 + i \sin 2)$. **7.** If $z_1 = r_1$
$(\cos \theta_1 + i \sin \theta_1)$ and $z_2 = r_2 (\cos \theta_2 + i \sin \theta_2)$, then $z_1 z_2 = r_1 r_2 [\cos (\theta_1 + \theta_2)$
$+ i \sin (\theta_1 + \theta_2)]$ and $z_1/z_2 = (r_1/r_2) [\cos (\theta_1 - \theta_2) + i \sin (\theta_1 - \theta_2)]$. Hence,
$|z_1 z_2| = r_1 r_2 = |z_1| |z_2|$ and $|z_1/z_2| = r_1/r_2 = |z_1|/|z_2|$. **9.** $z_1 - z_2 = (a - c) +$
$(b - d)i$, and $|z_1 - z_2| = (a - c)^2 + (b - d)^2$, which is the distance between the
points $(a, b), (c, d)$. **11.** If $z = a + bi, |z| = \sqrt{a^2 + b^2} = |a - bi|$. **13.** (a)$-4 + 4i$;
(b) $2^{15}i$; (c) $-\sqrt{3}/2 - i/2$; (d) $-\frac{1}{2} - \sqrt{3}i/2$; (e) $2^{11}i$; (f) $-64(\sqrt{3} + i)$; (g) -2^9.
15. $[r(\cos \theta + i \sin \theta)] [r(\cos \theta + i \sin \theta)] = r^2(\cos 2\theta + i \sin 2\theta)$. **17.** $|z| =$
$\sqrt{a^2 + b^2}$, so that $a \leq |z|$ and $b \leq |z|$.

Section 8.4

1. Since $1 = \cos 0 + i \sin 0 = \cos 2k\pi + i \sin 2k\pi$, it follows by De Moivre's
theorem that the nth roots of 1 are $\cos 2k\pi/n + i \sin 2k\pi/n, n = 0, 1, 2, \ldots, n - 1$.

If we let $\omega = \cos 2\pi/n + i \sin 2\pi/n$ (i.e., $k = 1$), it is immediate that the complete set of roots is $\omega, \omega^2, \omega^3, \ldots, \omega^n = 1$. **3.** $\sqrt{2}/2 + \sqrt{2}i/2$, $-\sqrt{2}/2 + \sqrt{2}i/2$, $-\sqrt{2}/2 - \sqrt{2}i/2$, $\sqrt{2}/2 - \sqrt{2}i/2$. **5.** $\sqrt[3]{2}(\cos \pi/18 + i \sin \pi/18)$, $\sqrt[3]{2}(\cos 13\pi/18 + i \sin 13\pi/18)$, $\sqrt[3]{2}(\cos 25\pi/18 + i \sin 25\pi/18)$. [See accompanying figure.]

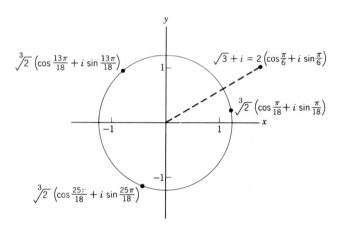

7. $\sqrt[6]{13}(0.95 - 0.32i)$, $\sqrt[6]{13}(-0.19 + 0.98i)$, $\sqrt[6]{13}(-0.75 - 0.66i)$. **9.** $\cos 0 + i \sin 0 = 1$, $\cos 2\pi/5 + i \sin 2\pi/5$, $\cos 4\pi/5 + i \sin 4\pi/5$, $\cos 6\pi/5 + i \sin 6\pi/5$, $\cos 8\pi/5 + i \sin 8\pi/5$. **11.** [See accompanying figures. Parts (a) and (b) are below; parts (c) and (d) are on opposite page.]

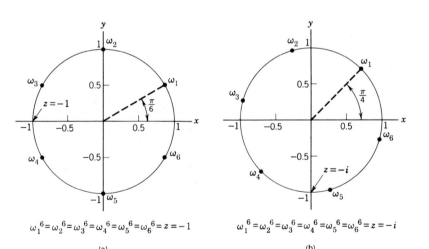

$$\omega_1^6 = \omega_2^6 = \omega_3^6 = \omega_4^6 = \omega_5^6 = \omega_6^6 = z = -1$$

(a)

$$\omega_1^6 = \omega_2^6 = \omega_3^6 = \omega_4^6 = \omega_5^6 = \omega_6^6 = z = -i$$

(b)

11. (*cont.*)

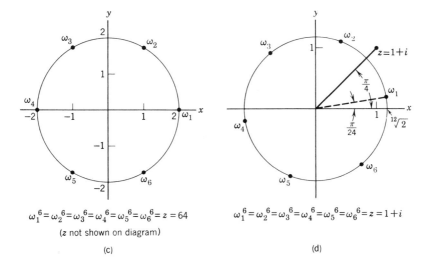

$\omega_1{}^6 = \omega_2{}^6 = \omega_3{}^6 = \omega_4{}^6 = \omega_5{}^6 = \omega_6{}^6 = z = 64$

(*z* not shown on diagram)

(c)

$\omega_1{}^6 = \omega_2{}^6 = \omega_3{}^6 = \omega_4{}^6 = \omega_5{}^6 = \omega_6{}^6 = z = 1 + i$

(d)

13. Yes, because $\cos(\theta + \pi) = -\cos\theta$, and $\sin(\theta + \pi) = -\sin\theta$. **15.** $(\cos\theta + i\sin\theta)^{p/q} = [(\cos\theta + i\sin\theta)^p]^{1/q} = (\cos p\theta + i\sin p\theta)^{1/q} = [\cos(p\theta + 2k\pi) + i\sin(p\theta + 2k\pi)]^{1/q} = \cos(p\theta + 2k\pi)/q + i\sin(p\theta + 2k\pi)/q, \ k = $ p, 1, 2, ..., $q - 1$. **17.** (a) true; (b) true. **19.** $1 + z + z^2 + z^3 = (1 + z) + z^2(1 + z) = (1 + z)(1 + z^2) = [(1 + z)(1 + z^2)(1 - z)]/(1 - z) = [(1 - z^2)(1 + z^2)]/(1 - z) = (1 - z^4)/(1 - z)$. **21.** $i, \ -\sqrt{3}/2 - i/2, \ \sqrt{3}/2 - i/2$. **23.** $[r_1e^{i\theta_1}][r_2e^{i\theta_2}] = r_1r_2e^{i(\theta_1 + \theta_2)}$, i.e., r_1 and r_2 are multiplied while θ_1 and θ_2 are added. This is similar for division. **25.** No. You answer it!

CHAPTER 9

Section 9.1

1. (a) algebraic; (b) algebraic; (c) nonalgebraic; (d) nonalgebraic; (e) algebraic; (f) algebraic; (g) algebraic. **3.** (a) $-x^3 + 4x - 7$; (b) $-3x^4 + 3x^3 - 3x^2 + 3x - 6$; (c) $x^3 - 2x^2 + 3x - 1$. **5.** (a) $x^2/2 + x + 1 + 7/(2x - 4)$; (b) $x + 1 + (3x^2 + 2x + 6)/(3x^3 - 3x^2 + x - 5)$; (c) $x^2/2 - 7x/4 + \frac{41}{8} - 107/[8(2x + 3)]$.
7. $\dfrac{1 - i}{2}x - \dfrac{i}{2} + [(6i - 2)x + i - 8]/[2(2x^2 - (1 - i)x + 1)]$. **9.** $3x^2 - 3x + 4 - (5x + 1)/(x^2 + x - 1)$. **11.** (a) 10; (b) 4; (c) 6. **13.** (a) $q = 4, r = 1$; (b) $q = 33, r = 6$; (c) $q = 3, r = 29$. **15.** (a) 0; (b) 21; (c) 1; (d) $\frac{3}{8}$. **17.** Each term is positive for any real substitution for x, and hence the expression can not equal 0. **19.** (a) $i + 1$; (b) $-i + 1$; (c) $-13i + 7$; (d) -2.

Section 9.2

1. (a) $\frac{2}{3}$; (b) $-\frac{3}{4}$; (c) $-t/k$; (d) t/s; (e) $\frac{7}{2}$; (f) $\frac{3}{2}$; (g) $\frac{21}{4}$; (h) $\frac{10}{9}$. **3.** (a) $1, \frac{1}{2}$; (b) $(-1 \pm \sqrt{37})/6$; (c) $(-1 \pm \sqrt{11}i)/4$; (d) $(5 \pm \sqrt{21})/2$. **5.** $\frac{2}{3}, \frac{1}{3}$; (b) $-\frac{1}{4}, \frac{3}{4}$; (c) $\frac{3}{2}, \frac{1}{2}$; (d) 3, 9; (e) $-p/3, q/3$; (f) $2/r, t/r$. **7.** (a) $-1.8, 0.28$; (b) $3.6, 1.4$; (c) $-0.4, -2.6$. [See accompanying figure.]

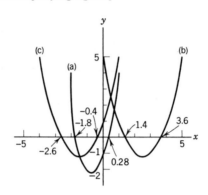

9. (a) $\pm \sqrt{5/2}i$; (b) $\pm \sqrt{3t}/2$; (c) $\pm kti$.

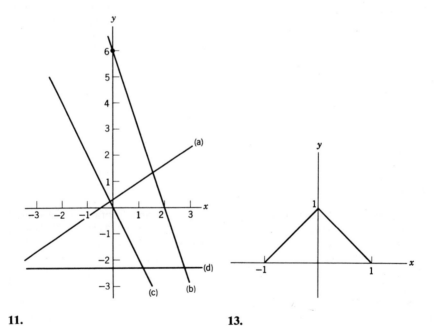

11.   **13.**

15. 12 years. **17.** 8, 9. **19.** 150 mph. **21.** (a) $\frac{11}{3}$; (b) None; (c) 2. **23.** $\pi/8$, $3\pi/8, 5\pi/8, 7\pi/8, 9\pi/8, 11\pi/8, 13\pi/8,$ $15\pi/8$. **25.** (a) 4; (b) 0; (c) 12.

Section 9.3

1. (a) $x^2 - 2x^2 - 5x + 6$; (b) $x^3 - 9x$; (c) $x^2 - 5x + 6$; (d) $x^4 - 4x^3 - 7x^2 + 22x + 24$; (e) $x^5 - 4x^4 - 7x^3 + 34x^2 - 24x$. **3.** (a) $x^3 - (2i - 1)x^2 - (3i + 3)x + 2i - 2$; (b) $x^4 - 7x^3 + (9 + i)x^2 - (54 + 2i)x - 56 - 8i$; (c) $x^4 + (1 - 2i)x^3 - (3 + 3i)x^2 + (2i - 2)x$; (d) $x^3 - (5 + i)x^2 + (12 + 5i)x$. **7.** (a) $\{2, -3, (-1 \pm \sqrt{3}i)/2\}$; (b) $\{3, -2, 7, -4\}$; (c) $\{3, 2, (1 + \sqrt{7}i)/2\}$; (d) $\{4, -6, 5, 1, -1\}$. **9.** (a) $n = 5$, $s = 3$, $n_1 = n_3 = 1$, $n_2 = 3$; $1 + 3 + 1 = 5$; (b) $n = 10$, $s = 4$, $n_1 = n_2 = 2$, $n_3 = n_4 = 3$; $2 + 2 + 3 + 3 = 10$; (c) $n = 15$, $s = 6$, $n_1 = n_5 = n_6 = 2$, $n_2 = n_3 = n_4 = 3$; $2 + 3 + 3 + 3 + 2 + 2 = 15$. **11.** (a) 46; (b) 5; (c) $7i/8 - 1$. **13.** $(-y)^n + y^n = 0$, if n is odd. **15.** (a) $(x - 2)(x + 2)(x + 2i)(x - 2i)$; (b) $(2x + i)(2x - i)(2x + 1)(2x - 1)$; (c) $(x - 1)(x + 1)^2$; (d) $(x - 1)[x + (1 + \sqrt{23}i)/6][x + (1 - \sqrt{23}i)/6]$. **17.** Yes; 1. **19.** (a) $a = -4$, $b = 2$; (b) $a = 1$, $b = -3$. **21.** If a and b are the leading coefficients of $P[x]$ and $Q[x]$, respectively, $(P[x])/a - (Q[x])/b$ is a polynomial of degree at least one less than P or Q, but with the *same* number of zeros. By Problem 20, coefficients are 0, and those of P are constant multiples of those of Q.

Section 9.4

1. (a) $2x^2 + x + 6$, $r = -4$; (b) $2x^2 - 3x + 8$, $r = -18$; (c) $2x^2 + 3x + 11$, $r = 12$; (d) $2x^2 - 5x + 15$, $r = -40$. **3.** (a) $3x^2 + x/2 + \frac{9}{4}$, $r = \frac{9}{8}$; (b) $3x^2 - 5x/2 + \frac{13}{4}$, $r = \frac{27}{8}$; (c) $3x^2 + x + \frac{8}{3}$, $r = \frac{61}{9}$; (d) $3x^2 - 3x + 4$, $r = \frac{7}{3}$. **5.** (a) -2; (b) -8; (c) 13; (d) -62. **7.** The "third row" of digits is: 1 3 6 32 168, and we note that all are positive; the "third row" of digits is 1 -5 6 -16 56 and these digits alternate in signs. **9.** (a) 1; (b) 3; (c) 9; (d) $\frac{17}{8}$. **11.** The successive quotients are: $2x^3 - x^2 - 2x = 1$, $2x^2 - 3x + 1$, $2x - 1$. **13.** (a) $-1, 2$; (b) $-2, 3$ (for example). **15.** $(5 \pm \sqrt{61})/6$. **19.**

x	-2	-1	0	1	2	3	4
y	-53	-11	1	-5	-17	-23	-11

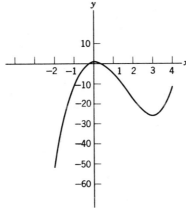

21. -4.   **23.** (a) $3x^2/2 + x/4 + \frac{5}{8}$, $r = -\frac{43}{8}$; (b) $x^2 - x + 1$, $r = -\frac{8}{3}$; (c) $3x^2/4 + 5x/16 + \frac{31}{64}$, $r = -\frac{291}{256}$.

Section 9.5

1. Degree in x is 2, but a, b, c are 3 distinct solutions.   **3.** (a) Degree in x is 2, but $-1, -2, 2$ are 3 solutions; (b) Degree in x is 3, but $0, 1, 2, -2$ are 4 solutions.
5. (a) $A = -\frac{1}{2}$, $B = 3$, $C = -\frac{3}{2}$; (b) $A = 1$, $B = 1$, $C = 2$.   **7.** (a) $2x^3 + 3x^2 + 5x + 2$; (b) $3x^4 + 2x^3 + x^2 + 5x + 1$; (c) $x^4 + 2x^2 + 6$; (d) $x^4 + 2x^3 + x^2 + 1$.
9. (a) 1 or 3 positive, no negative; (b) 0, 2, or 4 positive, no negative; (c) no real zeros; (d) 0 or 2 positive, no negative.   **11.** (a) $x^2 - 2x + 2 = 0$; (b) $x^3 - x^2 + x - 1 = 0$; (c) $x^4 - 8x^3 + 24x^2 - 32x + 20 = 0$; (d) $x^4 - 4x^3 + 9x^2 - 4x + 8 = 0$.   **13.** (a) $(2x - 3)(x^2 + 4x + 5)$; (b) $(x - 2)(x - 3)(x^2 - 2x + 5)$.
15. $(a + bi)^3 + p(a + bi)^2 + q(a + bi) + r = 0$, if and only if $(a - bi)^3 + p(a - bi)^2 + q(a - bi) + r = 0$. (Equate real and "imaginary" components.)
17. There are no negative solutions, and 1 is an upper bound (by synthetic division) of the positive solutions.   **19.** $\{2, -1, -1 + i, -1 - i\}$.   **21.** If it did, a polynomial equation of degree n could have more than n real solutions.

Section 9.6

1. (a) $\{\pm 1, \pm 2, \pm 3, \pm 6, \pm\frac{1}{2}, \pm\frac{3}{2}\}$; (b) $\{\pm 1, \pm 3, \pm\frac{1}{2}, \pm\frac{3}{2}, \pm\frac{1}{4}, \pm\frac{3}{4}\}$; (c) $\{\pm 1, \pm 2, \pm 4, \pm 8, \pm\frac{1}{3}, \pm\frac{2}{3}, \pm\frac{4}{3}, \pm\frac{8}{3}\}$; (d) $\{\pm 1, \pm 2, \pm 4, \pm 8, \pm\frac{1}{2}, \pm\frac{1}{4}, \pm\frac{1}{8}\}$.   **3.** (a) $\{-1, -5, -\frac{1}{3}, -\frac{5}{3}\}$; (b) $\{\pm 1 \pm \frac{1}{3}\}$; (c) $\{\pm 1, \pm 2, \pm 4, \pm 8, \pm\frac{1}{2}\}$; (d) $\{-1\}$.   **5.** (a) $\{\frac{1}{2}, 2, \pm\sqrt{2i}\}$; (b) $\{-1, 1, -\frac{1}{2}, \frac{2}{3}\}$; (c) $\{1, -1, 1 + i, 1 - i\}$; (d) $\{0, 2, -1, \frac{1}{3}, 2 - i, 2 + i\}$.   **7.** For example: (a) $x^4 + x^3 + 2 = 0$; (b) $x^4 - 3x^3 - 2x + 3 = 0$; (c) $x^4 + 2x^2 + 5 = 0$.   **9.** The only possible rational solutions are ± 5. But there are no negative solutions by Descartes' Rule, and 5 is not a solution.   **11.** (a) $[-2, -1]$, $[0, 1]$, $[1, 2]$; (b) $[-4, -3]$, $[0, 1]$, 1; (c) $[-4, -3]$, $[1, 2]$, $[3, 4]$; (d) $[-3, -2]$, $[3, 4]$.   **13.** 6,1.   **15.** If p/q occurs in the "third line," q must also be the denominator of the divisor when reduced to lowest terms. Successive multiplications increase the power of q and never reduce the term to an integer. Hence, the final position of the third line is never filled by 0.

CHAPTER 10

Section 10.1

1. 11025.   **3.** 6, 12.   **5.** (a) 18; (b) 9.   **7.** (9!) (8!).   **9.** 6!.   **11.** (a) 24; (b) 256.   **13.** 343.   **15.** 16, 256.

Section 10.2

1. (a) 6; (b) 40320; (c) 120; (d) 1; (e) 3628800.   **3.** (a) 20; (b) 30240; (c) 210; (d) 79833600.   **5.** (a) 9!; (b) 53(5!); (c) 7!.   **7.** (a) 45; (b) 15.   **9.** $2(7!) = 10080$.

11. (a) $\binom{52}{5} = 2598960$; (b) $\binom{52}{5} - 4^5 \binom{13}{5} = 1281072$; (c) 3744. **13.** 10.

15. $\binom{40}{3} \binom{50}{3} \binom{60}{3} - 1740$. **17.** (a) 120; (b) 210; (c) 968. **19.** $r \binom{n}{r} =$

$$\frac{r!n!}{r!(n-r)!} = \frac{n!}{(r-1)!(n-r)!} = \frac{n \cdot (n-1)!}{(r-1)!(n-r)!} = n \binom{n-1}{r-1}.$$

Section 10.3

1. 120. **3.** (a) 14400; (b) 57600; (c) $132(5!)^2 = 1900800$. **5.** (a) 511; (b) 315.
7. $n = 4, r = 3$. **9.** 90. **11.** 25200. **13.** (a) 18; (b) 270. **15.** (a) 120; (b) 12. **17.** 112.

Section 10.4

1. $27x^3 + 135x^2 + 225x + 125$. **3.** $\frac{1}{16} - x + 6x^2 - 16x^3 + 16x^4$. **5.** $1 + 12x^2$
$+ 60x^4 + 160x^6 + 240x^8 + 192x^{10} + 64x^{12}$. **7.** $1 - 8x + 28x^2 - 56x^3 + 70x^4$
$- 56x^5 + 28x^6 - 8x^7 + x^8$. **9.** $769824x^7y^5$. **11.** $(63\sqrt{2}\, x^8)/2, (63x^{10})/4$.

13. $\dfrac{12!6^6}{6!6!}$ **15.** $(1+x)^n = 1 + \binom{n}{1}x + \binom{n}{2}x^2 + \binom{n}{3}x^3 + \cdots + \binom{n}{n}x^n$.

Now put $x = 1$, and get $2^n - 1 = \binom{n}{1} + \binom{n}{2} + \cdots + \binom{n}{n}$.

17. $\dfrac{n!}{(r+1)!(n-r-1)!} = \dfrac{n-r}{n-r} \cdot \dfrac{n!}{(r+1)!(n-r-1)!} = \dfrac{n-r}{r+1} \cdot \dfrac{n!}{r!(n-r)!} =$

$\dfrac{n-r}{r+1} \binom{n}{r}$. Now let $s = r+1$, so that $s - 1 = r$. Then, $\binom{n}{s} = \dfrac{n-s+1}{s} \binom{n}{s-1}$.

19. $\binom{n}{r} + \binom{n}{r-1} = \dfrac{n!}{r!(n-r)!} + \dfrac{n!}{(n-r+1)!(r-1)!} = \dfrac{(n-r+1)}{(n-r+1)}$.

$\dfrac{n!}{r!(n-r)!} + \dfrac{r}{r} \cdot \dfrac{n!}{(n-r+1)!(r-1)!} = \dfrac{(n-r+1)n! + r \cdot n!}{(n-r+1)!r!} = \dfrac{n!(n+1)}{(n-r+1)!r!}$

$= \dfrac{(n+1)!}{(n+1-r)!r!} = \binom{n+1}{r}$.

Section 10.5

1. $1 + 3x/2 - 9x^2/8 + 27x^3/16, |x| < \frac{1}{3}$. **3.** $\sqrt[3]{2}\left[1 + \dfrac{5}{6}x^2 - \dfrac{25}{36}x^4 - \dfrac{625}{648}x^6\right]$,

$x^2 < \frac{2}{5}$. **5.** $1 + 2x + 4x^2 + 8x^3, |x| < \frac{1}{2}$. **7.** $\sqrt[3]{4}\ (1 + 5a/12 - \frac{25}{144}a^2 +$
$\frac{625}{5184}a^3), |a| < \frac{4}{5}$. **9.** $1 + 3(a-b) + 3(a-b)^2 + (a-b)^3 = 1 + 3a - 3b +$
$3a^2 - 6ab + 3b^2 + a^3 - 3a^2b + 3ab^2 - b^3$. **11.** 0.9803. **13.** 0.6742. **15.** 4.9330.

17. (a) $(1+x)^{1/2} = 1^{1/2} + (\frac{1}{2})1^{-1/2}x + \dfrac{(\frac{1}{2})(-\frac{1}{2})1^{-3/2}}{2}x^2 + \cdots \doteq 1 + x/2$;

(b) $(1+x)^{-2/3} = 1^{-2/3} + (-\frac{2}{3})1^{-5/3}x + \cdots \doteq 1 - 2x/3$; (c) $(1-x)^{-1} =$
$1^{-1} + (-1)(1^{-2})(-x) + \cdots \doteq 1 + x$. **19.** 0.004 secs. **21.** $\sqrt{6h}/2$ miles.

Section 10.6

1. $x^2 - y^2 = (x - y)(x + y)$, i.e., $P(1)$ is true. Assume $P(k)$ is true. Then $x^{2(k+1)}$ $- y^{2(k+1)} = x^2(x^{2k} - y^{2k}) + y^{2k}(x^2 - y^2)$, so that $P(k + 1)$ is true. **3.** $2^{1-1} = 2^0$ $= 1 = 1!$, so that $P(1)$ is true. Assume $P(k)$ is true. Then $2^{k-1} \leq k!$, by assumption, and we know that $2 \leq k + 1$ for $k \geq 1$. Then, $2^{k-1} \cdot 2 \leq k!(k + 1)$, i.e., $2^k \leq (k + 1)!$, so that $P(k + 1)$ is true. **5.** $a + 1 = 1 + a$, so that $P(1)$ is true. Assume $P(k)$ is true, i.e., $(a + 1)^k \geq 1 + ka$. Then $(a + 1)^{k+1} \geq (1 + ka)(1 + a)$ $= 1 + (k + 1)a + ka^2 \geq 1 + (k + 1)a$, so that $P(k + 1)$ is true. **7.** $(a + b)^1 =$ $a + b$, so that $P(1)$ is true. Assume $P(k)$ true. The $(r + 1)$st term of the product indicated in the hint is $a^{k+1-r}b^r \left[\binom{k}{r} + \binom{k}{r-1} \right] = \binom{k+1}{r} a^{k+1-r}b^r$, so that $P(k + 1)$ is true. **9.** No. The statement is not true for *every* natural number n and arbitrary integers x and y. Even if it were (!), an inductive proof could not be given for n not a natural number. **11.** $|\sin \theta| = |\sin \theta|$, so that $P(1)$ is true. Assume $P(k)$ is true, i.e., $|\sin k\theta| \leq k|\sin \theta|$. Then $|\sin (k + 1)\theta| = |\sin (k\theta + \theta)| = |\sin k\theta \cos \theta$ $+ \cos k\theta \sin \theta| \leq |\sin k\theta \cos \theta| + |\cos k\theta \sin \theta| \leq |\sin k\theta| + |\sin \theta| \leq k|\sin \theta| +$ $|\sin \theta| = (k + 1)|\sin \theta|$. Hence, $P(k + 1)$ is true. **13.** $P(1)$ is true as in Problem 5. Assume $P(k)$ is true, i.e., $(a + 1)^k \geq 1 + ka$. Since $a + 1 > 0$, for $a > -1$, $(a + 1)^{k+1} \geq (1 + ka)(1 + a) = 1 + (k + 1)a + ka^2 \geq 1 + (k + 1)a$, since $ka^2 \geq 0$. Hence, $P(k + 1)$ is true, if $a > -1$. If $a < -1$, $a + 1 < 0$, and the above argument fails.

Section 10.7

1. (a) $3, 5, 7, 9, 11$; (b) $4, 2, 4, 2, 4$; (c) $1, \frac{1}{2}, \frac{1}{4}, \frac{1}{8}, \frac{1}{16}$; (d) $2, 4\frac{1}{2}, 9\frac{1}{3}, 16\frac{1}{4}, 25\frac{1}{5}$. **3.** (a) $2, \frac{5}{2}$; (b) $-1, 1$. **5.** $7, 8, 5; 7, 15, 20$. **7.** $P(1)$ is true since S_1 is given. Assume $P(k)$ true, i.e., S_k is given. Then $S_{k+1} = S_k + a_{k+1}$, so that S_{k+1} is defined and $P(k + 1)$ is true. **9.** $1, 30, 119, 300, 605$. **11.** $\frac{1}{2}, \frac{2}{3}, \frac{3}{4}, \frac{4}{5}, \frac{5}{6}$. $S_n = n/(n + 1)$. Since $S_1 = \frac{1}{2}$, $P(1)$ is true. Assume $P(k)$ is true. Then $S_{k+1} = S_k + a_{k+1} = k/(k + 1) + 1/[(k + 1)(k + 2)]$ $= (k + 1)^2/[(k + 1)(k + 2)] = (k + 1)/(k + 2)$, so that $P(k + 1)$ is true. **13.** Since $1 = 1(1 + 1)/2$, $P(1)$ is true. Assume $P(k)$ is true. Then, $\sum_{i=1}^{k+1} i = \sum_{i=1}^{k} i + (k + 1)$ $= k(k + 1)/2 + (k + 1) = [(k + 1)(k + 2)]/2$, so that $P(k + 1)$ is true. **15.** Since $2(2^1 - 1) = 2$, $P(1)$ is true. Assume $P(k)$ is true. Then $\sum_{i=1}^{k+1} 2_i = \sum_{i=1}^{k} 2_i + 2^{k+1} =$ $2(2^k - 1) + 2^{k+1} = 2[2(2^k) - 1] = 2(2^{k+1} - 1)$, so that $P(k + 1)$ is true.

Section 10.8

1. $S_n = a_1 + a_2 + \cdots + a_{n-1} + a_n = a_1 + (a_1 + d) + \cdots + (a_n - d) + a_n = a_n$ $+ (a_n - d) + \cdots + (a_1 + d) + a_1$. Hence, $2S_n = (a_1 + a_n) + (a_1 + a_n) + \cdots +$ $(a_1 + a_n) + (a_1 + a_n) = n(a_1 + a_n)$, and so, $S_n = n(a_1 + a_n)/2$. **3.** $35, 222$. **5.** -59. **7.** (a) -63; (b) 54. **9.** $S_n = 1 + 3 + \cdots + (2n - 3) + (2n - 1) = (2n - 1) +$ $(2n - 3) + \cdots + 3 + 1$. Hence, $2S_n = 2n + 2n + \cdots + 2n + 2n = n(2n) = 2n^2$, and so $S_n = n^2$. **11.** (a) 275; (b) 783; (c) 1425; (d) -1530. **13.** $5, 8, 11, 14, 17, 20$.

15. Total interest $= \frac{10}{2}(18 + 18) = \$180$. Hence, amount of investment $= \$300 + \$180 = \$480$. **17.** 16, 2. **19.** 10. **21.** $n(a_1 + a_n)/2 = 322$ ft/sec. **23.** \$1260.

Section 10.9

1. $S_n = a_0 + a_0r + \cdots + a_0r^{n-1}, rS_n = a_0r + a_0r^2 + \cdots + a_0r^{n-1} + a_0r^n$. Hence, $S_n - rS_n = S_n(1 - r) = a_0 - a_0r^n = a_0(1 - r^n)$, and so $S_n = a_0(1 - r^n)/(1 - r)$.
3. (a) 162; (b) -0.000001; (c) 0.0001024. **5.** 116050/19683. **7.** 6, 2, $\frac{2}{3}$. **9.** 4.
11. (a) 6; (b) $\frac{3}{2}$; (c) $\frac{8}{9}$. **13.** 13. **15.** (a) 2; (b) $\frac{3}{4}$. **17.** 125 feet. **19.** $4\sqrt{3}/3$. **21.** $2^{21}/5^9$.
23. (a) Equivalent formulation: $2^{n+3} < (n + 3)!$, for $n \geq 1$. Since $2^4 = 16 < 24 = 4!$, $P(1)$ is true. Assume $P(k)$ is true. Then, $2^{(k+1)+3} = 2 \cdot 2^{k+3} < 2(k + 3)! < 2^2(k + 3)!$ $< (k + 4) \cdot (k + 3)! = (k + 4)!$, so that $P(k + 1)$ is true. (b) Equivalent formulation: $(n + 1)! < (n + 1)^{n+1}$, for $n \geq 1$. Since $2! = 2 < 4 = 2^2$, $P(1)$ is true. Assume $P(k)$ is true. Then $[(k + 1) + 1]! = (k + 1)! (k + 2) < (k + 1)^{k+1} \cdot (k + 2) < (k + 2)^{k+1} (k + 2) = (k + 2)^{k+2} = [(k + 1) + 1]^{[(k+1)+1]}$, so that $P(k + 1)$ is true.

ANSWERS TO PROBLEMS IN APPENDIX A

Section 1

1. Divide numerator and denominator by the number "canceled." **2.** (a) 2^6; (b) $2^2 \cdot 3^2$; (c) $2^3 \cdot 3^2$; (d) $2^5 \cdot 5$; (e) $2 \cdot 3 \cdot 7$; (f) $2 \cdot 3^2$; (g) 5^3; (h) $2^2 \cdot 3 \cdot 5$; (i) $2^4 \cdot 5$; (j) $2 \cdot 3^2 \cdot 5$; (k) $2 \cdot 3 \cdot 17$. **3.** (a) 1; (b) 3; (c) 2; (d) 15; (e) 1. **4.** (a) $\frac{1}{3}$; (b) $\frac{2}{3}$; (c) $\frac{1}{3}$; (d) $\frac{10}{3}$; (e) $\frac{15}{4}$; (f) $\frac{6}{13}$. **5.** (a) $\frac{10}{15}$; (b) $\frac{15}{20}$; (c) $\frac{25}{15}$; (d) $\frac{20}{30}$; (e) $\frac{20}{45}$. **6.** (a) $\frac{40}{30}$; (b) $\frac{20}{70}$; (c) $\frac{50}{80}$; (d) $\frac{50}{60}$; (e) $\frac{30}{40}$. **7.** (a) $2\frac{13}{24}$; (b) $2\frac{43}{60}$; (c) $1\frac{9}{70}$. **8.** (a) $4\frac{1}{3}$; (b) $\frac{1}{12}$; (c) $\frac{19}{56}$; (d) $3\frac{4}{7}$; (e) $\frac{2}{7}$. **9.** (a) $1\frac{19}{24}$; (b) $1\frac{7}{120}$; (c) $2\frac{226}{315}$. **10.** (a) $\frac{1}{12}$; (b) $\frac{8}{25}$; (c) $1\frac{7}{18}$. **11.** (a) $\frac{9}{8}$; (b) $\frac{5}{8}$; (c) $\frac{15}{32}$; (d) $\frac{1}{14}$; (e) 32; (f) $\frac{2}{9}$. **12.** (a) $\frac{11}{12}$; (b) $\frac{49}{72}$; (c) $\frac{83}{240}$; (d) $5\frac{5}{6}$; (e) $3\frac{3}{5}$. **13.** $4\frac{37}{40}$. **14.** $10\frac{7}{8}$; $12\frac{1}{3}$. **15.** $4\frac{1}{4}$ feet. **16.** $41\frac{5}{8}\cancel{c}$. **17.** $16\cancel{c}$. **18.** $2\frac{9}{10}$; $3\frac{31}{33}$.

Section 2

1. (a) 6; (b) 7; (c) 4; (d) $\frac{3}{5}$; (e) $\frac{5}{7}$. **2.** (a) 17; (b) -21; (c) $-2\frac{3}{8}$; (d) $1\frac{77}{120}$. **3.** (a) -3; (b) -17; (c) 1; (d) -2. **4.** (a) $\frac{5}{12}$; (b) $2\frac{1}{56}$; (c) $2\frac{13}{280}$. **5.** (a) $1\frac{1}{28}$; (b) $-2\frac{1}{15}$; (c) $5\frac{3}{4}$; (d) $-3\frac{2}{7}$; (e) $-\frac{14}{15}$; (f) $4\frac{3}{5}$; (g) $\frac{1}{4}$. **6.** (a) $\frac{2}{5}$; (b) -8; (c) $-3\frac{6}{7}$. **7.** (a) $-\frac{3}{7}$; (b) $\frac{5}{9}$; (c) $-6\frac{1}{4}$; (d) $-\frac{3}{10}$. **8.** (a) $-7\frac{1}{2}$; (b) $\frac{128}{245}$; (c) $-18\frac{37}{80}$. **9.** (a) $-10\frac{1}{2}$; (b) $7\frac{1}{4}$; (c) 2; (d) $2\frac{1}{3}$. **10.** (a) $5\frac{1}{4}$; (b) $\frac{3}{8}$; (c) $\frac{2}{9}$.

Section 3

1. (a) $-8x^3$; (b) $2ab$; (c) $24x^3$; (d) $3aby^2$; (e) $-7x^2y$. **2.** (a) $16a$; (b) $5ab$; (c) $4ac - 4ab$; (d) $2a^2 + 2a + 5b$. **3.** $-6a - 7b - 3c$. **4.** $-14x^2 + 12x - 8$. **5.** (a) $-15abc$; (b) $5m - 8m^2$; (c) $8x^2 - 8y$. **6.** (a) $3a - 11b + 6c$; (b) $-13x - y$; (c) $9x^2 - 2y + 15$. **7.** (a) $9y - xy$; (b) $9y - x^2$; (c) $4b^2 - 24b - a - 8$. **8.** (a) $3a^2 + ab - 2b^2$; (b) $5x - 3y$; (c) 1. **9.** (a) $4x^2 - 25y^2$; (b) $9x^4 - 4y^4$; (c) $4x^2 + 4xy + y^2$; (d) $x^3 - 6x^2y + 12xy^2 - 8y^3$. **10.** (a) $25x^2 - 4y^2$; (b) $x^4y^2 - 9a^2$; (c) $4x^2 - 36y^2$; (d) $27x^3 - 27x^2y + 9xy^2 - y^3$. **11.** (a) $4a^2 - 4ax + x^2$; (b) $1 + 3x + 3x^2 + x^3$; (c) $8x^3 - 12x^2 + 6x - 1$; (d) $x^2 + 5x + 6$; (e) $9x^2y^2 + 18xyz - 7z^2$. **12.** (a) $2x^2 - 6xy + 4y^2$; (b) $2a^2 + 11ab - 21b^2$; (c) $x^4 + x^2 - 12$; (d) $x^2/4 - 25y^2$; (e) $x^2/4 - xy/4 + y^2/16$. **13.** (a) $36x^2 - 6x + \frac{1}{4}$; (b) $8 + 36x + 54x^2 + 27x^3$; (c) $25m^6 - 25m^3s^2 - 6s^4$, (d) $9x^2y^2 - 42xy + 49$. **14.** (a) $3m + 2 - 5m^2$; (b) $2x^2 - x$; (c) $x^2 - 12x + 6$; (d) $a - a^2b + b^3$; (e) $5y^2$. **15.** (a) $-20m^2n^4$; (b) $12b^3c^3$; (c) $-40ty^5z$; (d) $8x^4y^2 - 14x^3y^3$; (e) $-a^4$. **16.** (a) $4x^2 + y^2 + 9z^2 - 4xy + 12xz - 6yz$; (b) $x - 2x^2 + x^3 - 2y + 4xy - 2x^2y$; (c) $2x^5 + x^4 - 24x^3 - 12x^2 + 72x + 36$; (d) $2x^3 - 3x^2y - 8xy^2 - 3y^3$; (e) $8x^3 + y^3 - z^3 - 12xyz - 12x^2z + 12x^2y + 6xz^2 + 6xy^2 - 3y^2z + 3yz^2$.

Section 4

1. $(3x^4 - 2y^3)(3x^4 + 2y^3)$. **2.** $(15 - a^3)(15 + a^3)$. **3.** $(r^2 - 5)(r^2 - 6)$. **4.** $(8x + 3)(2x + 3)$. **5.** $3(y + 2)(y^2 - 2y + 4)$. **6.** $(3x - 1)(2x + 3)$. **7.** $(c + 3d)$

334

$(c^2 - 3cd + 9d^2)$. **8.** $(x - 12)(x - 4)$. **9.** $(y - 3z)(y^2 + 3yz + 9z^2)$. **10.** $(x + 1)$ $(4x - 7)$. **11.** $(3 - 5t)(2 + 3t)$. **12.** $(5t^2 - 1)(5t^2 + 1)$. **13.** $(6a - 11)^2$. **14.** $(u^3 - 10)(u^3 + 11)$. **15.** $3(x^2 - 2)(x^2 + 2)$. **16.** $(x^4 + y^4)(x^2 + y^2)(x + y)$ $(x - y)$. **17.** $(x^2 + y^2)(x - y)^2(x + y)$. **18.** $(x - y)^2(x^2 + xy + y^2)$. **19.** $(x - 1)^3$. **20.** $(x + y - a)(x + y + a)$. **21.** $(c + a + b)(c - a - b)$. **22.** $(xy + 1)$ $(x^2y^2 - xy + 1)$. **23.** $(2 - 3x)(4 + 6x + 9x^2)$. **24.** $(2m + 3n)(12m - 7n)$. **25.** $(8x + 9)(2x - 3)$. **26.** $(1 + 4x)(9 - x)$. **27.** $(2x^2 - 3y^2)(x^2 + 7y^2)$. **28.** $(x - y - 2z)(x - y + 2z)$. **29.** $(5x - 6)(5x - 8)$. **30.** $y(2x - y)$. **31.** $(5y - 4)(y + 14)$. **32.** $y^4(x^2 - 3)(x^2 + 3)$. **33.** $(2x^2 + 2y + x - 9)(2x^2 + x - 2y + 9)$. **34.** $2(x + 2y)(x - y)$. **35.** $a(a + b)(x + y)$. **36.** $x^3(a - 8y)$ $(a + 8y)$. **37.** $a(x - y)(x + y)(a + b)$. **38.** $(x^2 + 1)(x + 1)$. **39.** $(1 - 2x)$ $(1 + 2x)(2 + 3x)$. **40.** $(7 - 4a)(8 + 3a^2)$. **41.** $(x + y - z)(x^2 + y^2 + z^2 - xy + xz - 2yz)$. **42.** $(m + n + 2t)(m^2 + n^2 + 4t^2 + 2mn - 2mt - 2nt)$. **43.** $(2a + b)$ $(13a^2 - 5ab + b^2)$. **44.** $(x + y - xy)(x + y + xy)$.

Section 5

1. $(5x + y)/6$. **2.** $(x + 4)/4$. **3.** $-(4a + b)/(ab)$. **4.** $(25x^2 + 12x - 14)/(20x^3)$. **5.** 0. **6.** $(x + 45)/70$. **7.** $2(x^2 - 2)/(x^2 - 1)$. **8.** $2x/[(x + 1)(x + 2)(x + 3)]$. **9.** $y(7y - 12)/[(y - 2)(3y - 2)]$. **10.** $x(a - b)/[(x + a)(x + b)]$. **11.** $1/[(1 - a)(1 + 2a)(2 - 3a)]$. **12.** $4x/(x^2 - 4)$. **13.** $3a(2a + 3)/[(2a - 1)(a - 1)]$. **14.** $x^3/(x^2 - 1)$. **15.** $2(x^3 + x^2 - 9)/[x(x - 3)(x + 3)]$. **16.** $1/[(x + 1)(x + 2)]$. **17.** 0. **18.** $(x^2 - 3x + 1)/(x - 2)$. **19.** $(x - y)(x + y)^2/(x^2y^2)$. **20.** $(x + 1)/(x - 1)$. **21.** $(x - 1)/[x(x + 3)]$. **22.** $(x + 1)/2$. **23.** $(x + 1)(x^2 + 1)(x^4 + 1)/x^3$. **24.** $(x + 1)/(x - 1)$.

Section 6

1. 4. **2.** $\frac{1}{2}$. **3.** -3. **4.** $-\frac{1}{2}$. **5.** 2. **6.** $7\frac{2}{3}$. **7.** -2. **8.** 5. **9.** $\frac{1}{2}, -3$. **10.** $-\frac{7}{3}, \frac{5}{2}$. **11.** $(-5 \pm \sqrt{37})/2$. **12.** $4, 1$. **13.** $-\frac{7}{3}, 1$. **14.** $-9, 4$. **15.** $-\frac{9}{4}, 5$. **16.** $60, 45$.| **17.** $4, 2$. **18.** $6, -1$. **19.** $4, -\frac{10}{3}$. **20.** $\pm 2, \pm 5$. **21.** $(-5 \pm \sqrt{65})/8$. **22.** $3 \pm \sqrt{15}$. **23.** $\dfrac{2 \pm 2\sqrt{3}}{3}$. **24.** $(-1 \pm \sqrt{6})/2$. **25.** $(2 \pm \sqrt{10})/4$. **26.** $3, -\frac{5}{3}$. **27.** No real solution. **28.** $\pm 5, \pm 2$. **29.** ± 7. **30.** $5, -3$. **31.** $\frac{1}{3}, 3, 1$. **32.** $\sqrt[3]{7}, \sqrt[3]{5}$. **33.** $\frac{5}{3}, -\frac{3}{2}$. **34.** $-\frac{1}{2}$. **35.** $\frac{2}{3}, 1$. **36.** $-\frac{1}{3}, \frac{1}{3}$. **37.** $-\frac{11}{6}, 2$. **38.** $(-10 \pm \sqrt{110})/10$. **39.** $a, 1/a$. **40.** $\dfrac{-2 \pm 2\sqrt{13}}{3}$.

Section 7

1. $x = 7, y = -2$. **2.** $x = 5, y = 4$. **3.** $x = -1, y = 1$. **4.** $x = \frac{15}{13}, y = -\frac{5}{13}$. **5.** $x = 5, y = 3$. **6.** $x = 15, y = 10$. **7.** $x = 4, y = 3$. **8.** $x = 2, y = 3$. **9.** $x = 2, y = 3$. **10.** $x = -\frac{1}{2}, y = \frac{5}{2}$. **11.** $x = -2, y = 1, z = 3$. **12.** $x = 3, y = 1, z = 2$. **13.** $x = 2, y = -1, z = -\frac{1}{3}$. **14.** $x = 2, y = -1, z = 0$. **15.** $x = 6, y = 18, z = 12$. **16.** $x = 2, y = 4, z = 8$. **17.** 6 m.p.h., 3 m.p.h. **18.** 55, 40.

Section 8

1. (a) $a^{1/2}$; (b) $x^{3/4}$; (c) $a^{7/5}$; (d) $a^{3/2}$; (e) $(a+2)^{1/5}$.   **2.** (a) $3^{1/2}$; (b) $2^{5/3}$; (c) $4^{4/5}$; (d) $5^{1/2}$; (e) $(2+x)^{1/3}$.   **3.** (a) 3; (b) 729; (c) 3125; (d) 32; (e) 2.   **4.** (a) $\sqrt[3]{a}$; (b) $\sqrt[6]{x^5}$; (c) $\sqrt[3]{b^n}$; (d) $\sqrt[4]{n^3}$; (e) $\sqrt[6]{s^7}$.   **5.** (a) x^{n+3}; (b) a^{2n+1}; (c) u^{2n}; (d) p^{21}; (e) a^{12}.   **6.** (a) x^{2n}; (b) 10^{r+1}; (c) u^{2v}; (d) x^4; (e) $(pq)^{3s}$; (f) $(rs)^{10}$; (g) e^{n+2}.   **7.** (a) $x^{8/3}$; (b) $a^{9/20}$; (c) $a^{23/21}$; (d) $x^{1/2}$.   **8.** (a) $a^{1/6}$; (b) $x^{1/2}$; (c) $a^{5/3}$; (d) $ab^{1/4}$.   **9.** (a) 1; (b) $x^{13/5}$; (c) $(\frac{27}{8})x^{21/40}$; (d) $2^{4/3}a^{1/6}b$.   **10.** (a) $\frac{1}{2}$; (b) $\frac{1}{8}$; (c) $\frac{1}{3}$; (d) 1; (e) 1.   **11.** (a) 18; (b) 8; (c) 1; (d) $\frac{1}{4}$.   **12.** (a) a/b^2; (b) $1/(a+b)^3$; (c) $3/(x^2y^{1/2})$; (d) x^4y^5; (e) x^2.   **13.** (a) x^{-2}; (b) $xy^2c^{-3}d^{-4}$; (c) $2^{-1}a^3b^{-3}r^2t^{-5}$; (d) $ab^{1/2}x^{1/3}y^{-s/t}$.   **14.** (a) a^7; (b) $1/x^4$; (c) $(a^9x^9)/(b^3y^6)$; (d) $r^{1/2}$.

Section 9

1. 5.   **2.** 10.   **3.** 65.   **4.** 4.   **5.** −2.   **6.** No solution.   **7.** No solution.   **8.** 2, 6.   **9.** No solution.   **10.** 4.   **11.** 9.   **12.** 6.   **13.** 2.   **14.** 4.   **15.** $\frac{1}{4}$.   **16.** $\frac{1}{81}$.   **17.** 4.   **18.** 0.

Section 10

1. (a) 1:2; (b) 10:13; (c) 13:18; (d) 16:17; (e) $(x-y)$:1.   **2.** (a) 1:18; (b) 8:27; (c) 2:3; (d) 10:9.   **3.** (a) 1:6; (b) 1:6; (c) 1:25.   **4.** (a) a:$(a-1)$; (b) $(x-3)$:2; (c) x:3.   **5.** 75, 50.   **6.** 8, 20.   **7.** (a) $\frac{16}{5}$; (b) $\frac{27}{2}$; (c) 12; (d) 9.   **8.** (a) 6; (b) 4; (c) 8; (d) $2\sqrt{6}$; (e) $2\sqrt{15}$.   **9.** (a) $\frac{81}{4}$; (b) $\frac{100}{3}$; (c) 72.   **10.** (a) 6; (b) 33; (c) $-\frac{80}{3}$.   **11.** $x=0$.   **12.** $x=-6$.

Test

1. (a) $-1\frac{5}{12}$; (b) $-\frac{31}{60}$.   **2.** (a) $-1\frac{7}{8}$; (b) $-1\frac{17}{18}$; (c) $\frac{3}{25}$; (d) -10.   **3.** (a) -1; (b) $(x+1)/(x^2-9)$.   **4.** (a) $2+2x-5x^2/12$; (b) $a+b$.   **5.** (a) $(m-2n)(m+2n)$; (b) $(t+11)(t-5)$; (c) $(1+y)(1-y)(1+y+y^2)(1-y+y^2)$.   **6.** (a) $(a+b)(m+1)$; (b) $(1-y)(1-2x+y)$; (c) $(4x-1)(3x+7)$.   **7.** (a) $(1-x-y)(1+x+y)$; (b) $x(x+1)(x-7)$.   **8.** (a) $(5\pm\sqrt{17})/4$; (b) $-\frac{1}{2}$, -1.   **9.** (a) $-\frac{1}{2}$, 1; (b) $\frac{2}{3}$, $-\frac{3}{2}$.   **10.** (a) -1, $\frac{3}{4}$; (b) $(2\pm\sqrt{6})/2$.   **11.** (a) $x=11$, $y=0$; (b) $y=\frac{7}{2}$, $z=-1$.   **12.** (a) $x=5$, $y=13$, $z=0$; (b) $x=\frac{1}{2}$, $y=\frac{1}{3}$, $z=2$.   **13.** (a) $\sqrt{2}$, $\sqrt[3]{9}$, $\sqrt{64}$, $\sqrt{\frac{1}{6}}$, $\sqrt[3]{\frac{1}{4}}$; (b) $5^{1/5}$, $3^{2/3}$, $3^{-1/2}$, $3(5^{-2/3})$.   **14.** (a) $y^6/(3x^4z)$; (b) $64x^2/(9y)$.   **15.** (a) 3:7; (b) $x=3\frac{2}{5}$.   **16.** $x=-1$.   **17.** $x=6$.

INDEX

337

S

T